JUNIOR
SCIENCE

by

STUART MIALL

Volume Three

THE CAXTON PUBLISHING COMPANY, LIMITED
CLUN HOUSE, SURREY STREET, LONDON, W.C.2

First Published . . . . June 1930

PRINTED AND BOUND IN ENGLAND BY
HAZELL WATSON AND VINEY LTD
AYLESBURY AND LONDON
J.S. 1

CONTENTS

VOLUME THREE

SECTION I—MATHEMATICS

SECTION II—CHEMISTRY

CONTENTS

CHAPTER III

SECTION III—NATURAL SCIENCE

CHAPTER I

LIST OF PLATES

VOLUME THREE

COLOUR PLATES

BLACK-AND-WHITE PLATES

JUNIOR SCIENCE

VOLUME THREE

INTRODUCTION TO MATHEMATICS

The greatest deterrent to the study of science is the almost universal dislike of mathematics. So soon as the reader of a science manual espies an equation he feels inclined to shut the book up and think about something else.

Knowing how distasteful to students the subjects of algebra and geometry generally are, I would gladly keep my treatment of science non-mathematical, but if I did this I should be in danger of creating a wrong impression; I should incline my readers to believe that mathematics could be dispensed with in passing examinations or in the pursuit of a scientific career. It is a fact that while the groundwork in science may be discussed in non-mathematical terms, the development and application of theories to meet everyday requirements involve the need for an ever-increasing skill in the science of measurement and calculation.

Mathematics is in reality a pleasant and easy study, but it has been made repellent in many schools because it has been divorced from the immediate needs and interests of those studying it. In this book the sciences have been dealt with first and the student is brought face to face with problems to which mathematics can be usefully applied. By the time he reaches this section on mathematics the reader will be aware that it contains knowledge he really requires.

In schools where the pupils do endless exercises in algebraic multiplication, division, factorisation, etc., etc., before they are allowed to hear of natural science, the question "What is the sense of doing all this?" is ever present in the youthful mind. It is because the answer to this question is so long deferred that boys and girls eventually come to detest mathematics, regarding it as only another disagreeable medicine for the strengthening of unwilling minds.

To people like engineers, surveyors, architects, navigation officers, etc., mathematics is like a kit of ever-useful tools. The professional man could accomplish nothing were he not proficient in arithmetic, algebra, geometry and trigonometry. This is not to say that boys and girls should be drilled in mathematics until they are nauseated by the monotony of it. We allow children to read long before they know all the words in the dictionary, and similarly we should permit children to start applying their mathematical knowledge before they are in possession of very much. A common but very wrong procedure is to make pupils do hundreds of examples in the factorisation of different expressions before they can appreciate why even the simplest quantity should ever need to be resolved. The old saying that you should not cross your bridges before you come to them is one that ought to be constantly borne in mind when showing people how to read or to calculate. Facility in dealing with awkward words or unwieldy algebraic expressions comes with practice, but it is a mistake to be always practising and never venturing into the field of real achievement. The tyro who is kept at five-finger piano exercises soon loses all interest in his instrument and in music, and a similar loss of interest in mathematics occurs when the beginner is required to be infallible too soon in an art of symbolical jugglery that cannot begin to have any meaning or attractiveness for him until he is shown that it has concrete applications.

In what follows I have passed lightly over many dull passages in arithmetic, algebra and so on, not stopping to set exercises in such pedestrian operations as multiplication, division, factorisation, etc., etc. The student will find that the mathematics in this book is directed as soon as possible to concrete ends, and that he is assumed to have some slight acquaintance with the more elementary steps. If he encounters difficulty on meeting some such transformation as, let us say, $x^2 + 7x + 12$ into $(x + 3)(x + 4)$ he will know that he needs more drill in the art of recognising or finding factors. We all need more drill in one elementary branch of calculation or another (and this applies even to the greatest of our scientists) but we should be foolish if we spent all our time drilling ourselves; many operations of an elementary kind are so rarely used that it hardly matters if we set about them in slow and clumsy fashion. Facility in finding factors is not immediately necessary and it will come in time whether we concentrate on exercises in this particular branch alone or just deal with such examples as come our way in the course of our other work.

It has not been thought desirable to work through a great many numerical examples, or to set exercises, for the reason that a few well-chosen examples directly connected with science have seemed more enlightening than a score of artificially concocted ones. If the number of equations dealt with seems inadequate and not sufficiently representative of all the types occurring in practice, the reader can turn to the chapters on physics and engineering in the assurance that there he will find further examples of great diversity.

Old-time teachers of algebra and geometry may wish to quarrel with me for going so fast through their subjects and missing out so much of value and interest, but my aim has been to reveal the utility of mathematics as soon as possible and in as many ways as possible. Once the student has glimpsed into the promised land, he is likely to seek proficiency in the duller and more mechanical parts of the art of calculation of his own accord, voluntarily undertaking drudgery that would gravely deter him were he to be confronted with it at an earlier stage. None of us shows a willingness to trudge long and far into what seems like an arid waste, but if journey's end is represented to us in an attractive light, we are likely to proceed without being driven from behind.

I have tried to make the story of mathematics one that constantly sustains reader interest, realising that constant stoppages and digressions for the detailed consideration of every process encountered *en route* are likely to prove a distraction fatal to the success of my purpose. The reader is advised to read straight through what is set before him, not delaying too long over apparent difficulties. The thing that puzzles him on one page may be made plain by what he reads a page or two farther on. The first reading should be followed by a second reading during which any obscurity that still persists should be noted for special consideration. If the reader feels that he is insufficiently grounded in any process touched upon in the following chapters, he could refer to a standard text for exercises on which to practise and so make himself proficient. With his weaknesses corrected in this way the student could then give the following chapters a third and final reading. After this he could follow farther any study that particularly interested him. For instance, he could set himself different expressions to plot as graphs, or he could take the conic sections one by one and derive from their definitions the relation between x and y which represent them algebraically.

The really keen student is rarely satisfied to sit at the feet of one master or assimilate learning from one book. It would gratify me to think that certain of my readers coming upon the theory of equations or of conics would take the trouble to read up these same subjects again in other books—in their *Encyclopædia Britannica*, say, or in texts obtainable from the local public library.

The present work cannot pretend to be exhaustive; it is but a guide to point out the main road to learning and the student is expected to trace and retrace this road, noticing at last the interesting byways that branch off and invite him to digress. Strange though it may seem, many a student has come at last to love mathematics for its own sake and to find in the solution of its many problems an occupation so peaceful and absorbing as to out-rival all other pleasures. It is to be regretted that the widespead liking for crossword puzzles and the game of chess never led people to seek problems more worthy of attention, for plenty of such problems exist, and given some facility in manipulating symbols and numbers, anybody can be as happy in the land of mathematical mysteries as in playing conventional games or solving conventional puzzles.

Time spent on recreations of a mathematical nature is never wasted, because they exercise the faculty that is most useful of all to the student of science. Not until he is perfectly at home with the shorthand language of the mathematician can a man hope to read the more advanced works on scientific subjects with pleasure and profit.

CHAPTER I

HOW MATHEMATICS BEGAN

Mathematical studies originated thousands of years ago, and the Greeks were already in possession of a vast amount of geometrical knowledge before the opening of the Christian era. This knowledge might have spread quickly throughout the world, but for many centuries the Christians opposed the teaching of anything that came from Greek or other "heathen" sources. The cleverness of some of the early mathematicians caused them to be persecuted for practising magic; it was thought that they owed their inspiration to the devil.

A certain amount of knowledge, geometrical and otherwise, was gained by practical men seeking the solution of day-to-day problems, but mathematics would never have become the vast body of knowledge that it is to-day had its development been left to people intent on making themselves prosperous. Such people were too busy to occupy themselves with learning for its own sake. Most of the progress made in mathematics is owing to men of more leisured habits who loved to set themselves puzzles and then find the solutions. In geometry the Greek teachers saw wonderful material for exercising and training the mind. They delighted in arranging logically the known facts about lines, triangles, circles and so on, making a sort of staircase of knowledge up which the student climbed step by step. Each step surmounted afforded the possibility of mounting one step higher. By demonstrating one almost self-evident geometrical truth after another the student arrived at last to the point where he was able to perceive highly useful and much less obvious geometrical relations—for instance, the relation between the squares on the three sides of a right-angled triangle, discovery of which is usually attributed to Pythagoras (see page 88).

Much of the geometrical knowledge of the Greeks was embodied in the famous text-book of Euclid entitled *Elements*. This came into use about 300 years before Christ, and it has been the bane of the duller sort of scholar ever since, although bright boys and girls find it of interest. Geometry was making great progress in Euclid's time, and it must not be thought that the *Elements* represents the sum total of what was then known. Archimedes and Apollonius pushed their inquiries so far beyond what is contained in the *Elements* that not until the advent of Newton in the seventeenth century of our own era did geometry again receive a definite forward impetus. Isolated discoveries and some useful suggestions were made by various able mathematicians between the time of the Greeks and that of Sir Isaac Newton, but credit is usually given to Newton for carrying on with the researches of Archimedes at the point where Archimedes left off. It is impossible to say now how much more the world might have benefited from the genius of Archimedes had he lived longer; he was a great scientist as well as a mathematician, but he was killed by a Roman soldier while in the midst of his studies at Syracuse when this city was eventually captured and sacked after a long siege. Nobody else of his immense ability was to be born for nearly 2000 years.

Ordinary arithmetical operations that we consider simple to-day presented considerable difficulty to the Greeks, the Romans and many another civilised people, and consequently arithmetical problems were solved by geometry which, as we have seen, became a highly developed science in Greek hands. Numbers were represented by lines of different lengths, and it was not until the Arabs (who seemed to have borrowed the idea from the Hindus of India) started using the ten different symbols we know (1, 2, 3, 4, 5, 6, 7, 8, 9, 0) that the manipulation of numbers could conveniently be divorced from geometrical representation. Roman numerals were too clumsy and easily confused to suggest practicable methods for carrying out complicated calculations, and the limit to the enumerating powers of the ancients was set by the abacus, a mechanical device still used in kindergarten schools and enabling addition or subtraction to be carried out without much difficulty.

We, who begin our mathematical studies as children by dealing with integral numbers in the operations of addition, subtraction and multiplication, escape acquaintance with fractions until we come to division and encounter sums which do not divide out exactly. Our early sums have to do with "whole" things such as sheep or people, which cannot be subdivided. The Greeks were confronted with fractions from the outset, because when the unit is represented by a line of given length it becomes apparent that there could be fractional parts of this unit; a line 1 inch long can be divided into two, three, four or any number of shorter lines, each representing a fractional part of an inch.

In course of time (long after the Greek ascendancy) lengths and numbers not precisely known came to be represented by alphabetical symbols, and to-day we often put a, b, c for the magnitudes used to construct a triangle. The measures of the opposite angles are denoted by A, B, C.

In co-ordinate geometry we indicate the position of a point in space by its distances from three fixed planes; in general these are shown as x, y and z until numerical values can be substituted for the symbols. Angles of uncertain amount are provisionally represented by the Greek equivalents of our letters such as α (for a), β (for b), γ (for c) and so on. These are "alpha," "bēta" and "gamma." Other frequently used Greek letters are pī (π), thēta (θ), phī (ϕ), ōmega (ω) and psī (ψ). For some of these a fixed meaning is assigned; thus π is always used to denote the ratio of a circle's circumference to its diameter, or the radian measure of 180 degrees. In the various physical sciences the Greek letters are again given special significance; thus in mechanics an angular velocity in radians per second is nearly always represented by ω; in electricity a magnetic flux is commonly represented by ϕ, and the same symbol appears again to represent yet another quantity in the science of thermodynamics.

When the letter "a" is used to signify the length of one side of a triangle we understand that a can be anything, not necessarily an integral number of inches or feet. Numbers stand for fixed quantities, either integers or definite fractions, but a symbol such as a, b, c, x, y or z can be made to stand for whatever quantity satisfies the conditions. Such symbols are the shorthand of the mathematician, for they enable statements to be made very concisely. Thus the statement: "a man walking for a given time will cover a distance equal to the time in hours multiplied by his rate of travelling," can be written very briefly

$$S = vt,$$

where S is the distance and vt is the product of v the speed (or velocity) and t the time. The short lines in between S and vt form the symbol of equality. If $v = 4$ miles an hour, then

$$S = 4t$$

means that in t hours the man will walk a distance $S = 4t$ miles. If

$t = 1, S = 4 \times 1 = 4$; if $t = 2$, $S = 4 \times 2 = 8$; if $t = 3$, $S = 4 \times 3 = 12$ and so on, the result being in miles in every instance.

You should notice that the relation $S = vt$ holds good for all values of t, so that t can change continuously from one value to another and S will faithfully and truthfully alter to correspond. The value of t does not have to jump from integer to integer in the way suggested above; $S = 4t$ is equally true for values of t lying between integers; for $t = 2\frac{1}{2}$ for instance, or for $t = 3 \cdot 7258$.

Needless to say, the truth of the relation $S = 4t$ is dependent upon the constancy of the speed at which the man walks and the precision with which his speed is measured. You would not want t to be measured to four places of decimals (to tenths of a second) if the man's speed were estimated to be only roughly 4 m.p.h.

3	6	6
8	5	2
4	4	7

(a)

a	b	c
c	a	b
b	c	a

(b)

10	3	8
5	7	9
6	11	4

(c)

15	-4	10
2	7	12
4	18	-1

(d)

Here is a problem the solution of which is helped by the use of symbols standing for integers. The problem is not of any practical importance, but it is a puzzle that intrigued the ancients and it would probably provide some minutes' amusement to your brighter friends. You have a large square divided into nine smaller ones, as shown in the diagram (*a*) on this page; you have to put integers in the nine spaces so that the sum of any three taken horizontally across the square, down the square, or diagonally from corner to corner is always the same. In the particular solution shown the total is 15. Could you fill up the nine spaces in some other way to satisfy a different condition—to give a common sum of 10 say, or 20? If you experiment with different numbers you will find that the problem is never easy and often it seems to be quite impossible to solve.

To find a rule for solving it you can experiment with symbols. Suppose you wished to achieve a solution using only the numbers a, b and c. You could write these in the given order across the top row, and again in the next two rows but starting one place and two places to the right. When you have done this (see diagram (*b*)) you will find that the sum across or down is $a + b + c$ in every instance. The diagonal sum from top right to bottom left is also $a + b + c$, but the remaining diagonal is $a + a + a$ or $3a$. Thus the numbers represented by a, b and c will fulfil the conditions only if a is a third of the total sum. Another way of putting it is to say that the sum must be a multiple of 3;

thus you could never solve the puzzle if you tried to make the three numbers add up to 10 or 20.

The number in the central space is a and so you should be able to solve the puzzle easily if you will put in this space a number equal to a third of the sum you are aiming to get. Suppose you are trying to make the numbers across, down and diagonally come to 21; then you should put 7 in the central space (see diagram (c)). After this you can fill in the numbers as you please, putting anything anywhere so long as the sums across, down and diagonally are made to come to 21.

If you choose large numbers to begin with you may be driven to fill in some of the remaining spaces with zeros or even negative (to be taken away) numbers; diagram (d) shows an instance of this. The numbers 15 and 10 in the top row were chosen at random, with the result that two of the remaining numbers had to be negative.

Diagram (e) shows a square divided into sixteen spaces. Once again we wish to fill in the spaces with integers so that horizontal rows, vertical rows and diagonal rows all add up to the same sum. If, as shown in diagram (e), we use the symbols a, b, c, d in such a way as to make the rows come right, then the diagonals become equal to $4a$

a	b	c	d
b	a	d	c
c	d	a	b
d	c	b	a

(e)

2	4	8	4
6	5	3	4
5	6	4	3
5	3	3	7

(f)

and $4d$ respectively. Thus we could achieve our result with integers provided that two of them (a and d) were the same and each equal to a fourth part of $a + b + c + d$. The integers might be 4, 3, 5 and 4 or 5, 6, 4 and 5.

Need we tie ourselves to using only four integers of which two are alike? In the nine-space square we found that we could use any integers we liked provided that the one we put at the centre was a third of the sum aimed at for the rows and diagonals. In the sixteen-space square, the possibility suggests itself that provided we do the right thing in filling the central group of four spaces we shall reach a solution. The diagonal sum for this central group is $2a$ or $2d$ and in each case it is half the sum for the whole diagonal. Let us then start with some number for the whole square which is divisible by 2, the number 18, say. Half of this is 9 and $9 = 5 + 4$ or $3 + 6$. In diagram (f) the four numbers 5, 4, 3 and 6 have been put in the four central spaces. The corner spaces have then been filled up to give complete diagonal sums of 18. Two of the figures used were optional and the others were obligatory differences. Four more optional numbers were then filled in, one in each side row and one each in the top and bottom rows. The last four spaces had to receive obligatory numbers and they were found to satisfy all the conditions so that, finally, diagram (*f*) gave a solution to the puzzle.

If you proceed in the way indicated here, choosing to begin with a sum divisible by 2 and making sure that the diagonal sums for the central group of four squares is equal to half the sum aimed at for the rows and diagonals of the complete square, *you cannot go wrong*.

Next we shall seek a solution for the twenty-five-space square. There is scope here for using five integers a, b, c, d and e, so that all the rows and both diagonals add up to $a + b + c + d + e$, and diagram (*g*) shows the filling required. No limit whatever is placed on the integers used or on the sum they are required to yield. Let us choose to aim at a sum of 25. Beginning by filling in any numbers we please, we find ourselves free to fill in a great many before our hand is forced. With a nine-space square we could put in only two more from choice after the central number; beyond this the numbers were dictated by the terms of the problem. With a twenty-five-space square we can put in 14 numbers from choice after the central one. If we aim at getting all the down rows and the diagonals to add up correctly, we shall probably find two of our cross rows coming out wrong, but as the amount by which one exceeds the chosen sum equals the amount by which the other is short, we can adjust the two rows until both are made correct without affecting the downward rows. In filling up diagram (*h*) the number 5 was put in the centre; then the four rows top and bottom right and left framing the figure were filled up, 12 figures being chosen and 4 being obligatory. Then the diagonal sums were made to come right, one figure in each being chosen freely and the other being obligatory. The downward rows on either side of the central one were then made right and in the course of doing this one cross row (the central one) was unavoidably made to add up to 2 too many. The second cross row from the top and the central down row were then made right, and in doing this the second cross row from the bottom was unavoidably made 2 too few.

a	b	c	d	e
d	e	a	b	c
b	c	d	e	a
e	a	b	c	d
c	d	e	a	b

(*g*)

3	4	11	4	3
8	4	3	8	2
6	7	5	7	2
5	6	3	2	7
3	4	3	4	11

(*h*)

The figures shown deleted were then adjusted to give the correct solution, one being made 2 more and the other 2 less. We now see that particular symbolical solutions to all these puzzles have led us to discover the rules whereby numerical solutions can readily be obtained. You could have juggled with figures for hours without finding a single solution to the nine-, sixteen- or twenty-five-space squares, and when eventually you arrived at a numerical solution it would not have been likely to suggest to you the way in which you could find an alternative solution. *The symbols have compelled the secret to divulge itself*, for symbols do not lose their identity by mingling together as numbers do when you operate with them.

Work with symbols instead of numbers is called *algebra*, and you can see now that it is productive of results not easily obtained in any other way.

Here is another mystery that easy algebra will clear up for you:

Ask your friends to write down any sum of money less than £12 in which the pence figure is less than the pounds figure. A typical amount would be £9 2s. 6d. You now ask your friend to reverse this sum of money, writing it under the original amount with the pounds figure in the pence place and the pence figure in the pounds place. This having been done, your friend must subtract the lower sum of money from the top one. The result will be as given below:

£	s.	d.
9	2	6
6	2	9
£2	19	9

The "answer" must now be reversed and added to itself as shown below:

£	s.	d.
2	19	9
9	19	2
£12	18	11

The peculiarity of this result is that it is *always the same* no matter what sum of money was originally thought of. Here, for instance, is the same set of calculations performed with £10 6s. 8d.

£	s.	d.
10	6	8
8	6	10
1	19	10
10	19	1
£12	18	11

This agreement between the final results when, say, ten of your friends all carry out your instructions and all reach the same answer proves very mystifying at first, but if you will work with *a* pounds, *b* shillings and *c* pence, you will see that the agreement is inevitable. Here is the working when the sum of money first thought of is £*a b*s. *c*d.:

£	s.	d.
a	*b*	*c*
c	*b*	*a*
$a - 1 - c$	$(b-1) + 20 - b$	$c + 12 - a$
$c + 12 - a$	$(b-1) - 20 - b$	$a - 1 - c$
12	18	11

Some explanation of the above may be necessary.

Since pence were to be less than pounds, *c* is less than *a*, and before *a* can be subtracted from *c* a shilling (12 pence) must be borrowed from the amount of *b* shillings; thus we have to take *a* not simply from *c* but from $c + 12$, and the subtraction gives us $c + 12 - a$.

Coming now to the shillings, we find we must take *b* from $b - 1$ (a shilling having been previously borrowed). We cannot perform this subtraction until we have borrowed a pound (20 shillings). Then we take *b* from $(b - 1) + 20$ and the result is $(b - 1) + 20 - b$, or 19. In the pounds column we have to take *c* from $a - 1$ (a pound having been borrowed from *a*); this leaves us with $a - 1 - c$ pounds.

When this "answer" to the subtraction sum is reversed and we start to add we find that the symbols all cancel out. Thus in the pence column we have *a* and *c* but we have also $- a$ and $- c$, and $a - a$ equals nothing; so does $c - c$. This leaves us with $12 - 1 = 11$.

In the shillings column we have $(b - 1) + 20 - b$ to add to its like. Here you can see that $b - b = 0$, so that you are left with $20 - 1 = 19$, and 19*s.* added to itself is £1 18*s.* Thus of necessity the shillings will always be 18 just as the pence will always be 11. In the pounds column we have $a - a = 0$; $c - c = 0$; and $12 - 1 = 11$. But there is 1 pound to carry over from the shillings column, and $11 + 1 = 12$ so that, of necessity, this figure which represents the number of pounds will always be 12. Finally, then, we have juggled with the three symbols *a*, *b* and *c* in such a way as to get rid of them, leaving three numbers in their place—the numbers 12, 18, 11.

The puzzle is in reality only another of those old favourites which go something like this:

Think of a number, double it, add 10, subtract 5, take away twice the number you first thought of—and your answer is 5. In symbols this one would work out like this:

$$2a + 10 - 5 - 2a = 5,$$

showing you that it is immaterial what number you initially choose for *a*. Small children are mystified by this transparently explicable "magic," but you will be able to "see through it" at once. The pounds, shillings and pence jugglery is not so obviously a trick, and even the adult intelligence is duped by it.

Some mathematical puzzles have a long and interesting history because the more difficult ones excited the interest of really able mathematicians. The problem of filling in the spaces of a square so that the numbers added up to the same whether taken across, down or diagonally is a very old one and it can be varied to make it more difficult. Thus you could restrict yourself to the use of consecutive numbers, not allowing yourself to omit any or to use any number twice. This would mean that in doing the nine-space square you would have to solve the puzzle using the numbers 1 to 9 only. Not knowing the sum to which the lines of three numbers must add up, you cannot at once put the right figure in the central square, though, of course, this will still have to be a third of that sum. We know that the sum could never be less than 9 + 1 + 2 = 12, so that 4 is the lowest figure we need to try in the centre. The sum with 4 in the centre would be 12, but the number 9 has to be used twice at least in forming this sum and this is impossible with the given figures because the next lowest sum involving 9 is 9 + 3 + 4 = 16. We can now try 5 in the centre; the sum to aim at is 15, and using 9 twice to get 15 we have the alternatives 9 + 5 + 1 and 9 + 4 + 2. Obviously 9 must not be at a corner, for here it would be involved in a diagonal sum also, and we cannot make three sums equal to 15 which include 9. Diagram (*a*) on this page shows the start (using 5 at the centre) that the logic of the case demands. Diagram (*b*) shows the next stage. After this our hand is forced, but when we fill in the obligatory numbers we find that they complete the sequence 1 to 9 and give us the solution to our puzzle. The ancients called this result a "magic square of the 3rd order." A magic square of the 5th order would be one having twenty-five spaces filled with the numbers 1 to 25 in such a way as to give the same sum across, down and diagonally. One of the 4th order would be filled with the numbers 1 to 16.

It is not necessary for me to go into the general theory of magic squares, but you can see that they afford scope for much thought. In the fourth or fifth century of our era a mathematician of Constantinople called Moschopulus wrote a treatise on magic squares showing how they could be filled in irrespective of the order. Seemingly useless investigations of this kind led to the improvement of algebraical methods and provided an instrument of research that could be turned to real account.

Another of the puzzles that led to speculations of value was that associated with the old legend of the race between Achilles and the tortoise. Achilles runs, let us say, ten times as fast as the tortoise, but the tortoise has a start of 100 yards to help him win. When Achilles has run the first 100 yards the tortoise has advanced 10 yards; when Achilles has run 10 yards the tortoise has advanced 1 yard more; when Achilles has run 1 yard the tortoise has advanced $\frac{1}{10}$ yard; when Achilles has run $\frac{1}{10}$ yard the tortoise has advanced $\frac{1}{100}$ yard.

We can go on like this for ever proving (apparently) that the tortoise always remains in front of Achilles. This seems contrary to common sense and of course it *is* contrary to common sense; the tortoise is in reality speedily overtaken. How, then, are the two points of view to be reconciled?

Our confusion results from considering the actions of Achilles and the tortoise stage by stage. Each stage takes as long to describe as the one before though in reality the stages are accomplished in ever-diminishing times. Though we could imagine an infinite number of stages and take an infinite time describing them, the real times for each stage get shorter and shorter and their sum is *not* infinite.

Let us imagine that Achilles was able to run at 5 yards per second, then the first stage of 100 yards took him 20 seconds, the next stage of 10 yards took him 2 seconds, the next stage of 1 yard took him $\frac{1}{5}$ second and so on; each stage took only a tenth of the time of the stage before. If we add up all these times (an infinite number of them) we get a definite and quite small sum. The numbers involved form what is called a geometric series or progression, and there is a formula for adding them up. Here are some numbers forming geometrical progressions, beginning with the ones already discussed:

$$20 \quad 2 \quad \tfrac{1}{5} \quad \tfrac{1}{50} \quad \tfrac{1}{500} \quad \tfrac{1}{5000}, \text{ etc.}$$
$$1 \quad \tfrac{1}{2} \quad \tfrac{1}{4} \quad \tfrac{1}{8} \quad \tfrac{1}{16} \quad \tfrac{1}{32}, \text{ etc.}$$
$$3 \quad 9 \quad 27 \quad 81 \quad 243 \quad 729, \text{ etc.}$$

In each series any one number is obtained from the preceding one by using a multiplier called the "common ratio." The common ratio is $\frac{1}{10}$ for the first series; for the others it is $\frac{1}{2}$ and 3 respectively. To get a generally applicable formula for the sum of the numbers in such a series, we must resort to symbols. Let a be the first term of our series (it is 20, 1 and 3 in the above examples) and let r be the common ratio (it is $\frac{1}{10}$, $\frac{1}{2}$ and 3 in the above examples). If S is the sum of the terms, then we can write:

$$S = a + (a \times r) + (a \times r \times r) + (a \times r \times r \times r) + \text{etc.}$$

A shorter way of writing $r \times r$ is usual in algebra—we write it r^2 and in the same way we put $r \times r \times r = r^3$; $r \times r \times r \times r = r^4$ and so on. Notice that the second term is ar, the third term ar^2, the fourth term ar^3 and so on; the nth term would obviously be ar^{n-1}. Now we will write our series again thus:

$$S = a + ar + ar^2 + ar^3 + ar^4 \ldots ar^{n-1}.$$

The next step is what you might call a "wangle." I am going to multiply everything in this equality by r. This gives me:

$$Sr = ar + ar^2 + ar^3 + ar^4 + ar^5 + \ldots ar^n.$$

Continuing in my artfulness, I shall now subtract the multiplied series from the unmultiplied one, thus:

$$
\begin{aligned}
S &= a + ar + ar^2 + ar^3 + \ldots ar^{n-2} + ar^{n-1} \\
Sr &= ar + ar^2 + ar^3 + \ldots ar^{n-2} + ar^{n-1} + ar^n \\
\hline
S - Sr &= a \phantom{+ ar + ar^2 + ar^3 + \ldots ar^{n-2} + ar^{n-1}} - ar^n
\end{aligned}
$$

Everything disappears on the right except for a couple of end terms. My cunning has greatly simplified the expression for S. I have:

$$S - Sr = a - ar^n.$$

This simplifies to

$$S(1 - r) = a(1 - r^n).$$

Dividing both sides by $(1 - r)$ I get:

$$S = \frac{a(1 - r^n)}{1 - r}.$$

Shall we apply this formula to the problem of Achilles and the tortoise and so find out how long it took Achilles to catch up the tortoise?

The series for the times was

$$20, 2, \tfrac{1}{5}, \tfrac{1}{50}, \text{ etc., seconds.}$$

Here $a = 20$, $r = \frac{1}{10}$ and $n =$ infinity (written ∞). Filling in these figures we get:

$$S = \frac{20\ \{1 - (\frac{1}{10})\infty\}}{1 - \frac{1}{10}}\ \text{seconds.}$$

Now what should you think a tenth multiplied by itself an endless number of times would be? Try it and see: $\frac{1}{10} \times \frac{1}{10} = \frac{1}{100}$; $\frac{1}{100} \times \frac{1}{10} = \frac{1}{1000}$; $\frac{1}{1000} \times \frac{1}{10} = \frac{1}{10000}$ and so on. Obviously if we go on like this we shall end up with a fraction so tiny that it is just nothing at all. So our result simplifies to:

$$S = \frac{20 \times 1}{1 - \frac{1}{10}} = \frac{20}{\frac{9}{10}} = \frac{200}{9} = 22\frac{2}{9}\ \text{seconds.}$$

Achilles runs at the rate of 5 yards a second, so in $22\frac{2}{9}$ seconds he runs:

$$5 \times 22\frac{2}{9} = 111\frac{1}{9}\ \text{yards.}$$

In other words, Achilles catches up the tortoise after he has run 111 yards 4 inches. Thereafter he will be in front of the tortoise.

Is not algebra a wonderful thing? It has enabled us to deal in a few minutes with an infinite series of numbers, adding them up and giving the right answer.

The Geometrical Progression is only one kind of series out of many possible ones. You could make up a series like this:

$$1,\ 1\frac{1}{2},\ 2,\ 2\frac{1}{2},\ 3,\ 3\frac{1}{2},\ \text{etc.}$$
$$\text{or}\ 12,\ 10,\ 8,\ 6,\ 4,\ 2,\ 0,\ -2,\ -4,\ \text{etc.}$$

Here you have added or taken away the same amount each time in going from one turn to the next. Such a series is called an Arithmetical Progression, and the amount added or subtracted each time is called the "common difference." How would you add up a series of numbers like this? Let us try the general case, putting a for the first term and d for the common difference. The sum S of n terms is:

$$S = a + (a + d) + (a + 2d) + (a + 3d) + \ldots [a + (n - 1)d].$$

The "wangle" here is to write the same series again but backwards and then add to the original series, as follows:

$$S = a + (a+d) + (a+2d) + (a+3d) + \ldots [a+(n-1)d]$$
$$S = [a + (n-1)d] + [a + (n-2)d] + [a+(n-3)d] + \ldots (a+d) + a$$
$$\overline{2S = a + [2a+nd] + [2a+nd] + [2a+nd] + [2a+nd] + a}$$
$$= 2a\ \text{taken}\ n\ \text{times plus}\ nd\ \text{taken}\ (n-1)\ \text{times}$$
$$= 2an + nd(n-1)$$
$$= n\{2a + (n-1)d\}$$
$$\therefore S = n\left\{\frac{2a + (n-1)d}{2}\right\}$$

This formula can be remembered in words because $2a + (n-1)d$ is the sum of the first and last terms of the progression, and half of this sum is called their *average* or *mean*. Thus the *sum of an Arithmetical Progression is the mean of the first and last terms multiplied by the number of terms.*

Problem 1.—A motor car travels 8 feet in the first second of its motion, 10 feet in the next, 12 feet in the next and so on. How far does it travel in half a minute? The first term of this series is 8 and there are 30 terms. The common difference is $+2$, so that the last term is $8 + 29 \times 2 = 64$. The sum S is given by

$$S = \frac{\text{1st term} + \text{30th term}}{2} \times 30$$

$$= \frac{8 + 64}{2} \times 30 = 1080 \text{ feet.}$$

Numbers behave in ways that are puzzling until you can see the algebraic or geometrical interpretation. Here is something that at first sight seems inexplicable. The "squares" of the natural numbers are $1 \times 1 = 1$, $2 \times 2 = 4$, $3 \times 3 = 9$, $4 \times 4 = 16$ and so on. The odd numbers (numbers not divisible by 2) are 3, 5, 7, 9, 11 and so on. Take the square of 1 and add the

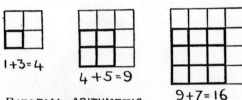

PICTORIAL ARITHMETIC

first odd number to it and we get $1 + 3 = 4$ the next square. Take 4 and add the next odd number to it, and we get $4 + 5 = 9$, the next square. From 9 we get $9 + 7 = 16$ the square of 4, and from 16 we get $16 + 9 = 25$, the square of 5. Farther than $25 + 11 = 36$ or 6×6 we need not go, for we can see now that all the squares are to be got in this way by combining a previous square with an odd number. Why is this?

If we show a pictorial representation of what occurs (see the diagrams on this page), we shall cease to be puzzled, for the results now seem obvious and natural.

The same pictorial method turns the colourless and apparently useless truisms of algebra into meaningful statements. Every multiplication of two terms yields an area; if the terms are equal you get a square; if they are unequal you get a rectangle. When you multiply compound lengths together—for instance $a + b$ by $c + d$—your result is made up of four terms, since each term in the first expression must multiply each term in the second, and where all terms are different there can be no reduction of terms by amalgamation in the final result. The rule for squaring an

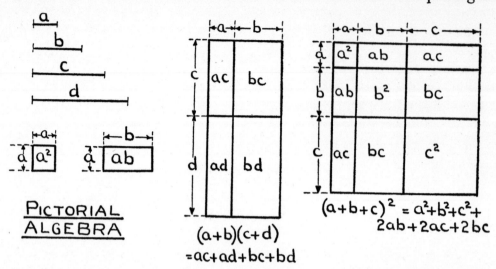

PICTORIAL ALGEBRA

$(a+b)(c+d)$
$=ac+ad+bc+bd$

$(a+b+c)^2 = a^2+b^2+c^2+2ab+2ac+2bc$

expression is also clearly justified—you must take the square of every term and twice the product of all possible pairs. Thus:

$$(a + b + c)^2 = a^2 + b^2 + c^2 + 2ab + 2ac + 2bc.$$

Euclid gave all these results in long-winded fashion, and for some centuries all algebraical results were formulated in words and not in symbols. The elimination of diagrams and the substitution of symbolical for verbal methods of expression gave us our algebra.

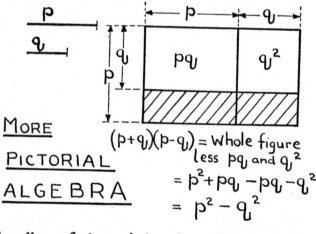

MORE PICTORIAL ALGEBRA

$(p+q)(p-q) =$ Whole figure less pq and q^2
$= p^2+pq -pq -q^2$
$= p^2 - q^2$

Geometry can give us a pictorial interpretation of a^3 or of $a \times b \times c$, or even of $(a+b)(c+d)(e+f)$, all these being solid figures; but what can it tell us of a^4 or $abcd$ or $(a+ b)\ (c+ d)\ (e+ f)\ (g+ h)$ or $(1 + x)^n$?

The rules for multiplying which apply to two or three quantities (and give areas and solids according to geometrical interpretation) can be extended to deal with four and more factors, but here geometry is left behind, for it cannot present us with visual justification for our methods. We adhere to these methods, referring to the quantities involved as "factors" rather than as "dimensions," blindly hoping that they will lead us to truth of some sort, though not geometrical truth; and happily we are vindicated in our faith.

Advanced mathematics deals nowadays with ideas that are not susceptible to any but symbolical interpretation. The Greeks refused to contemplate a product of more than three quantities—they said that it had no geo-

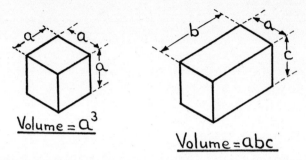

Volume $= a^3$

Volume $= abc$

SIMPLE 3-DIMENSIONAL QUANTITIES

metrical significance and therefore did not make sense. Modern algebra is happy in more than three dimensions, however, and we no longer tie ourselves to this old geometrical limit of three.

If the Greeks had ever got as far as evaluating

$$(1 + x)^2 = 1 + 2x + x^2$$

and
$$(1 + x)^3 = 1 + 3x + 3x^2 + x^3$$

by symbolical methods they would have felt very pleased with themselves, but they would have hesitated before writing the next result, namely

$$(1 + x)^4 = 1 + 4x + 6x^2 + 4x^3 + x^4,$$

saying that it could not mean anything real. We no longer suffer from such scruples and, in fact, Sir Isaac Newton worked out the value of $(1 + x)^n$ in the seventeenth century, obtaining a result called the Binomial Theorem which we are quite happy to accept as true even though n may be fractional or negative! The Binomial Theorem says that:

$$(1 + x)^n = 1 + nx + \frac{n(n-1)}{1 \times 2} x^2 + \frac{n(n-1)(n-2)}{1 \times 2 \times 3} x^3 + \text{etc.}$$

You can easily verify that it is true for $n = 2$, 3 or 4, but how are you to feel about its veracity when $n = \frac{1}{2}$ say, or -3?

On page 15 we resorted to writing r^2 for $r \times r$ as a matter of convenience, and we know what we mean by r^n when n is a positive integer. But what can n mean when we put $\frac{1}{2}$ or -3 for it? I will explain:

Suppose we wish to divide r^4 by r^2 we should proceed as follows:

$$\frac{r \times r \times r \times r}{r \times r} = r \times r = r^2 \ (= r^{4-2}).$$

Again:

$$r^6 \div r^3 = \frac{r \times r \times r \times r \times r \times r}{r \times r \times r} = r^{6-3} = r^3.$$

The rule for division of one "power" of r by another, then, is to *subtract the indices* corresponding to that power. If we divide r^2 by r^4 we get the quite intelligible result:

$$\frac{r \times r}{r \times r \times r \times r} = \frac{1}{r^2}$$

but applying the rule we get $r^{2-4} = r^{-2}$. If, then, r^{-2} means anything it must mean the reciprocal of r^2, namely $\frac{1}{r^2}$, and we accept this meaning.

If we want to find out what quantity multiplied by itself gives us r^4, we have only to write $r^4 = r \times r \times r \times r$ and we see at once that the required quantity is $r \times r$. Thus, what we call the "square root" of r^4 is r^2 and we find it by halving the power index. You can satisfy yourself that $\sqrt{r^6} = r^3$, but applying the rule in every case you are forced to write $\sqrt{r^3} = r^{1\frac{1}{2}}$ or $\sqrt{r} = r^{\frac{1}{2}}$.

A particularly curious result is r^0; what can this mean? We get it from dividing r^2 by r^2 or r^n by r^n, for the one comes to $r^{2-2} = 0$ if we apply the rule, and the other likewise comes to r^0. But we know that the division comes to 1 in each case; thus $r^0 = 1$ if it means anything at all.

After this explanation you will be able to work out $(1 + x)^{-3}$ quite easily; it is simply

$$\frac{1}{1 + 3x + 3x^2 + x^3}$$

and $(1 + x)^{\frac{1}{2}}$ is the same thing as $\sqrt{1 + x}$. Suppose that $x = 0 \cdot 21$; then $\sqrt{1 + x} = \sqrt{1 \cdot 21} =$ (by ordinary arithmetic) $1 \cdot 100$. This result could be got from the Binomial Theorem, for we have:

$$(1 + x)^{\frac{1}{2}} = 1 + \tfrac{1}{2}x + \frac{\tfrac{1}{2}(\tfrac{1}{2} - 1)}{1 \times 2} x^2 + \frac{\tfrac{1}{2}(\tfrac{1}{2} - 1)(\tfrac{1}{2} - 2)}{1 \times 2 \times 3} x^3 + \ldots$$

$$= 1 + 0 \cdot 5x - 0 \cdot 125x^2 + 0 \cdot 0625x^3 - \ldots$$

If we put $x = 0 \cdot 21$ and take enough terms of this series, we shall approach the right answer. The first two terms give it very nearly, for

$$1 + 0.05x = 1 + \frac{0.21}{2} = 1.105.$$

This provides us with a useful mental approximation for the square or square root of any number very near to unity.

If x is small:

$$\sqrt{1 + x} = 1 + \tfrac{1}{2}x$$
$$\sqrt{1 - x} = 1 - \tfrac{1}{2}x$$
$$(1 + x)^2 = 1 + 2x$$
$$(1 - x)^2 = 1 - 2x$$

Thus:

$$\sqrt{1.1} = 1.05$$
$$\sqrt{0.9} = 0.95$$
$$1.1^2 = 1.2$$
$$0.95^2 = 0.9$$

and so on.

CHAPTER II

LABOUR-SAVING ARITHMETIC

When an expression $(a + b + c)$ is multiplied by another such as $(d + e + f)$ the work is performed in steps, for first we multiply by d, getting $da + db + dc$; then we multiply by e, getting $ea + eb + ec$; then we multiply by f, getting $fa + fb + fc$, and finally we add all these results together.

Now arithmetical multiplication is performed in the same way, though usually the work proceeds from right to left instead of from left to right. An example in multiplication is given below.

	THOUSANDS	HUNDREDS	TENS	UNITS
		3	1	2	8
		6	1	3	2
			6	2	5	6
		9	3	8	4	0
	3	1	2	8	0	0
1	8	7	6	8	0	0	0
	1	9	1	8	0	8	9	6

Notice that we multiply 3128 first of all by 2, an operation which should not require explaining or justifying to anybody; then we multiply it by 3, but because this numeral really signifies 30, or 3×10, we have to multiply by 10 also. This we do by shifting our result one place to the left to make room for a o in the units place. Multiplying next by 1, which is really 1×100, we shift our result two places to the left. Our next line is shifted three places to the left. All our lines are then added up to give the product of

$$(3000 + 100 + 20 + 8)\,(6000 + 100 + 30 + 2).$$

We can deal with numbers involving decimal fractions in exactly the same way, thus:

TENS	UNITS		TENTHS	HUNDREDTHS		
3	1	·	2	8		
	6	·	1	3	2	
1 8	7	·	6	8		
	3	·	1	2	8	
		·	9	3	8	4
		·	0	6	2	5 6
1 9	1	·	8	0	8	9 6

Here, however, the work is most likely to be conducted without mistake if we multiply by the 6 to form our first row, 6 standing for units. Our first figure of 8, resulting from multiplying 8 by 6, is put under the 8 which is multiplied. The other rows go one, two and three places to the right because the multiplying numerals do not stand for units but for tenths, hundredths and thousandths, so that the multiplications must be corrected by simultaneous division by 10, 100 and 1000 respectively.

Very rarely in practice would the scientist or engineer perform a multiplication such as is shown in the second example here. The figures forming the factors in a practical calculation are usually the result of measurements made with some instrument for which only a limited degree of accuracy can be claimed. The figures 31·28 and 6·132 might be obtained with such an instrument. Clearly the results are supposed to be correct to one part in less than 10,000. The result of multiplying out these figures is an "answer" which pretends to an accuracy of one part in nineteen million! The last figures in this answer are clearly valueless because it would make all the difference to them whether the product were really 31·277 × 6·1318 or 31·283 × 6·1322. The *reliable* part of the "answer" goes only to four figures, the same as in the original factors; it is 191·8. These figures are called "significant" figures.

In general, when we work with factors containing n significant figures we shall get an answer of which only the first n figures are to be regarded as significant.

The engineer's way of evaluating $31 \cdot 28 \times 6 \cdot 132$ is set out below:

$$
\begin{array}{r}
3\cancel{1}\cancel{2}\cancel{8} \\
2\cancel{3}\cancel{1}\cancel{6} \\
\hline
18768 \\
313 \\
94 \\
6 \\
\hline
1918\cdot1
\end{array}
$$

Notice first of all that the decimal place is ignored in both numbers. Anyone can see that the answer will be *about* 180 and so, when the answer comes out to be 19181, we know it is really 191·81. To keep track of the decimal point is unnecessary when its final position can be so easily determined.

Notice next that the multiplier is reversed so that the rows are staggered to the right instead of to the left as is more usual. When a number has been used as multiplier it is crossed out together with the figure above it. The next figure thus has one fewer figures to multiply and labour is saved. The rows all begin under each other and they get shorter and shorter. Figures which would normally spread out towards the right are omitted because these are the ones affected by any approximation in the last figures of the two factors.

When 6 and 8 have been crossed out and multiplication by 1 commences, the operator looks at what has been crossed out to see if its multiplication would have given a figure to "carry." He says "1 by 8 is 8 and since this is nearer to 10 than to nothing I shall carry a 1; 1 by 2 is 2 and 1 to carry makes 3." This explains how the second row begins with 3 and not 2.

The third row is commenced after the 1 and the 2 have been crossed out. Three times the crossed-out figure of 2 is 6 and this is the better half of 10, so 1 is carried; $3 \times 1 = 3$ and 1 more is 4, so the third row starts with 4. In general the figure to be carried forward from multiplication of the crossed-out figure is the nearest multiple of ten; it is 1 for a product of 5 to 14, 2 for a product of 15 to 24, and so on.

This method of multiplication saves much time and it is therefore called the "contracted" method; it gives as many figures in the answer as can be trusted.

Contracted division also has for its object the limitation of work to what is really useful. Suppose we had 31·28 to divide by 6·132, we could either go on for ever as shown on the left (being very foolish to do so) or we could cut down the work to what is really useful as shown on the right. Here a figure of the divisor is crossed out after every division yielding a fresh numeral (or a cipher) in the quotient.

```
6132)31280(5101108...        6132)31280(5101
     30660                        30660
     ─────                        ─────
      6200                          620
      6132                          613
      ─────                         ───
       6800                           7
       6132                           6
       ─────                         ───
        6680                           1
        6132
        ─────
        54800
      and so on.
```

The decimal place is again left to look after itself; we know that the quotient must be about 5 and so its real value is 5·101. There can be no going wrong here because it could not be 0·5101 or 51·01.

The above example does not provide any instance of figures having to be carried over as a result of multiplying a crossed-out figure; consequently another will now be worked out. We will divide 73·281 by 387·64.

```
38764)73281(18905
      38764
      ─────
      34517
      31011
      ─────
       3506
       3488
       ────
         18
         19
```

The answer must plainly be in the neighbourhood of a fifth, or 0·2, so it is 0·18905.

When the 4 is crossed out the divisor is seen to give a figure of 8 for the quotient. Multiplying by 8 we see that if the crossed-out 4 were taken into account there would be 3 to carry; consequently we have $8 \times 6 = 48$ and 3 make 51. Put down 1 and carry 5.

When the 6 has been crossed out the divisor is seen to give a figure of 9 for the quotient. Multiplying by 9 we see that if the crossed-out 6 were taken into account there would be 5 to carry (because $9 \times 6 = 54$); So we say $9 \times 7 = 63$ and 5 make 68. Put down 8 and carry 6. How we get a carrying figure from crossed-out numbers is now plain. When a multiplication yields 28 we carry 3 and not 2; if it yields 25 we carry 3 also, but if it yields 24, 20, 18 or 15 we carry only 2.

The only other operation in simple arithmetic that we need to study in detail is the obtaining of square roots.

In algebra we know that $(a + b)^2 = a^2 + 2ab + b^2$, so that if we were finding the square root of $a^2 + 2ab + b^2$, the work would go like this:

$$
\begin{array}{r|l}
 & a + b \\
\hline
a & a^2 + 2ab + b^2 \\
 & a^2 \\
\hline
2a + b & + 2ab + b^2 \\
 & + 2ab + b^2 \\
\end{array}
$$

Here we have found the square root of the first term, namely of a^2; it is a. We put a on top and at the side. Then we multiply top and side terms, getting a^2 which we put under the original term of a^2. We subtract and bring down the outstanding terms $2ab + b^2$. We now divide this remainder by *twice that part of the root already obtained*, namely by $2a$, and we see that the result is $+ b$. We put $+b$ at the top and at the side and we multiply the total side expression by b; this gives us $2ab + b^2$, which we put under the $2ab + b^2$ already laid out. Subtraction leaves us with no remainder, so this is the end of our work and $a + b$ (the top expression) is the square root we want.

A similar process is employed in arithmetic, but we need to note that there are always *two* square roots possible in arithmetic, depending on the position of the decimal point. Thus $\sqrt{9} = 3$ but $\sqrt{90} = 9 \cdot 5$, also $\sqrt{900} = 30$ but $\sqrt{9000} = 95$ and so on.

Thus we cannot now ignore the decimal point. To prepare our number for the work of extracting its square root we must mark off the digits in pairs on either side of the decimal point. Thus, if we wanted the square root of $327 \cdot 581$ we should write it $\overline{3}\,\overline{27} \cdot \overline{58}\,\overline{1}$ and recognise that to begin with we had to find the approximate square root of 3, *not* of 30; it means that we start our answer with a 1 and *not* a 5. Below is the complete working:

$$
\begin{array}{r|l}
 & 18\cdot09\ldots \\
\hline
1 & 327\cdot58\overline{1} \\
 & 1 \\
\hline
28 & 227 \\
 & 224 \\
\hline
3609 & \quad 35810 \\
 & \quad 32481 \\
\hline
\end{array}
$$

and so on.

The decimal point is inserted when further figures can be obtained only by bringing down more figures after the decimal point (in this case the figures 58).

Later on we shall want certain square roots and so we will start to find them now. The working out of the above will become easier to follow after we have put in more practice. First of all we are going to evaluate $\sqrt{10}$ (proceeding to four significant figures).

$$
\begin{array}{r|l}
 & 3 \\
\hline
3 & 10\cdot00 \\
 & 9 \\
\hline
 & 100 \\
\end{array}
$$

Above is given the first step. Now we double the part of the root already obtained and use it as a divisor, thus:

$$
\begin{array}{r|l}
 & 3\cdot1 \\
\hline
3 & 10\cdot00 \\
 & 9 \\
\hline
61 & 100 \\
 & 61 \\
\hline
 & 3900 \\
\end{array}
$$

When 6 has another figure joined on to make it sixty-something it is contained by 100 only once, so the next part of the root is 1, as shown. 1 × 61 is 61 and when this is subtracted from 100 we have 39.

This is turned into 3900 for the next step. Notice that *two* digits are brought down each time (zeros in this case) to enable the work to proceed; in division only one digit is brought down at a time. The next step in our work is as follows:

```
                    3·16
                   ‾‾‾‾‾‾
        3    │   10·00
             │    9
             │   ‾‾
       61    │   100
             │    61
             │   ‾‾‾
      626    │   3900
             │   3756
             │   ‾‾‾‾
             │   14400
```

In our division here we had to think of how many times 3900 contained not 62 but six hundred and twenty-something; the obvious answer was 6, so six was added on top and at the side. We will now obtain two more figures so that we can adjust our final result correctly to four significant figures.

Here is our working as it appears when completed:

```
                     3·1622
                    ‾‾‾‾‾‾‾‾
        3     │   10·00
              │    9
              │   ‾‾
       61     │   100
              │    61
              │   ‾‾‾
      626     │   3900
              │   3756
              │   ‾‾‾‾
      6322    │    14400
              │    12644
              │   ‾‾‾‾‾‾
     63242    │    175600
              │    126484
              │   ‾‾‾‾‾‾‾
              │     49116
```

The next figure (if we wanted it) would be more than 5, so that the square root of 10 correct to five significant figures is 3·1623; correct to four significant figures it is 3·162.

We shall presently be wanting the fourth root of 10, i.e. $\sqrt[4]{10}$; it is $\sqrt{3\cdot1623}$ and the necessary calculation is set out on the next page.

$$\begin{array}{r|l}
 & 1\cdot778 \\ \hline
1 & 3\cdot\overline{1623} \\
 & 1 \\ \hline
27 & 216 \\
 & 189 \\ \hline
347 & 2723 \\
 & 2429 \\ \hline
3548 & 29400 \\
 & 28384 \\ \hline
3556 & 101600
\end{array}$$

The next figure would be nearer to 3 than to 2, so that the square root of $3\cdot1623$ to five significant figures is $1\cdot7783$.

Finally we shall require $\sqrt{1\cdot7783}$, which is the eighth root of 10, or $\sqrt[8]{10}$. Here is the necessary calculation:

$$\begin{array}{r|l}
 & 1\cdot333 \\ \hline
1 & 1\cdot\overline{7783} \\
 & 1 \\ \hline
23 & 77 \\
 & 69 \\ \hline
263 & 883 \\
 & 789 \\ \hline
2663 & 9400 \\
 & 7989 \\ \hline
2666 & 141100
\end{array}$$

The next figure would be 5, so that the square root of $1\cdot7783$ to five significant figures is $1\cdot3335$.

All the results so far calculated can now be gathered together as follows:

$$\sqrt{10} = 10^{\frac{1}{2}} = 3\cdot1623$$
$$\sqrt[4]{10} = 10^{\frac{1}{4}} = 1\cdot7783$$
$$\sqrt[8]{10} = 10^{\frac{1}{8}} = 1\cdot3335$$

Referring to page 20 in Chapter I, you will find an account of the theory of indices. Read this again carefully and then you will understand that:

$$10^{\frac{3}{4}} = 10^{\frac{1}{2}} \times 10^{\frac{1}{4}} = 3 \cdot 1623 \times 1 \cdot 7783 = 5 \cdot 6234$$
$$10^{\frac{3}{8}} = 10^{\frac{1}{4}} \times 10^{\frac{1}{8}} = 1 \cdot 7783 \times 1 \cdot 3335 = 2 \cdot 3713$$
$$10^{\frac{5}{8}} = 10^{\frac{1}{2}} \times 10^{\frac{1}{8}} = 3 \cdot 1623 \times 1 \cdot 3335 = 4 \cdot 2170$$
$$10^{\frac{7}{8}} = 10^{\frac{3}{4}} \times 10^{\frac{1}{8}} = 5 \cdot 6234 \times 1 \cdot 3335 = 7 \cdot 4988$$

The multiplications on the left are of powers of 10, and when powers are multiplied the indices are added; that is why $10^{\frac{3}{4}} = 10^{\frac{1}{2}} \times 10^{\frac{1}{4}}$; it is $10^{(\frac{1}{2}+\frac{1}{4})}$.

The multiplications on the right are all carried out by the contracted method. Here are the four sums:

```
3·1623        1·7783        3·1623        5·6234
3·8···        5····         5····         5····
-------       -------       -------       -------
31623         17783         31623         56234
22136          5335          9487         16870
 2213           533           949          1687
  253            53            95           169
    9             9            16            28
-------       -------       -------       -------
56234         23713         42170         74988
```

Collecting results again, we have the following table:

Index of 10	Number represented
0	1 (see page 20)
0·1250 (or $\frac{1}{8}$)	1·3335
0·2500 (or $\frac{1}{4}$)	1·7783
0·3750 (or $\frac{3}{8}$)	2·3713
0·5000 (or $\frac{1}{2}$)	3·1623
0·6250 (or $\frac{5}{8}$)	4·2170
0·7500 (or $\frac{3}{4}$)	5·6234
0·8750 (or $\frac{7}{8}$)	7·4988
1·0000	10·0000
2·0000	100·00
3·0000	1000·00

If we make a graph showing the numbers corresponding to various powers of 10, using the above figures for this purpose, we could (in theory at least) find from this graph the power of 10 corresponding to *any* number. The diagram on this page is the graph for numbers 1 to 10 for which the *power* of 10 ranges between 0 and 1. We can see from

this that $2 = 10^{0.3}$ and $3 = 10^{0.48}$ and $5 = 10^{0.7}$.

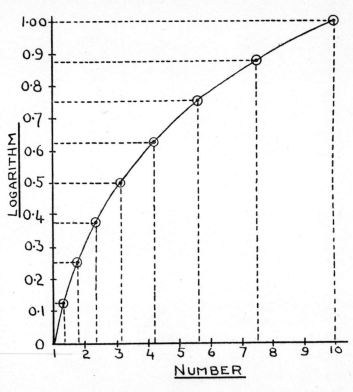

When a graph of this kind is drawn to a very large scale you can get the index of 10 for the various numbers more accurately. Thus in reality $2 = 10^{0.3010}$, $3 = 10^{0.4771}$, $5 = 10^{0.6990}$ and so on. The table below gives some results obtained from a very large graph indeed. Notice that the power or index of 10 corresponding to a given number is called the *logarithm* of that number. Thus log $2 = 0.3010$, log $3 = 0.4771$, log $10 = 1$, log $100 = 2$ and so on.

Number	Logarithm	Number	Logarithm
1·000	0·0000	1·500	0·1761
2·000	0·3010	2·500	0·3979
3·000	0·4771	3·500	0·5441
4·000	0·6021	4·500	0·6532
5·000	0·6990	5·500	0·7404
6·000	0·7782	6·500	0·8129
7·000	0·8451	7·500	0·8751
8·000	0·9031	8·500	0·9294
9·000	0·9542	9·500	0·9777
10·000	1·0000		

The value of logarithms is that with their help you can *turn a multiplication sum into a simple addition sum and a division sum into a simple subtraction sum.*

Let us take a very easy multiplication, say 2×3. To do this by logarithms we have (using the above table):

$$2 = 10^{0.3010}$$
$$3 = 10^{0.4771}$$
$$2 \times 3 = 10^{(0.3010+0.04771)}$$
$$= 10^{0.7781} = 6.$$

There is a very slight discrepancy in the last figure because $\log 6 = 0.7782$ according to the table.

Let us now try 4×2:

$$\log 4 = 0.6021$$
$$\log 2 = 0.3010$$
$$\text{Sum} = 0.9031$$
$$\text{Antilog} = 8.$$

Going from number to power of 10 is called "finding the logarithm," and a table of logarithms is used for this; going from logarithm back to an ordinary number is called " finding the *antilogarithm*." You can go back using a logarithm table or you can refer to a special antilogarithm table. The expert prefers *not* to use an antilogarithm table but to refer to a logarithm table for both operations. If you have both tables you are quite likely to use the wrong one in error, but if only one is used you cannot make mistakes in this way.

The above calculations are absurdly easy, and you can do them in your head. Here is a slightly harder one:

$$3 \times 2.5$$
$$\log 3 = 0.4771$$
$$\log 2.5 = 0.3979$$
$$\text{Sum} = 0.8750$$
$$\text{Antilog} = 7.5.$$

Now let us try a division sum:

$$9 \div 2$$
$$9 = 10^{0.9542}$$
$$2 = 10^{0.3010}$$
$$9 \div 2 = 10^{(0.9542-0.3010)}$$
$$= 10^{0.6532} = 4.5.$$

The next division sum is set out in a more conventional manner:

$$6 \div 1 \cdot 5$$
$$\log. 6 = 0 \cdot 7782$$
$$\log. 1 \cdot 5 = 0 \cdot 1761$$
$$\text{Difference} = 0 \cdot 6021$$
$$\text{Antilog} = 4.$$

Now we will try something quite ambitious:

$$\frac{7 \times 4 \cdot 5 \times 5 \times 2}{2 \cdot 5 \times 1 \cdot 5 \times 3 \cdot 5 \times 6}$$

$\log 7 \ \ = 0 \cdot 8451$	$\log 2 \cdot 5 = 0 \cdot 3979$
$\log 4 \cdot 5 = 0 \cdot 6532$	$\log 1 \cdot 5 = 0 \cdot 1761$
$\log 5 \ \ = 0 \cdot 6990$	$\log 3 \cdot 5 = 0 \cdot 5441$
$\log 2 \ \ = 0 \cdot 3010$	$\log 6 \ \ = 0 \cdot 7782$
$\text{Sum} = 2 \cdot 4983$	$\text{Sum} = 1 \cdot 8963$

$$1 \cdot 8963$$
$$\text{Difference} = 0 \cdot 6020$$
$$\text{Antilog} = 4$$

The abbreviated table of logarithms given above is not of any real use because the calculations it assists could easily be done mentally. However, it shows the application of a principle that can be extended to cover really laborious calculations. There follows part of a table giving logarithms to four significant figures enabling us to find the logarithm of $2 \cdot 573$ and of $3 \cdot 267$.

	0	1	2	3	4	5	6	7	8	9	1	3	5	7	9
25	3979	3997	4014	4031	4048	4065	4082	4099	4116	4133	2	5	9	12	15
32	5051	5065	5079	5092	5105	5119	5132	5145	5159	5172	1	4	7	9	12

To "look up" the logarithm of a number we must disregard the decimal point at first. Opposite 25 on the left and under the numbers 0, 1, 2, 3, 4, etc., appear the logarithms corresponding to 250, 251, 252, 253, etc. They are to be read as $0 \cdot 3979$, $0 \cdot 3997$, $0 \cdot 4014$, etc., for $2 \cdot 50$, $2 \cdot 51$, $2 \cdot 52$, $2 \cdot 53$, etc. The number for which we require our first logarithm is $2 \cdot 573$. Opposite 25 and under 7 we get the part $0 \cdot 4099$ corresponding to $2 \cdot 570$. But our number is $2 \cdot 573$. To the right of the second thick vertical line are given what are termed "proportional parts," and under the figure 3 in the top row we find 5; we must add this on to 0·4099 mentally, making it 0·4104 because the 5 really stands for 0·0005. Thus, finally,

$$\log 2\cdot573 = 0\cdot4104.$$

In the same way we find that

$$\log 3\cdot267 = 0\cdot5141$$
$$\log 2\cdot573 + \log 3\cdot267 = 0\cdot9245.$$

To find the antilog we need another part of the table; this is reproduced below:

	0	1	2	3	4	5	6	7	8	9	1	3	5	7	9
84	9243	9248	9253	9258	9263	9269	9274	9279	9284	9289	1	2	3	4	5

From this section of the table we see that ·9243 is log 8·400; our logarithm is greater by 0·0002 and this figure of 2 appears in the "proportional parts" on the right under 3 so that, finally,

$$\text{Antilog } 0\cdot9243 = 8\cdot403.$$

Let us now evaluate $8\cdot451 \div 3\cdot269$.

Referring to the three sections of a complete logarithm table given above, we have:

$$\log 8\cdot451 = 0\cdot9270$$
$$\log 3\cdot269 = 0\cdot5144$$
$$\text{Difference} = \overline{0\cdot4126}$$
$$\text{Antilog} = 2\cdot585$$

You will perceive now that the use of logarithms is a saving of time when longer sums in multiplication and division have to be performed. Here is a lengthy calculation performed by logarithms. To check the working you must refer to the complete table printed on pages 254 and 255 at the end of this volume.

$$\frac{3\cdot142 \times 8\cdot635 \times 1\cdot761}{4\cdot223 \times 7\cdot137 \times 2\cdot954}$$

log 3·142 = 0·4972	log 4·223 = 0·6256
log 8·635 = 0·9363	log 7·303 = 0·8635
log 1·761 = 0·2457	log 2·954 = 0·4704
Sum = 1·6792	Sum = 1·9595
1·9595	

Difference =

The above work is not completed because there is the apparent difficulty of dealing with logarithms greater than 1, especially when we have to subtract a greater logarithm from a smaller.

Above we have logarithmic sums adding to 1·6792 and 1·9595. What do they mean?

Well, $10^{1·6792}$ is the same as $10^{1·0} \times 10^{0·6792}$, so that since the antilog of 0·6792 is 4·778, the antilog of 1·6792 must be 47·78, that is, ten times greater.

When you see a logarithm such as 1·6792, you must imagine it to consist of two parts, namely the part obtainable from the table, which is 0·6792 and is called the "mantissa," and the additional whole number, namely 1, which is called the "characteristic." The purpose of the characteristic is to indicate where the decimal point comes in the antilog. Thus, antilog 0·9595 = 9·110 (since this figure taken from the table is *always* between 1 and 10) but antilog 1·9595 = 91·10. Similarly, antilog 2·9595 = 911·0 and antilog 3·9595 = 9110·0.

How about numbers less than unity? What, for instance, would be log 0·5 or log 0·05 or log 0·005? From the table we find log 5 = 0·6990, 0·5 = $\frac{5}{10}$, and therefore:

$$\log 0·5 = \log 5 - \log 10$$
$$= 0·6990 - 1·0000$$
$$= - 0·3010$$
$$\log 0·05 = \log \tfrac{5}{100} = \log 5 - \log 100$$
$$= 0·6990 - 2·0000$$
$$= - 1·3010$$

From the above we see that fractions have entirely different logarithms from those of numbers in excess of unity, though the digits of the original numbers may be the same. This is seemingly very awkward, but the difficulty is overcome by not working out the subtraction 0·6990 − 1 or 0·6990 − 2, or any subtraction like these two; instead we use negative characteristics. Thus we write:

$$\log 0·5 = \bar{1}·6990$$

meaning that the figure 1 with a "bar" over it is negative. Similarly, log 0·05 is bar two point six nine nine nothing ($\bar{2}·6990$) and log 0·005 = $\bar{3}·6990$.

Above we were confronted with the subtraction of $1 \cdot 9595$ from $1 \cdot 6792$. We work this out as follows:

$$1 \cdot 6792$$
$$1 \cdot 9595$$
$$\overline{1} \cdot 7197$$

Here the subtraction has gone according to rule to the point where we take away the 9, borrowing the top 1 in order to do so. Finally we have the bottom 1 to take from a top 1 which has already been borrowed. So we have 1 to take from nothing. But $0 - 1$ is simply $- 1$ or, as we now prefer to write it $\overline{1}$; hence the above result.

We find antilog $0 \cdot 7197$ from the table in the ordinary way; it is $5 \cdot 245$. We then allow for the *negative* characteristic by shifting the decimal point one place to the *left*, indicating division by 10. Thus, the final answer to the long calculation above is $0 \cdot 5245$.

Problem 2.—Use logarithms to evaluate $0 \cdot 6321 \times 12 \cdot 73$.

$$\log 0 \cdot 6321 = \overline{1} \cdot 8008$$
$$\log 12 \cdot 73 = 1 \cdot 1048$$
$$\text{Sum} = 0 \cdot 9056$$
$$\text{Antilog} = 8 \cdot 046.$$

Here we find the logs of the numbers $6 \cdot 321$ and $1 \cdot 273$ from the tables, adding the characteristics $\overline{1}$ and 1 to allow for the real position of the decimal point. In adding the amended logarithms we find that we have 1 to add to $\overline{1}$; this is the same thing as $1 - 1$, and so it comes to 0.

Problem 3.—Use logarithms to evaluate $0 \cdot 08274 \times 93 \cdot 27$.

$$\log 0 \cdot 08274 = \overline{2} \cdot 9177$$
$$\log 93 \cdot 27 = 1 \cdot 9697$$
$$\text{Sum} = 0 \cdot 8874$$
$$\text{Antilog} = 7 \cdot 716.$$

Here we see that in the addition of the mantissæ there is a carrying figure of 1 which, together with the characteristic of the underneath logarithm, makes 2. The combination of 2 and $\overline{2}$ yields 0.

Problem 4.—Use logarithms to evaluate $7 \cdot 213 \div 0 \cdot 6315$.

$$\log 7 \cdot 213 = 0 \cdot 8581$$
$$\log 0 \cdot 6315 = \overline{1} \cdot 8003$$
$$\text{Difference} = 1 \cdot 0578$$
$$\text{Antilog} = 11 \cdot 42.$$

Here we have to take $\overline{1}$ from o; subtraction of a *negative* quantity is always equivalent to the addition of the same quantity, that is $- (- 1) = + 1$ (see page 50).

Problem 5.—Evaluate $6 \cdot 723 \div 0 \cdot 8507$.

$$\log 6 \cdot 723 = 0 \cdot 8276$$
$$\log 0 \cdot 8507 = \overline{1} \cdot 9298$$
$$\text{Difference} = 0 \cdot 8978$$
$$\text{Antilog} = 7 \cdot 903.$$

Here we have to "borrow" a 1 we have not got, and then we have to take $\overline{1}$ from the minus 1 thus obtained. This gives us $- 1 - (- 1) = - 1 + 1 = 0$.

Problem 6.—Use logarithms to evaluate $372 \cdot 1 \div 0 \cdot 7623$.

$$\log 372 \cdot 1 = 2 \cdot 5706$$
$$\log 0 \cdot 7623 = \overline{1} \cdot 8822$$
$$\text{Difference} = 2 \cdot 6884$$
$$\text{Antilog} = 487 \cdot 9.$$

Here we eventually have to subtract $\overline{1}$ from 1 which gives $1 - (- 1) = 1 + 1 = 2$.

Problem 7.—Use logarithms to evaluate:

$$\frac{1357 \times 21 \cdot 33 \times 0 \cdot 0005129}{216 \cdot 5 \times 33 \cdot 29 \times 0 \cdot 01355}$$

$\log 1357 = 3 \cdot 1326$	$\log 216 \cdot 5 = 2 \cdot 3355$
$\log 21 \cdot 33 = 1 \cdot 3290$	$\log 33 \cdot 29 = 1 \cdot 5223$
$\log 0 \cdot 0005129 = \overline{4} \cdot 7101$	$\log 0 \cdot 01355 = \overline{2} \cdot 1319$
$\text{Sum} = \overline{1} \cdot 1717$	$\text{Sum} = \overline{1} \cdot 9897$

$$\underline{1 \cdot 9897}$$
$$\text{Difference} = \overline{1} \cdot 1820 \qquad \text{Antilog} = 0 \cdot 1521.$$

Logarithms can be used to evaluate many quantities not easily obtainable by ordinary arithmetic. Thus we can find the square root, cube root, fourth root, fifth root or any other root of a number very quickly, the method being to divide the logarithm of the number in question by 2, 3, 4, 5 or whatever is necessary, and then find the antilogarithm. The theory justifying this is quite simple. Suppose we wish to evaluate $\sqrt[3]{10^9}$ we know that it must be $10^{\frac{9}{3}}$ because $10^3 \times 10^3 \times 10^3 = 10^{3+3+3} = 10^9$.

Problem 8.—Use logarithms to evaluate $\sqrt[5]{3\cdot000}$ and $\sqrt[3]{174\cdot5}$.

$$\log 3\cdot000 = 0\cdot4771$$
$$\tfrac{1}{5} \text{ ,, \quad ,, } = 0\cdot0954$$
$$\text{Antilog} = 1\cdot246$$
$$\log 174\cdot5 = 2\cdot2417$$
$$\tfrac{1}{3} \text{ ,, \quad ,, } = 0\cdot7472$$
$$\text{Antilog} = 5\cdot587.$$

A possible difficulty suggests itself here: what happens when the root of a fractional quantity has to be found? The logarithm of, say, 0·3000 is $\bar{1}\cdot4771$; how can this be divided by 5 in order to evaluate $\sqrt[5]{0\cdot3000}$? The method is to *make* the characteristic divisible by 5 by changing it to $\bar{5}$ and then adding + 4 to the mantissa to compensate for the alteration. We then have for the division of $\bar{1}\cdot4771$ by 5 the following result:

$$5\,|\!-\!5 + 4\cdot4771$$
$$-\ 1 + 0\cdot8954 = \bar{1}\cdot8954$$
$$\text{Antilog} = 0\cdot7860.$$

The work of dividing can usually be done without setting it out if we remember that after an adjustment to the characteristic such as is described above, the first positive number is obtained by the division not of 4 by 5 but of 44 by 5.

Problem 9.—Divide $\bar{2}\cdot3261$ by 3 and $\bar{4}\cdot3695$ by 5.

The results are : $\bar{1}\cdot4420$ and $\bar{1}\cdot2739$.

To evaluate the power of any number we must obtain the logarithm of the number, multiply this by the power and then find the anti-logarithm. Thus to evaluate $(3\cdot142)^3$ we have:

$$\log 3\cdot142 = 0\cdot4972$$
$$3\times \log 3\cdot142 = 1\cdot4916$$
$$\text{Antilog} = 31\cdot02.$$

Problem 10.—Evaluate $(0\cdot6234)^5$.

$$\log 0\cdot6234 = \bar{1}\cdot7948$$
$$5 \log 0\cdot6234 = \bar{2}\cdot9740$$
$$\text{Antilog} = 0\cdot09419.$$

You will notice here that when the mantissa is multiplied by 5 there results a positive characteristic of 3, but since $5 \times \bar{1} = \bar{5}$ the net result is $\bar{2}$, this being $-5 + 3$.

Problem 11.—When a volume V_1 of air at a pressure of P_1 is expanded adiabatically to volume V_2 and pressure P_2 (see Volume II, page

151), the quantities P_1, V_1, P_2 and V_2 are connected by the relation
$$P_1 V_1^{1\cdot4} = P_2 V_2^{1\cdot4}$$
If 10 cub. ft. of air at 15 lb. per sq. in. are compressed adiabatically to a pressure of 90 lb. per sq. in., what will be the final volume?

We have:
$$15 \times 10^{1\cdot4} = 90 \times V_2^{1\cdot4}$$
$$\text{whence } V_2^{1\cdot4} = \frac{15}{90} \times 10^{1\cdot4} = \frac{10^{1\cdot4}}{6}$$
$$V_2 = \sqrt[1\cdot4]{\frac{10^{1\cdot4}}{6}} = \frac{10}{\sqrt[1\cdot4]{6}}$$

$$\log 10 = 1\cdot0000$$
$$\log 6 = 0\cdot7782$$
$$\log 6 \div 1\cdot4 = 0\cdot5558$$
$$\log 10 - \frac{1}{1\cdot4} \log 6 = 0\cdot4442$$
$$\text{Antilog} = 2\cdot781.$$

Thus the final volume $V_2 = 2\cdot781$ cub. ft.

Problem 12.—The formula for the period p of oscillation of a simple pendulum is:

$$p = 2\pi \sqrt{\frac{l}{g}}$$

where $l =$ length of string in feet and g is the acceleration due to gravity in feet per second per second. If $g = 32\cdot2$, find what length of string will give a period of 2 seconds.

We have, squaring both sides,

$$p^2 = 4\pi^2 \frac{l}{g}$$

$$\therefore \quad l = \frac{gp^2}{4\pi^2}$$

$$= \frac{32\cdot2 \times 4}{4 \times (3\cdot142)^2} = \frac{32\cdot2}{3\cdot142 \times 3\cdot142}$$

$$\log 32\cdot2 = 1\cdot5079$$
$$\log 3\cdot142 = 0\cdot4972$$
$$2 \log 3\cdot142 = 0\cdot9944$$
$$\log 32\cdot2 - 2 \log 3\cdot142 = 0\cdot5135$$
$$\text{Antilog} = 3\cdot262.$$

Thus the length of a "seconds" pendulum is $3\cdot262$ ft. or $39\cdot144$ in.

Logarithms can be represented by lengths marked out along a straight line. We could use the graph on page 31 as a means to obtaining such a logarithmically divided scale, or we could take the requisite lengths direct from a table; the result would be the same in either case and would be as shown on this page.

Logarithmic scales are of great utility because if we have two of them to place one against another we can speedily arrive at the results of a multiplication or division sum. A slide rule is a contrivance in which logarithmic scales can be moved relatively to one another so that logs represented by lengths can be rapidly added or subtracted and antilog readings directly obtained.

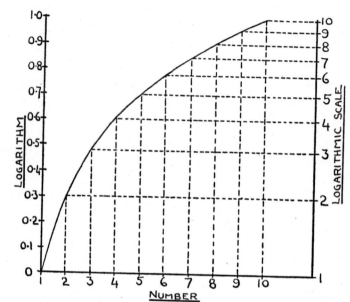

In the diagram (a) of two scales shown on page 41, length pq on one scale represents log 2 whereas length qr on the other represents log 3; the combined length pr represents log (2 × 3), so that opposite the figure 3 on the bottom scale we find 6 on the top scale, and this is the product of 2 × 3. When the scale is more finely divided (as on a real slide rule) you can employ the same method to evaluate any product of factors having three significant figures; for instance, you could multiply 2·36 by 3·72 nearly as quickly as you could multiply 2 by 3.

Division is performed on the slide rule just as quickly as multiplication, the method being to subtract lengths. In sketch (b) you see the scales set for dividing 9 by 3. The number 3 on the bottom scale is brought opposite the number 9 on the top scale and the top scale is then read opposite the number 1 on the bottom scale; the quotient is 3. You can see that log 9 − log 3 = st − tu = su = log 3.

When a lengthy calculation such as the following is to be done on a slide rule you will find that it is advantageous to do the multiplications and divisions alternately so that you go to and fro on the top scale

instead of quickly running off it as you would do were you to do all the
multiplying first, and as you would again when you performed a series
of divisions. The sequence for working out

$$\frac{3 \cdot 21 \times 4 \cdot 57 \times 2 \cdot 93}{5 \cdot 61 \times 0 \cdot 385 \times 112}$$

would be to divide $3 \cdot 21$ by $5 \cdot 61$, then multiply by $4 \cdot 57$, then divide
by $3 \cdot 85$, then multiply by $2 \cdot 93$ and finally divide by 112. The decimal
point is ignored in all operations and its position in the final result is
determined by making a rough mental check of this. Thus my small
slide rule gives 177 as
the result of working
out the above. Looking
at the original figures
and mentally rounding
them into

$$\frac{3 \times 5 \times 3}{6 \times 0 \cdot 4 \times 100}$$

I can see that the result
is about $\dfrac{7 \cdot 5}{40}$; thus it
must be $0 \cdot 177$ and
not $1 \cdot 77$ or $17 \cdot 7$ or 177
or $0 \cdot 0177$.

Instructions are sometimes given for keeping a check on the decimal
point when using the slide rule, but the mental approximation method is
far the best because it obliges you to check the figures at the same time
and you will be sure to perceive any gross error in your working if there
happens to be one.

To find a square root on the slide rule you must first make up your
mind what this will be *approximately*. The square root of 4 (ignoring the
decimal place) could be 200 or 633 on the slide rule and you must
decide which of the two it is going to be. For $4 \cdot 0$ it is $2 \cdot 0$, for $40 \cdot 0$ it
is $6 \cdot 33$, for $400 \cdot 0$ it is 20, and so on. Diagram (*c*) shows that in seeking a
square root you must seek to divide your number (4 in this instance) by
some other number that gives a quotient equal to the divisor. What you
have to do is move the sliding scale slowly and watch the number
passing under 4 until it is the same as the number on the fixed scale
above 1 on the sliding scale. In diagram (*c*) the sliding scale has been

moved until equality has been reached, and the figure sought comes to 2.

Some slide rules are made with other scales drawn to one-half of the size of the full-length scale; these half-length scales are repeated twice in the full length of the rule, and although they do not give quite such accurate results they are handier for long calculations because it is not so often that you will run off the end of the rule in the course of your work.

The combination of full-length with half-length scales also facilitates the finding of square roots, and it affords a method for finding cube

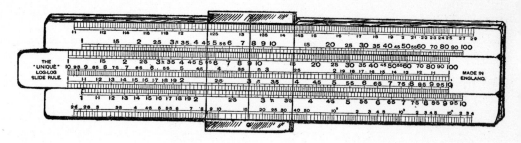

roots as well. The diagram on this page shows the scales provided on a general-purpose rule priced at less than 10*s*. More expensive rules are made with ivorine engine-divided scales, but the rule shown, which has a plastic-protected printed-paper scale, is satisfactory for all practical purposes.

The little plastic or glass window usually provided to slide over the scales is called the "cursor." It has a fine line engraved or etched on it and the purpose of the cursor is to "keep your place" on the scales while you look away from the rule to do something else. You can still use a slide rule even when the cursor is missing, but there is some loss of convenience. The bottom picture facing page 74 shows a slide rule in which the upper pair of scales is shifted relatively to the lower pair in order to bring the unit figure to the centre. With this arrangement of scales the number of slide movements is reduced so that there is a further economy in the time needed to work out problems.

CHAPTER III

CALCULATIONS OF ALL KINDS

Before children are accepted for the better kind of secondary education they must pass an intelligence test in which questions like this are put to them:

"In the sentence which follows you can see a clear relation between the things mentioned:

"Hand is to Arm as Foot is to Leg.

"Now complete the sentences given below, writing the correct word in the blank space.

"Sun is to Day as Moon is to . . . .
"Water is to Thirst as Food is to . . . . . .
"Bird is to Cage as Dog is to . . . ."

If you have met this kind of test before, you will know that the correct words are Night, Hunger and Kennel respectively.

Ability to pass this kind of test may be a measure of your ability to do calculation in simple proportion. You know that:

4 is to 8 as 3 is to 6

because 4 is *half* of 8 and 3 is *half* of 6. Could you fill in the missing figures in the following?

2 is to 12 as 5 is to . . . .
. . . . is to 3 as 6 is to 18
5 is to . . . . as 1 is to 2
3 is to 12 as . . . . is to 28

In the first one 2 is a sixth of 12, so the missing figure must be 6 times $5 = 30$ and we can write:

$$\frac{2}{12} = \frac{5}{30}$$

this being the shorthand for:

2 is to 12 as 5 is to 30.

Sometimes (in old books) you see the same thing expressed as follows:

2 : 12 :: 5 : 30.

In the next problem we know that 6 is a third of 18 and so we must find out what is a third of 3; the missing figure is 1 and so the complete statement is:

1 is to 3 as 6 is to 18

or

1 : 3 :: 6 : 18

or

$$\frac{1}{3} = \frac{6}{18}.$$

Next we have:

$$\frac{5}{10} = \frac{1}{2}$$

and lastly we have:

$$\frac{3}{12} = \frac{7}{28}.$$

When you see the quantity $\frac{7}{28}$ by itself you say that it is a fraction— a "vulgar fraction" to give it its full name. If I had to give you $\frac{7}{28}$ of a cake I should first of all cut it into twenty-eight slices and then give you seven of them. However, as 7 is a quarter of 28, I could save myself a lot of trouble by cutting it into four large slices and giving you one. In that way you would get exactly the same amount of cake but it would be in one piece instead of in seven.

Problem 13.—A cake has to be divided between three children whose ages are 4, 5 and 6, and they are allowed to have amounts proportional to their ages. How much is to be given to each?

To share out this cake we must cut it into four plus five plus six equals fifteen equal parts and then give four of these to the 4-year-old, five of them to the 5-year-old and six of them to the 6-year-old. Their shares are $\frac{4}{15}$, $\frac{5}{15}$ and $\frac{6}{15}$ respectively, these being in the proportion of 4 to 5 to 6.

Notice that $\frac{5}{15} = \frac{1}{3}$ and $\frac{6}{15} = \frac{2}{5}$. We can put their shares as:

$$\tfrac{4}{15}, \tfrac{1}{3} \text{ and } \tfrac{2}{5},$$

but now it is not so clear that they are in the proportion 4 to 5 to 6. Nor is it so clear that:

$$\tfrac{4}{15} + \tfrac{1}{3} + \tfrac{2}{5} = 1 \text{ (the whole cake).}$$

Problem 14.—Three children are given a whole cake between them, their shares being in proportion to their ages. The amounts of cake are $\frac{5}{12}, \frac{1}{3}$ and $\frac{1}{4}$ of the whole. If the eldest child is 10 years old, what are the ages of the other two?

To solve this problem we must have our fractions alike so far as their denominators are concerned. The denominator is the underneath figure and the numerator is the top figure. Looking at the three denominators 12, 3 and 4, we see that 12 contains the others 4 and 3 times and therefore it can serve us as "common denominator." We can rewrite our fractions:

$$\tfrac{5}{12}, \tfrac{4}{12} \text{ and } \tfrac{3}{12}.$$

In this form they can be compared with one another; they are to one another as 5 to 4 to 3. But this is also the proportion of the children's ages and the eldest is 10; therefore:

5 is to 4 as age of eldest is to age of next child, i.e. as 10 is to 8. So the second child is 8 years old.

Also 5 is to 3 as age of eldest is to age of last child, i.e. as 10 is to 6. So the last child is 6 years old.

When comparing fractions, or when adding and subtracting fractions, it is always necessary to make them alike as regards their denominators. Suppose, for instance, we wish to add $\frac{1}{3}$ and $\frac{1}{4}$, we can do it by making the denominator equal to 3×4, or 12 for both.

Then $\tfrac{1}{3} = \tfrac{4}{12}$

and $\tfrac{1}{4} = \tfrac{3}{12}$

so we have $$\frac{4}{12} + \frac{3}{12} = \frac{4+3}{12} = \frac{7}{12}.$$

You can always find a common denominator by multiplying all the given denominators together, but this method may give you one which is larger than you really need. If the given denominators are 8, 12, 15 and 30, you could use $8 \times 12 \times 15 \times 30$ for a common denominator, but this would be very clumsy. You can find a smaller figure by which each of the given figures is contained an exact number of times, and the smallest possible one is called the "Least Common Multiple," often abbreviated to L.C.M. and referred to wonderingly by small children as "Elsie Em."

To find the L.C.M. of the above figures we factorise them as shown below:

$$8 = 2 \times 2 \times 2$$
$$12 = 3 \times 2 \times 2$$
$$15 = 3 \times 5$$
$$30 = 3 \times 5 \times 2$$

We now take as many of these factors as are needed to contain the factors of 8 and of 12 and of 15 and of 30. For 8 we must have $2 \times 2 \times 2$. If we bring in the factor 3 we shall have enough for 12 also, because $2 \times 2 \times 2 \times 3$ contains all the factors of 12. To make this product include the factors of 15 also we must bring in 5, thus:

$$2 \times 2 \times 2 \times 3 \times 5.$$

The above product contains all the factors of 8, 12 and 15; it also contains all the factors of 30 because these are $3 \times 5 \times 2$ and they are already present. Thus the L.C.M. of 8, 12, 15 and 30 is:

$$2 \times 2 \times 2 \times 3 \times 5 = 120.$$

No *smaller* number is exactly divisible by 8, 12, 15 and 30, though many larger numbers are—for instance the huge number $8 \times 12 \times 15 \times 30 = 43,200$!

Suppose we are confronted with the sum:

$$\tfrac{1}{8} + \tfrac{5}{12} + \tfrac{7}{15} + \tfrac{11}{30},$$

our first care must be to find the L.C.M. of 8, 12, 15 and 30. Already we have done this and we know that it is 120. Each fraction must have a new numerator when it is given the new denominator of 120. We find out by how much the denominator has been multiplied and we multiply the numerator by the same amount, because *multiplying numerator and denominator of a fraction by the same amount does not change its value*. The fraction $\tfrac{1}{8}$ is going to have its denominator multiplied by $120 \div 8 = 15$, so it becomes $\dfrac{15 \times 1}{120}$; the fraction $\tfrac{5}{12}$ is going to have its denominator multiplied by $120 \div 12 = 10$, so it becomes $\dfrac{5 \times 10}{120}$. Altogether, then, our sum becomes:

$$\frac{(15 \times 1) + (5 \times 10) + (7 \times 8) + (11 \times 4)}{120}$$

$$= \frac{15 + 50 + 56 + 44}{120} = \frac{165}{120} = 1\frac{45}{120} = 1\frac{3}{8}.$$

In the form $\frac{165}{120}$ our sum is called an "improper" fraction because the numerator is greater than the denominator. Plainly $\frac{120}{120} = 1$ and so we can take 120 from 165, leaving 45, and write our result $1\frac{45}{120}$, meaning 1 together with $\frac{45}{120}$. Just as we can *multiply* numerator and denominator of a fraction by any given number without affecting the result, so also we can *divide* numerator and denominator by any given amount. In the fraction $\frac{45}{120}$ numerator and denominator are divisible by 15, the former containing it 3 times and the latter 8 times; consequently, $\frac{45}{120} = \frac{3}{8}$ and our sum reduces finally to $1\frac{3}{8}$.

Problem 15.—The formula for electrical resistances in parallel is (see Volume II, page 297):

$$\frac{1}{R} = \frac{1}{r_1} + \frac{1}{r_2} + \frac{1}{r_3} + \text{etc.}$$

where r_1, r_2, r_3, etc., are the separate resistances and R is the combined or equivalent resistance. What is the equivalent resistance when $r_1 = 5$, $r_2 = 3$ and $r_3 = 8$?

We have

$$\frac{1}{R} = \frac{1}{5} + \frac{1}{3} + \frac{1}{8}.$$

The L.C.M. of 5, 3 and 8 is $5 \times 3 \times 2 \times 2 \times 2 = 120$

$$\therefore \quad \frac{1}{R} = \frac{(1 \times 24) + (1 \times 40) + (1 \times 15)}{120} = \frac{79}{120}.$$

When a fraction is turned upside down we get its "reciprocal." *If two fractions are equal their reciprocals will also be equal.* Thus $\frac{1}{2} = \frac{7}{14}$ and it is evident that

$$\frac{2}{1} = \frac{14}{7}$$

because both are equal simply to 2.

Above we have

$$\frac{1}{R} = \frac{79}{120}.$$

It follows that

$$\frac{R}{1} = \frac{120}{79}$$

i.e.

$$R = \frac{120}{79} = 1\frac{41}{79}$$

The fraction $\frac{41}{79}$ is irreducible because there is no number contained an exact number of times in 41 which is also contained an exact number of times in 79; the numbers 41 and 79 have no common factor.

Problem 16.—The formula connecting the focal length f of a lens with the distances u and v of object and image from the lens itself is (see Volume II, page 222):

$$\frac{1}{f} = \frac{1}{v} - \frac{1}{u}.$$

If $f = 6$ and $u = 8$, what is v?
Putting in the values for f and u, we have:

$$\frac{1}{6} = \frac{1}{v} - \frac{1}{8}.$$

Now this is called an "equation" because it is a statement of equality between two things. We can do whatever we like to the two sides of an equation *provided that we do the same thing to both*. Here we are going to add $\frac{1}{8}$ to both sides. This gives us:

$$\frac{1}{6} + \frac{1}{8} = \frac{1}{v} - \frac{1}{8} + \frac{1}{8} = \frac{1}{v},$$

so simplifying our problem.

The L.C.M. of 6 and 8 is $3 \times 2 \times 2 \times 2 = 24$

$$\therefore \qquad \frac{1}{v} = \frac{(1 \times 4) + (1 \times 3)}{24} = \frac{7}{24}$$

$$\therefore \qquad v = \frac{24}{7} = 3\frac{3}{7}.$$

In the expression

$$2 : 8 :: 3 : 12$$

the numbers 2 and 12 (smallest and largest) are called "extremes" and the others (8 and 3) are called means. You will notice that the product of the extremes is equal to the product of the means, for $2 \times 12 = 8 \times 3 = 24$. Is this mere accident or does it always happen that way?

Let us try the general case:

$$a : b :: c : d.$$

Written thus the proposition gives us no rule for general application. In its modern form it is more suggestive, however, for when we put

$$\frac{a}{b} = \frac{c}{d}$$

we see that we can get rid of the fractions in this equation by multiplying both sides by the product bd. Then:

$$\frac{a \times bd}{b} = \frac{c \times bd}{d}$$

or $ad = cb.$

Comparing this result with the original statement $a : b :: c : d$, we see that the rule "the product of the extremes equals the product of the means" is generally applicable.

The quickest way to obtain $ad = cb$ from $\frac{a}{b} = \frac{c}{d}$ is to "cross multiply," taking the numerator of the first fraction with the denominator of the second for one product and the denominator of the first with the numerator of the second for the second product. This method of cross multiplication enables us to arrive quickly at the solution to an equation such as:

$$\frac{2}{x+1} = \frac{5}{2x+5}.$$

By cross multiplication we have:

$$2(2x + 5) = 5(x + 1)$$
$$4x + 10 = 5x + 5.$$

Take $4x$ from both sides and we get $10 = x + 5$.
Take 5 from both sides and we get $5 = x$.
As a check on this result let us go back to the original expression, putting 5 for x; then

$$\frac{2}{5+1} = \frac{5}{10+5}$$
$$\tfrac{2}{6} = \tfrac{5}{15}$$
$$\tfrac{1}{3} = \tfrac{1}{3}.$$

Problem 17.—A goods train travelling at an average speed of 24 miles an hour is dispatched on a 240-mile journey and some time afterwards an express train averaging 60 m.p.h. is sent from the same starting-point along the same line. If both trains are required to arrive at their destination 240 miles away at the same instant, what start in miles must be given to the goods train?

The easiest way to do this problem is to put s for the start in miles that must be given to the goods train, and then evaluate s.

At the time the express starts the goods train will still have $240 - s$ miles to go and therefore it will take $\dfrac{240 - s}{24}$ more hours to reach its destination. The express has 240 miles to go and it will take $\frac{240}{60}$ hours to reach the same destination. But the trains arrive together and so their running times as given above must be equal.

$$\therefore \qquad \frac{240 - s}{24} = \frac{240}{60} = 4.$$

Multiplying both sides by 24, we have $240 - s = 24 \times 4 = 96$.

Taking 240 from both sides, we have $- s = 96 - 240$.

And here a great many people would become confused and not know what to do next. We must multiply both sides by $- 1$.

Now if you are minus anything positive (in your possession), it means you are without it, so that multiplying anything by $- 1$ merely means taking it away. That is to say $(- 1)(10) = - 10$, or 10 to take away. If you are already in debt to someone by 10 pounds and have no money at all, your financial holding can be expressed as $- 10$. If now your creditor lets you off the debt, you will be $(- 1)(- 10)$ better off. But the result is the same as if some friend had given you 10 pounds to pay with. Thus $(- 1)(- 10) = + 10$.

This result is a little difficult to appreciate, and you must think hard about it because you will constantly find that when minus things are multiplied together they yield a plus answer. Here are some examples in multiplication for you to consider:

$(- 3)(5) = - 15$ because it is 5 taken away 3 times.

$(3)(5) = + 15$ because it is 5 added on (or given to you) 3 times.

$(- 3)(- 5) = + 15$ because it is three *debts* of 5 taken away from you or settled for you.

Notice that multiplication by a minus quantity changes the sign of whatever is multiplied no matter whether this is originally $+$ or $-$.

Thus $\qquad\qquad\qquad (- 3)(+ 5) = - 15$

and $\qquad\qquad\qquad (- 3)(- 5) = + 15.$

Going back to our problem and multiplying by $- 1$, the expression
$$- s = 96 - 240$$
we get
$$s = 240 - 96$$
because every sign is changed by this multiplication. Now we can evaluate s easily:
$$s = 240 - 96 = 144.$$
The goods train must be given a start of 144 miles.

The above problem shows you that when an unknown quantity is represented by a symbol, this symbol may become tied up with a lot of other figures in such a way as to make it difficult to evaluate numerically.

In the following expression the unknown quantity is represented by x. Can you find out what x is numerically?

$$3[50 - 2\{5x - 2(7x + 6)\}] = 330.$$

The way to do this is to get rid of the brackets, beginning with the innermost ones ( ), going on to the next in order { } and finishing with the outer ones [ ].

Rewriting the equation without the inner brackets, we have:

$$3[50 - 2\{5x - 14x - 12\}] = 330.$$

Notice that everything inside the brackets has been multiplied by $- 2$, so that it is numerically twice as large and with all signs reversed.

Next we get rid of the curly brackets as follows (everything within is multiplied by $- 2$):

$$3[50 - 10x + 28x + 24] = 330.$$

Now we get rid of the square brackets, multiplying by 3 everything inside them:

$$150 - 30x + 84x + 72 = 330.$$

To 150 we add 72, getting 222, and from $84x$ we take $30x$, getting $54x$.

$$\therefore \qquad 222 + 54x = 330.$$

Taking 222 from both sides, we have:

$$54x = 330 - 222 = 108.$$

Dividing both sides by 54, we have, finally:

$$x = \tfrac{108}{54} = 2.$$

The work could have been shortened in one or two ways; see now if you can follow it in its abbreviated form given below. To begin with we had:

$$3[50 - 2\{5x - 2(7x + 6)\}] = 330.$$

We could have done this next:

$$50 - 2\{5x - 2(7x + 6)\} = 110.$$

Then this:

$$- 2\{5x - 14x - 12\} = 60,$$

and this:

$$-\{- 9x - 12\} = 30$$
$$9x + 12 = 30$$
$$9x = 18$$
$$x = 2.$$

You may say that removing brackets on one side of an equation without doing anything on the other side is not playing fair. But when you eliminate brackets you are most careful not to alter the numerical value of all the quantities involved. They mean exactly the same after as before, but the expression is simpler, so that the operation of removing brackets is often called "simplification." It neither adds nor subtracts anything; nor does it multiply or divide the expression as a whole.

See now if you can simplify this horrifying-looking equation:

$$\frac{112 - 5(3x + 8)}{12 - (4x - 3)} = 16 - \{12x + 25 - 3(4x + 5)\}.$$

Before you do anything else start getting rid of brackets, as follows:

$$\frac{112 - 15x - 40}{12 - 4x + 3} = 16 - \{12x + 25 - 12x - 15\}$$

$$\frac{72 - 15x}{15 - 4x} = 16 - 25 + 15 = 6$$

Now multiply both sides by $15 - 4x$ to get rid of fractions; this re-introduces some brackets, thus:

$$72 - 15x = 6(15 - 4x),$$

but they are soon eliminated, as follows:

$$72 - 15x = 90 - 24x.$$

Taking $-24x$ and $+72$ from both sides, we get (remember (-1) $(-24x) = +24x$)

$$24x - 15x = 90 - 72$$
$$9x = 18$$
$$x = 2.$$

Do you notice that when anything showing on one side is taken from both sides of an equation it reappears on the other side with its sign changed? This happens in every case and it enables us to arrange the terms as we please without thinking too much about the matter; we merely transfer them from side to side, changing their signs as we move them.

Here is an example of this process:

$$3x + 15 - 2x - 7 = 12 - 6x + 3.$$

We can have all the x's on one side and all the numbers on the other by rearrangement; moving terms from side to side and changing their signs as we move them, thus:

$$3x - 2x + 6x = 12 + 3 - 15 + 7$$
$$7x = 7$$
$$x = 1.$$

On page 52 we multiplied the fraction $\dfrac{72 - 15x}{15 - 4x}$ by its denominator and then it ceased to be a fraction, becoming $72 - 15x$. We did not stop to justify this step, but now we ought to say something about the matter. The fraction $\frac{3}{4}$ multiplied by 4 becomes twelve quarters, for it is

$\dfrac{3 \times 4}{4} = \dfrac{12}{4}$ and that is 3.   Observe that when multiplying a fraction by an integer, *only the numerator is multiplied*; multiplying both numerator and denominator by a number leaves the value unaffected.

Thus, $\dfrac{3 \times 4}{4 \times 4} = \dfrac{12}{16}$ but this is the same as $\frac{3}{4}$, each of the three quarters being subdivided into four sixteenths, making twelve sixteenths in all.

When you multiply a fraction by an integer you can do one of two things: either you can multiply the numerator by the multiplier or you can divide the denominator by it, for the result is the same in each case.

Suppose $\frac{5}{12}$ has to be multiplied by 2; we can write the answer as $\frac{10}{12}$ or $\frac{5}{6}$ because the original fraction is doubled whether we double the numerator or halve the denominator. Half a cake ($\frac{1}{2}$) is twice as much as a quarter ($\frac{1}{4}$) of the same cake. The larger the denominator the smaller the divisions into which a thing is cut, there being more of them.

In the same way when a fraction is divided by an integer we can either divide the numerator by this integer or multiply the denominator by it. Thus $\frac{5}{12} \div 5$ is either $\frac{1}{12}$ or $\frac{5}{60}$.

A cake is divided into twelve parts and you are given five of them. Now you are told you must keep only a fifth of your share and part with the rest; would you care whether you were left with one slice ($\frac{1}{12}$) or with $\frac{5}{60}$?

If the icing on the five slices were different, a fair division might require each slice to be cut into five, so reducing the original five-twelfths to twenty-five-sixtieths of which you would retain five and give away the other twenty.

When a fraction is multiplied by a fraction you must treat the numerator of the multiplying fraction as a multiplier and the denominator of that fraction as a divisor. Thus:

$$\tfrac{3}{4} \times \tfrac{2}{3} \text{ is the same as } (\tfrac{3}{4} \times 2) \div 3$$

Now $\qquad\qquad \tfrac{3}{4} \times 2 = \tfrac{6}{4}$

but better still $\qquad \tfrac{3}{4} \times 2 = \tfrac{3}{2}$

and $\qquad\qquad\quad \tfrac{3}{2} \div 3 = \tfrac{3}{6}$

but better still $\qquad \tfrac{3}{2} \div 3 = \tfrac{1}{2}$

altogether, then,

$$\tfrac{3}{4} \times \tfrac{2}{3} = \tfrac{1}{2}.$$

Notice that you can get the same result by what is called "cancelling":

$$\frac{\overset{1}{\cancel{3}} \times \cancel{2}}{\cancel{4} \times \cancel{3}} = \frac{1}{2}.$$

This cancelling method is in order for big calculations such as the one which follows:

Problem 18.—Evaluate $\dfrac{7 \times 5 \times 125 \times 39}{13 \times 28 \times 20 \times 15}$.

This is the same as

$$\tfrac{7}{13} \times \tfrac{5}{28} \times \tfrac{125}{20} \times \tfrac{39}{15}$$

or $\qquad\qquad\qquad \tfrac{39}{13} \times \tfrac{7}{28} \times \tfrac{5}{20} \times \tfrac{125}{15}$

or any other arrangement we care to make keeping top numbers always on top and bottom numbers always underneath. To evaluate the expression we will do some cancelling of factors common to numerators and denominators, thus:

$$\frac{\overset{25}{\cancel{7}} \times \cancel{5} \times \overset{\overset{25}{\cancel{125}}}{} \times \overset{3}{\cancel{39}}}{\underset{4}{\cancel{13}} \times \underset{4}{\cancel{28}} \times \underset{}{\cancel{20}} \times \underset{3}{\cancel{15}}} = \frac{25}{16} = 1\frac{9}{16}.$$

Problem 19.—Evaluate $\tfrac{5}{7} \times \tfrac{2}{3}$.

There is no cancelling you can do here and so the result is simply:

$$\frac{5 \times 2}{7 \times 3} = \frac{10}{21}.$$

Problem 20.—Solve the following equation:

$$(x+1)\left\{\frac{2}{x+1}+\frac{3}{x-1}\right\}=10.$$

Everything inside the curly brackets has to be multiplied by $x+1$; consequently:

$$\frac{2(x+1)}{x+1}+\frac{3(x+1)}{x-1}=10.$$

Cancelling where we can, we get:

$$2+\frac{3(x+1)}{x-1}=10.$$

Taking 2 from both sides, we get:

$$\frac{3(x+1)}{x-1}=8.$$

Multiplying both sides by $x-1$ to get rid of fractions, we get:

$$3(x+1)=8(x-1)$$
$$3x+3=8x-8$$
$$3+8=8x-3x$$
$$11=5x$$
$$x=11/5.$$

When we divide one fraction by another we have to treat the numerator of the dividing fraction as a divisor and the denominator of the dividing fraction as a multiplier. Thus:

$$\tfrac{3}{4}\div\tfrac{3}{4} \text{ is } (\tfrac{3}{4}\times4)\div3=1.$$

We get the same result if we turn the dividing fraction bodily upside down and multiply by it, thus:

$$\tfrac{3}{4}\div\tfrac{3}{4} \text{ is } \tfrac{3}{4}\times\tfrac{4}{3}.$$

The reason for this is clear enough if you will think about it a little. If you were dividing $\tfrac{3}{4}$ by 3 you would use the 3 as a divisor and express your result as $\dfrac{3}{4\times3}$. But you are dividing by $\tfrac{3}{4}$ and not by 3. Your divisor of 3 has been made four times smaller to begin with, so your answer will have to be four times greater, namely $\dfrac{3\times4}{4\times3}$. You can see now that this is $\tfrac{3}{4}\times\tfrac{4}{3}$, so that as stated above

$$\tfrac{3}{4}\div\tfrac{3}{4} \text{ is } \tfrac{3}{4}\times\tfrac{4}{3}.$$

This is always true, so that if you have to work out $\frac{a}{b} \div \frac{c}{d}$ you know that

the result must be $\frac{a}{b} \times \frac{d}{c} = \frac{ad}{bc}$.

Problem 21.—Evaluate the following:

$$\frac{\frac{7}{8}(\frac{2}{3} + \frac{3}{4}) - \frac{1}{6}}{\frac{3}{5}}.$$

You must first work out the sum inside the brackets. The L.C.M. of 3 and 4 is 12, and so:

$$\frac{2}{3} + \frac{3}{4} = \frac{(2 \times 4) + (3 \times 3)}{12} = \frac{8 + 9}{12} = \frac{17}{12}.$$

Now you must evaluate the product:

$$\frac{7}{8} \times \frac{17}{12}.$$

There is no cancelling, so the result is:

$$\frac{7 \times 17}{8 \times 12} = \frac{119}{96}.$$

From this you must take $\frac{1}{6}$, the numerator of the main expression having been simplified to:

$$\frac{119}{96} - \frac{1}{6}.$$

The L.C.M. of 96 and 6 is 96, and therefore (since 96 contains 6 sixteen times):

$$\frac{119}{96} - \frac{1}{6} = \frac{119 - 16}{96} = \frac{103}{96}.$$

Finally, we have to evaluate:

$$\frac{103}{96} \div \frac{3}{5}$$

It is

$$\frac{103 \times 5}{96 \times 3} = \frac{515}{288} = 1\frac{227}{288}.$$

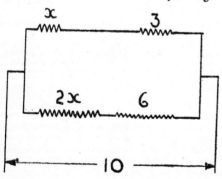

Problem 22.—Unknown resistances of x and $2x$ are grouped with known resistances of 3 and 6 as shown in the accompanying sketch, giving a combined resistance of 10. What are the values of x and $2x$?

From the formula for resistances in parallel (see Volume II, page 297) we have:

$$\frac{1}{10} = \frac{1}{x+3} + \frac{1}{2x+6}$$

$$= \frac{(2x+6)+(x+3)}{(x+3)(2x+6)} = \frac{3x+9}{(x+3)(2x+6)}$$

$$= \frac{3(x+3)}{(x+3)(2x+6)} = \frac{3}{2x+6}$$

$$\therefore \qquad 10 = \frac{2x+6}{3}$$

or $\qquad 2x + 6 = 30$

$$2x = 24$$

and $\qquad x = 12.$

Problem 23.—The resistance R_B, formed as shown in the accompanying sketch is four times the resistance R_A. What is the value of x?

$$\frac{1}{R_A} = \frac{1}{2x} + \frac{1}{10} = \frac{10+2x}{20x}$$

so $\qquad R_A = \frac{20x}{10+2x} = \frac{10x}{5+x}$

$$\frac{1}{R_B} = \frac{1}{9x} + \frac{1}{36} = \frac{36+9x}{324x} = \frac{4+x}{36x}$$

so $\qquad R_B = \frac{36x}{4+x}$

$$R_B \div R_A = 4, \text{ so} \frac{36x}{4+x} \times \frac{5+x}{10x} = 4$$

$$\frac{36(5+x)}{10(4+x)} = 4$$

$$180 + 36x = 160 + 40x$$

$$20 = 4x$$

$$x = 5.$$

Problems involving electrical resistances do not always work out as simply as this; neither do the problems in other departments of science. As a matter of fact, the last two problems were specially devised so as not to offer any perplexities;

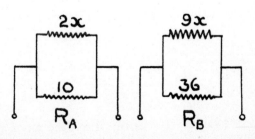

in real life most problems bristle with awkwardnesses. Just to show you what I mean I am going to alter Problem 22 slightly by changing the resistance of 3 into a resistance of 4; this will prevent the cancelling of $x + 3$ from numerator and denominator in the course of the working and present us with a difficulty we have not encountered before. Here is the amended problem:

Problem 24.—Unknown resistances of x and $2x$ are grouped with known resistances of 3 and 4 as shown in the accompanying sketch, giving a combined resistance of 10. What are the values of x and $2x$?
We have:

$$\frac{1}{10} = \frac{1}{x + 4} + \frac{1}{2x + 6}$$

$$= \frac{(2x + 6) + (x + 4)}{(x + 4)(2x + 6)} = \frac{3x + 10}{(x + 4)(2x + 6)}$$

$$10 = \frac{(x + 4)(2x + 6)}{3x + 10} = \frac{2(x + 4)(x + 3)}{3x + 10}$$

$$5 = \frac{(x + 4)(x + 3)}{3x + 10}$$

$$15x + 50 = x^2 + 7x + 12$$
$$x^2 - 8x = 38.$$

This equation is not a simple equation because x^2 appears in it; such an equation involving x and x^2 is called a "quadratic" equation, and one way to solve it is by the trial-and-error method. We guess at values of x and see whether they give us the required result.

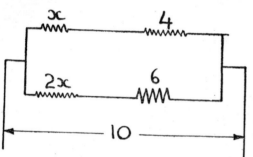

Let $x^2 - 8x = y.$

Then we must go on trying different values for x until we get the value of 38 for y. The work is best done in tabular form, thus:

x	10	11	12	13	14	15	16	17
x^2	100	121	144	169	196	225	256	289
$8x$	80	88	96	104	112	120	128	136
$y = x^2 - 8x$	20	33	48	65	84	105	128	153

Plainly the value of x that we want lies between 11 and 12.

Let us now make out another table trying values of x between these two limits.

x	11·2	11·4	11·6	11·8	11·3
x^2	125·4	130·0	134·6	139·2	127·7
$8x$	89·6	91·2	92·8	94·4	90·4
$y = x^2 - 8x$	35·8	38·8	41·8	44·8	37·3

We have now found that the value of x lies between 11·3 and 11·4. We could make out a third table evaluating y for values of x between these limits, but a better way of arriving at the final result is to make a picture of $y = x^2 - 8x$ and study closely that part where $y = 38$.

To make our picture we take a squared piece of paper and rule on it two lines at right angles to one another; these are called "axes," the vertical one being the axis of y and the horizontal one the axis of x. Any point on the paper can then have its position described accurately by giving two measurements, namely its vertical distance from the axis (called its *ordinate* or its "y") and its hori-

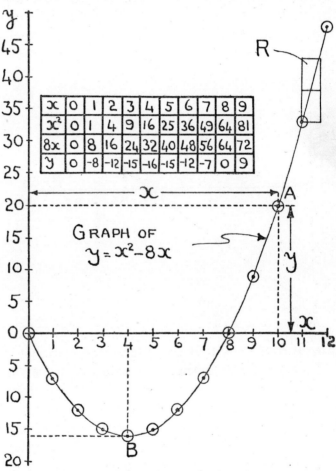

x	0	1	2	3	4	5	6	7	8	9
x^2	0	1	4	9	16	25	36	49	64	81
$8x$	0	8	16	24	32	40	48	56	64	72
y	0	-8	-12	-15	-16	-15	-12	-7	0	9

GRAPH OF
$y = x^2 - 8x$

zontal distance from the axis (called its *abscissa* or its "x"). Point A in the diagram on this page has an ordinate of 20 and an abscissa of 10. Clearly there can be only one point for which $y = 20$ and $x = 10$. Point B is fixed by the distances $y = -16$ (a distance below the x axis is always reckoned negative) and $x = 4$. Distances to the left of the y axis (when they occur) are reckoned negative.

Now our expression $y = x^2 - 8x$ gives a series of points. We can choose the x for all these points, but the y works out to values over which we have no control. Thus if $x = 1$, y must be $1^2 - 8 = -7$; if $x = 2$, y must be $2^2 - 16 = -12$, and so on. Values of y corresponding to some arbitrary values of x are tabulated in the diagram and others have been tabulated above in the text. To each value of x there is a value of y and therefore each pair of values gives us a point on our paper. When all these points are joined by a smooth curve we have a picture or "graph" of our expression $y = x^2 - 8x$. We are very interested in that point on the graph for which $y = 38$. Immediately below this point, on the x axis, we can read off the corresponding value of x that we have been trying to evaluate. The scale of the whole graph is rather small for our purpose, however, so what we do now is re-plot to a much larger scale that part of the graph enclosed in the small rectangle shown at R. We have some related values of x and y to help us do this and the second diagram shows the interesting part of our graph greatly

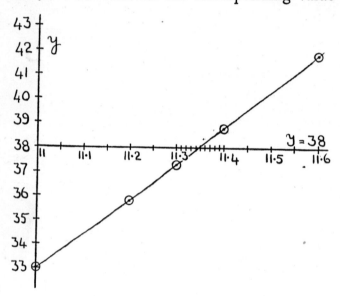

magnified. From it we are able to ascertain that when $y = 38$ $x = 11 \cdot 35$.

This graphical method of solving equations is extremely useful. The equation we have just solved *can* be solved by analytical methods, and these will be discussed presently, but you will often come across equations that resist all attempts to solve them analytically and then the graphical way is a very real aid in time of trouble.

Problem 25.—Somewhere between $x = 2$ and $x = 4$ there lies a solution to the equation $x^3 - 2x^2 + x = 24$. Find what this solution is by graphical means.

The first step is to write :

$$y = x^3 - 2x^2 + x$$

and then make a table giving values of y for different values of x between $x = 2$ and $x = 4$.

x	2	2·5	3	3·5	4
x^3	8	15·6	27	42·9	64
$x^3 + x$	10·0	18·1	30·0	46·4	68
$2x^2$	8	12·5	18	24·5	32
$y = x^3 + x - 2x^2$	2·0	5·6	12·0	21·9	36

The required solution is plainly between $x = 3·5$ and $x = 4$ and nearer to the first figure. To plot the graph in the neighbourhood of $x = 3·5$ we need some more points and the table below provides a sufficiency.

x	3·4	3·6	3·7
x^3	39·3	46·7	50·7
$x^3 + x$	42·7	50·3	54·4
$2x^2$	23·1	25·9	27·4
$y = x^3 + x - 2x^2$	19·6	24·4	27·0

From the graph derived from these figures it is plain that $x = 3·585$.

The expression we have just plotted is called a cubic quantity because it involves the three-dimensional quantity x^3.

Quadratic and cubic equations may have more than one solution. Thus the graph of $y = x^2 - 8x$ on page 59 shows us that if $-10 = x^2 - 8x$ there will be two solutions to satisfy the equation; x could be either between 1 and 2 or between 6 and 7. The precise values of x satisfying the equation are called *roots* of the equation.

The graph of $y = x^2 - 8x$ could be extended on the left and negative values of x would give positive values of y. For all values of y above -16 the equation has two roots. Between $y = -16$ and $y = 0$ the roots are both positive; when y is positive one root of the equation will be positive and the other will be negative. Very often we can find both roots of an equation without any trouble. Thus the equation $x^2 - 8x = 20$ would be an easy one to solve. Our graph

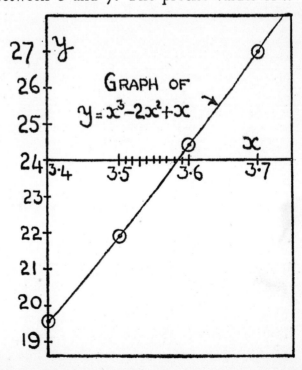

shows us that one root is $x = 10$ and we could easily extend it to show us what the other root must be. But we could solve it without drawing any graph at all. If we rewrite it

$$x^2 - 8x - 20 = 0$$

we see that the expression on the left can be factorised, giving us

$$(x + 2)(x - 10) = 0.$$

Now whenever two or more quantities yield a product of zero one of the quantities involved *must* be zero, so either $x - 10 = 0$ or $x + 2 = 0$. If $x - 10 = 0$ it means that $x = 10$, which result we have obtained already from the graph. If $x + 2 = 0$ it means that $x = -2$, which result we could also obtain from our graph if we liked to extend it far enough.

Let us now look at our cubic expression:

$$y = x^3 - 2x^2 + x.$$

The table on page 61 shows us that when $y = 12$, $x = 3$, but possibly another value of x would make $y = 12$. If we write:

$$12 = x^3 - 2x^2 + x$$

we have an equation for which 3 is one possible root. What are the others?

By rearrangement we have:

$$x^3 - 2x^2 + x - 12 = 0.$$

Because 3 is a root of the equation we know that $x - 3$ must be a factor of the left-hand expression. Let us divide by $x - 3$ to evaluate the other factor or factors.

$$
\begin{array}{r}
x^2 + x + 4 \\
x - 3{\overline{\smash{\big)}\,x^3 - 2x^2 + x - 12}} \\
\underline{x^3 - 3x^2} \\
x^2 + x \\
\underline{x^2 - 3x} \\
4x - 12 \\
\underline{4x - 12}
\end{array}
$$

Thus $(x - 3)(x^2 + x + 4) = 0$, and if this equation has other roots besides $x = 3$ they must be obtained by putting

$$x^2 + x + 4 = 0.$$

This is a quadratic equation. Can we factorise $x^2 + x + 4$? We cannot. The factors would have to be $(x +)(x +)$, where blank spaces are left for the factors of 4. These factors of 4 must add up to $+ 1$, but there are no such factors. No value of x can ever make the quantity $x^2 + x + 4$ equal to zero and so $x = 3$ is the only possible root of the original cubic equation.

Usually a cubic equation gives us three roots, but this only happens because it is possible to find three factors of the cubic expression which equals zero.

Problem 26.—Solve the equation $x^3 - 3x^2 - 4x + 12 = 0$, finding three roots if possible.

A way of finding the first factor is to try several in turn. Suppose we believed $x - 1$ to be a factor, we could divide out and see whether it gave a quotient without a remainder. A quicker way of finding out, however, is to remember that if $x - 1$ is a factor, $x = 1$ will be a root of the equation, and therefore substituting 1 for x in the above expression will give us a zero result. Putting $+ 1$ for x, we have:

$$1 - 3 - 4 + 12 = 6.$$

Plainly $x - 1$ is *not* a factor. Let us try $x + 1$ by putting $x = -1$. Our expression is then:

$$- 1 - 3 + 4 + 12 = 12,$$

so $x + 1$ is not a factor either.

Is $x - 2$ a factor?

Let us put 2 for x; this gives us:

$$8 - 12 - 8 + 12 = 0,$$

consequently $x - 2$ *is* a factor. Dividing out we get:

$$
\begin{array}{r}
x - 2\overline{)x^3 - 3x^2 - 4x + 12}(x^2 - x - 6 \\
\underline{x^3 - 2x^2} \\
- x^2 - 4x \\
\underline{- x^2 + 2x} \\
- 6x + 12 \\
\underline{- 6x + 12}
\end{array}
$$

The factors of $x^2 - x - 6$ can be seen at a glance. They must be $(x +)(x -)$ because the 6 bears the minus sign. The blanks are left for factors of 6 which differ by 1. Plainly they are 3 and 2. The larger one goes with the negative sign because x is negative. Thus:

$$x^2 - x - 6 = (x + 2)(x - 3).$$

Finally, then, we have:

$$(x - 2)(x + 2)(x - 3) = 0.$$

So that the equation has the three roots $x = 2$, $x = -2$ and $x = 3$.

To prove we are right let us make the graph of $y = x^3 - 3x^2 - 4x + 12$ between $x = -3$ and $x = +5$. Here is the necessary preliminary tabular work:

x	-3	-2	-1	0	$+1$	$+2$	$+3$	$+4$	$+5$
x^3	-27	-8	-1	0	$+1$	$+8$	$+27$	$+64$	$+125$
$A = x^3 + 12$	-15	$+4$	$+11$	$+12$	$+13$	$+20$	$+39$	$+76$	$+137$
$3x^2$	$+27$	$+12$	$+3$	0	$+3$	$+12$	$+27$	$+48$	$+75$
$4x$	-12	-8	-4	0	$+4$	$+8$	$+12$	$+16$	$+20$
$B = 3x^2 + 4x$	$+15$	$+4$	-1	0	$+7$	$+20$	$+39$	$+64$	$+95$
$A - B = y$	-30	0	$+12$	$+12$	$+6$	0	0	$+12$	$+42$

and here is the graph:

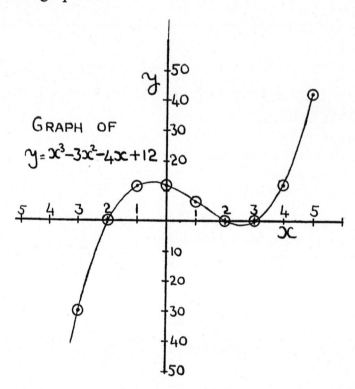

GRAPH OF
$y = x^3 - 3x^2 - 4x + 12$

The factors of an expression may not always be easy to determine by inspection. Thus you would probably be at a loss to factorise $x^2 - 2x - 11 \cdot 25$ and would therefore be baffled by the equation:

$$x^2 - 2x - 11 \cdot 25 = 0.$$

If you remember that

$$(x - a)^2 = x^2 - 2ax + a^2$$

and that $$(x + a)(x - a) = x^2 - a^2$$

you will be able to coax factors out of any quadratic expression that has them.

Thus $$(x - 1)^2 = x^2 - 2x + 1$$

so our original expression is the same as:

$$(x - 1)^2 - 11 \cdot 25 - 1 = (x - 1)^2 - 12 \cdot 25.$$

If we know the square root of $12 \cdot 25$ we can write out the factors straight away. As a matter of fact $\sqrt{12 \cdot 25} = 3 \cdot 5$, and therefore:

$$(x - 1)^2 - 12 \cdot 25 = (x - 1 + 3 \cdot 5)(x - 1 - 3 \cdot 5) = (x + 2 \cdot 5)(x - 4 \cdot 5).$$

The roots of the original equation are $x = -2 \cdot 5$ and $x = +4 \cdot 5$.

Problem 27.—Mechanics teaches us (see Volume II, page 16) that when a body is thrown vertically into the air with a velocity of v, the distance s it travels in time t is given by the relation:

$$s = vt - 16t^2.$$

A projectile is fired from a gun at a speed of 1600 feet per second. In how many seconds will it attain a height of 4800 feet?

Our equation is:

$$4800 = 1600t - 16t^2.$$

Rearranging and dividing throughout by 16, we have:

$$t^2 - 100t + 300 = 0$$
$$(t - 50)^2 + 300 - (-50)^2 = 0$$
$$(t - 50)^2 - 2200 = 0.$$

The square root of 2200 is $46 \cdot 8$,

$$\therefore \quad (t - 50 + 46 \cdot 8)(t - 50 - 46 \cdot 8) = 0$$
$$(t - 3 \cdot 2)(t - 96 \cdot 8) = 0.$$

So $t = 3 \cdot 2$ or $96 \cdot 8$ seconds.

The reason for the double answer is readily explained; the shell has to come down after going up, and whereas it is at a height of 4800 feet after only $3 \cdot 2$ seconds on the upward journey, $93 \cdot 6$ more seconds must elapse before it is at the same height on the downward journey.

The solution of a quadratic equation by the method employed in the last problem involves what is called "completing the square." The terms $t^2 - 100t$ are part of the expression $(t - 50)^2 = t^2 - 100t + 2500$, and we deliberately add in 2500 to "complete the square" and then take it away again so that the value of our original is not affected. Admittedly this is a trick, or "wangle," but the successful mathematician is one who constantly uses such tricks to get something familiar out of what appears unfamiliar.

In many text-books you can find a formula for solving quadratic equations. This formula applies to the general equation:

$$ax^2 + bx + c = 0$$

where a, b and c are any numbers whatsoever, and it is obtained by completing the square. To derive this formula we proceed as follows:

First we divide both sides by a, getting:

$$x^2 + \frac{b}{a}x + \frac{c}{a} = 0.$$

Now we complete the square:

$$x^2 + \frac{b}{a}x + \left(\frac{b}{2a}\right)^2 - \left(\frac{b}{2a}\right)^2 + \frac{c}{a} = 0$$

$$\left(x + \frac{b}{2a}\right)^2 - \left(\frac{b}{2a}\right)^2 + \frac{c}{a} = 0$$

$$\left(x + \frac{b}{2a}\right)^2 - \left(\frac{b^2 - 4ac}{4a^2}\right) = 0$$

$$\left[x + \frac{b}{2a} + \sqrt{\frac{b^2 - 4ac}{4a^2}}\right]\left[x + \frac{b}{2a} - \sqrt{\frac{b^2 - 4ac}{4a^2}}\right] = 0.$$

Now if we have an expression such as $\sqrt{\frac{p}{q}}$ we can put it equal to $\frac{\sqrt{p}}{\sqrt{q}}$.

In the numerical example $\sqrt{\frac{4}{9}}$, for instance, we shall get the same result whether we evaluate $\frac{4}{9}$ (which comes to $0\cdot4$ recurring) and then take the square root, or change it to $\frac{\sqrt{4}}{\sqrt{9}} = \frac{2}{3}$ and divide out to get $0\cdot6$ recurring. Realising this, we can write:

$$\sqrt{\frac{b^2 - 4ac}{4a^2}} = \frac{1}{2a}\sqrt{b^2 - 4ac}.$$

Finally, then, our factors are:

$$\left[x + \frac{b}{2a} + \frac{1}{2a}\sqrt{b^2 - 4ac}\right]\left[x + \frac{b}{2a} - \frac{1}{2a}\sqrt{b^2 - 4ac}\right] = 0$$

$$x = \frac{-b \pm \sqrt{b^2 - 4ac}}{2a}.$$

(Here the sign $\pm$ stands for "plus or minus.")

Problem 28.—Using the quadratic equation formula, find the roots of:

$$3x^2 + 2x - 16 = 0$$

$$x = \frac{-2 \pm \sqrt{4 + 12 \times 16}}{6} = \frac{-2 \pm \sqrt{196}}{6}$$

$$= \frac{-2 \pm 14}{6} = +2 \text{ or } -2\tfrac{2}{3}.$$

Many problems in science require the solution of equations having *two* unknown quantities or even more. Such equations are called simultaneous equations because they do not occur singly; they occur in pairs when there are two unknowns, in threes when there are three unknowns, and so on. *For the solution of simultaneous equations you must have as many separate equations as there are unknown quantities to be found.*

Problem 29.—Electrical resistances are connected across a 12-volt supply as shown in the accompanying sketch. The currents in the cross resistances are *x* and *y* and the other currents are as indicated.

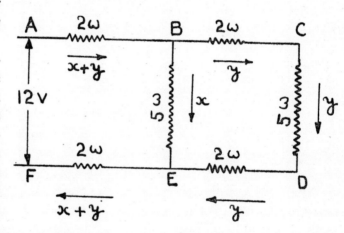

Applying Ohm's Law for voltage drops (see Volume II, page 282), evaluate *x* and *y*.

Going round ABEF we have:

$$12 = 2(x + y) + 5x + 2(x + y)$$

or $\qquad 12 = 9x + 4y$ .. .. (1)

Going round ABCDEF we have:

$$12 = 2(x + y) + (2 + 5 + 2)y + 2(x + y)$$

or $\qquad 12 = 4x + 13y$ .. .. (2)

One way to solve these equations would be to make graphs of *y* against *x* for both and find out where these graphs have a point in common.

From equation (1) we have:

$$4y = 12 - 9x$$

or

$$y = \frac{12 - 9x}{4}.$$

We can give x a number of values and obtain the corresponding values of y. The work is set out below in tabular form:

x	0	1	2	3
$9x$	0	9	18	27
$12 - 9x$	12	3	-6	-15
$y = \frac{1}{4}(12 - 9x)$	3	$\frac{3}{4}$	$-1\frac{1}{2}$	$-3\frac{3}{4}$

From equation (2) we have:

$$13y = 12 - 4x$$

or

$$y = \frac{12 - 4x}{13}.$$

Again we give x a number of values and calculate the corresponding values of y. The table for this work is below:

x	0	1	2	3
$4x$	0	4	8	12
$12 - 4x$	12	8	4	0
$7 = \frac{1}{13}(12 - 4x)$	$\frac{12}{13}$	$\frac{8}{13}$	$\frac{4}{13}$	0

When the graphs are plotted they are seen to be straight lines, and common to both is the point $x = 1 \cdot 07$, $y = 0 \cdot 595$. These values satisfy both equations and thus give us the required solution.

The graphical solution of simultaneous equations is laborious, and it cannot be employed when there are three or more unknowns to be found.

A better way of proceeding is to combine the equations so as to make one equation, at the same time ridding ourselves of all but one unknown. Reverting to our original equations:

$$12 = 9x + 4y \qquad \cdots \qquad \cdots \qquad \cdots \quad (1)$$
$$12 = 4x + 13y \qquad \cdots \qquad \cdots \qquad \cdots \quad (2)$$

we shall now demonstrate this method.

Equation (1) multiplied by 4 is:

$$48 = 36x + 16y \qquad \cdots \qquad \cdots \qquad \cdots \quad (3)$$

Equation (2) multiplied by 9 is:

$$108 = 36x + 117y \qquad \cdots \qquad \cdots \qquad \cdots \quad (4)$$

Looking at (3) and (4), we see that this artifice has made the coefficient of x equal to 36 in both equations. We can now get rid of x and form a new equation for y only by subtracting (3) from (4). This gives us:

$$108 - 48 = 117y - 16y$$
$$60 = 101y$$
$$y = \tfrac{60}{101} = 0 \cdot 595.$$

To find x we can substitute the discovered value for y in any of the

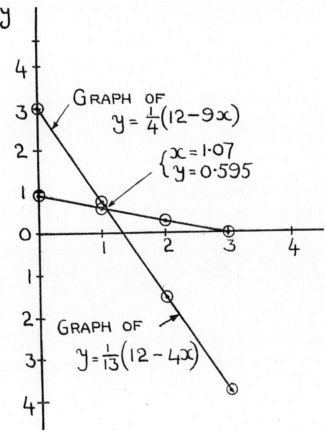

GRAPH OF
$$y = \tfrac{1}{4}(12 - 9x)$$

$$\begin{cases} x = 1 \cdot 07 \\ y = 0 \cdot 595 \end{cases}$$

GRAPH OF
$$y = \tfrac{1}{13}(12 - 4x)$$

equations, choosing the simplest for preference. Let us choose equation (1); then:

$$12 = 9x + 4 \times 0 \cdot 595$$
$$9x = 12 - 4 \times 0 \cdot 595$$
$$= 12 - 2 \cdot 38 = 9 \cdot 62$$

whence
$$x = \tfrac{9 \cdot 62}{9} = 1 \cdot 07.$$

For the solution of simultaneous equations with three unknown quantities you are referred to Volume II, page 301, where the theory of the Wheatstone Bridge network is investigated.

CHAPTER IV

EASY GEOMETRY

Engineers and other people who do practical things soon find themselves needing a knowledge of geometry, and the name of this science, meaning "measurement of the earth," testifies to its practical origins. When people first laid claim to plots of ground they drew boundary lines, and it is said that the science of geometry was developed in the region made fertile by the River Nile, which frequently overflowed its banks and obliterated all distinctions between one man's property and the next. Many square miles of land had to be marked out afresh, starting from one or two landmarks that the flood waters were unable to erase. It was a matter of necessity to be able to rule one straight line parallel to another and at a given distance from it, or to draw from a given point in a straight line another line perpendicular to it. Certain of these problems were easy to do, but others were more difficult. For instance, nobody knew of a method for dividing an angle into three equal angles, or how to draw a rectangle equal in area to a circle of a given diameter.

Philosophers began to take an interest in geometrical problems for their own sake and apart from any consequences useful or otherwise that might result from their solution. When the Greeks adopted geometry as one of their favourite studies the spur was no longer one of practical necessity but the love of exercising the mind. They purposely deprived themselves of the use of such useful aids in drawing as set-squares, protractors, etc., and set out to overcome all difficulties armed only with a ruler and a pair of compasses. Geometry thus divorced from all useful application became the basis of a liberal education, *and to this very day it is taught in some schools as though its sole object were to exercise and develop the mind.* From this point of view it is, of course, good and quite interesting, but considered as a prelude to practical occupations such as land surveying, astronomy, navigation or engineering it is vastly more absorbing. The top picture facing page 74 shows drawing instruments of the kind employed by the Romans.

In this book the truths of geometry will be presented in such an order that they lead logically from one to another, but at the same time many practical illustrations will be given. Almost everything is of value that can be learnt about triangles and circles, and no teacher of geometry should be at a loss for an answer when boy or girl asks: "But what is the *use* of knowing about triangles?"

In the beginning geometry was concerned only with the lines and figures that had to be drawn on flat level surfaces; this is what we call "plane geometry", because a flat level surface is termed a plane.

The Earth is not really flat, and if any considerable extent of its surface is involved in our calculations we must treat it as a sphere. The relations between lines and figures marked out on a sphere comprise another branch of geometry.

Solid bodies such as spheres, cubes, cones, pyramids, prisms, etc., may have nothing to do with the figure of the Earth, but geometrical methods can be applied to the study of their peculiarities, and so this study also is regarded as a branch of geometry; it is called "solid geometry."

Much interest has always been shown in the peculiar curves obtained when a cone is cut or sawn through at various angles. These curves are called "conic sections," and the branch of "geometry" concerned with them is often referred to as "conics." You would think that the conic sections (the ellipse, the parabola and the hyperbola, in addition to the circle) had no manner of practical importance whatever, but as a matter of fact all of them occur again and again in Nature and in the practical arts of engineering, building and optics. Nobody intent on architecture, shipbuilding or astronomy can afford to be ignorant of the properties of these remarkable curves.

Plane Geometry—Lines and Angles.—In reducing geometry to a science the Greeks began by defining their terms. Everyone knows what a point is, or a straight line or a plane, but it is not everyone who could clearly describe these things in words. The Greeks defined a point as that which has position but not magnitude. A star in the sky might be said to answer to this description because the most powerful telescopes ever made are incapable of giving us a measurable image of a star—it remains a mere dot, and a very precise indication of position. In a star catalogue each star has an identifying name, number or letter, and its place in the heavens is denoted by two angular measurements analogous to latitude and longitude on the Earth's surface.

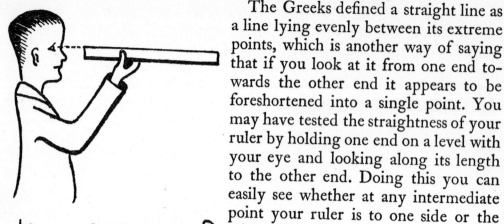

Is it STRAIGHT ?

The Greeks defined a straight line as a line lying evenly between its extreme points, which is another way of saying that if you look at it from one end towards the other end it appears to be foreshortened into a single point. You may have tested the straightness of your ruler by holding one end on a level with your eye and looking along its length to the other end. Doing this you can easily see whether at any intermediate point your ruler is to one side or the other of the line of sight between the extreme points.

The Greeks defined a plane surface as one such that any two points on it can be joined by a straight line lying wholly in that surface. The practical test for the flatness of any supposedly flat slab of glass or metal or stone is to place a straight-edge against it. If the surface is concave the two ends of the edge will rest on it, but light will show under it near its centre; if the surface is convex the straight-edge will rest on it near its centre but be clear of it at the ends and so rock to and fro like a see-saw. Extreme accuracy in the flatness of some things (a plane mirror for optical purposes, for instance) is very important, and more refined tests than that with a straight-edge have to be used in some cases. Certain gauge blocks used by

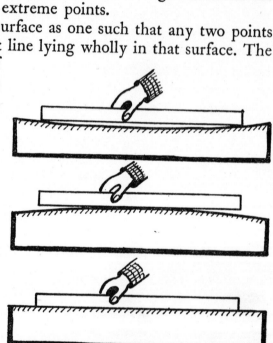

WHICH ONE IS FLAT?

engineers are so accurate that when two of them are placed with their plane or flat sides together they adhere to one another as though they were magnetised. The reason for this is that their fit, face to face, is so perfect as to exclude all atmospheric air, and consequently the atmospheric pressure on their backs becomes an unbalanced force holding them together. The Greek geometers would have been delighted beyond measure with such practical illustrations as this of the mathematically perfect plane.

Intersecting straight lines in a plane form an angle between them, and the measure of this angle is the amount of turning that one line must undergo in the plane in order that it may be brought to coincide with the other. The legs of your compass form an angle between them when you stretch the points apart. Holding one leg still, you can move the other round more and more until the two legs make a straight line. The total angular movement between "legs together" and the what dancers call the "splits" is two right angles. Continued movement of the rotating leg may not be feasible in practice either for your compass or for the supple human being, but if it could be rotated through four right angles it would be back at its

MEASUREMENT OF AN ANGLE
BY MEANS OF A PROTRACTOR

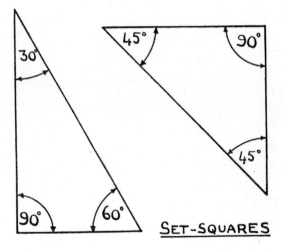

SET-SQUARES

starting-place again. Angles are commonly measured in degrees and the ordinary protractor shows you that there are 90 degrees (written 90°) in one right angle, 180 degrees between two lines so far apart as to form a single line and 360 degrees in a complete revolution.

Triangular set-squares are commonly made with the edges at one corner forming a right angle. The other two angles may be half a right angle or 45 degrees each, or they may be a third and two-thirds of a right angle (30 degrees and 60 degrees).

If you measure all the angles of a set-square, you will find that they add up to two right angles or 180 degrees in both cases. Later on we shall see that the three angles of *any* triangle must add up to two right angles or 180 degrees.

When two lines intersect, four angles are formed, as shown in the accompanying sketch. Angles marked with like symbols—two X's or two O's—are called "opposite" angles; angles on the same side of

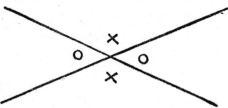

of a line and marked with unlike symbols—an X and an O—are called "adjacent" angles. The Greeks defined the *right angle* as either of the angles formed when one straight line stands on another making the adjacent angles equal. Their geometry books started with easy theorems setting out proofs of what we should now regard as obvious. Thus one theorem had for its object to prove that when one straight line stands on another, making the adjacent angles unequal (X and O in the diagram herewith), the sum of these two angles (X + O) is still equal to two right angles. The next theorem proves that the opposite angles (the two X's or the two O's) are equal.

Parallel straight lines were defined by the Greeks as lines which, being drawn in a plane, never meet however far they may be produced in either direction. The Greeks went to considerable trouble to prove certain things about

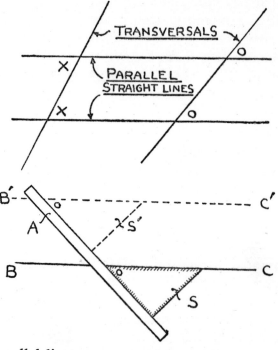

the angles formed when two parallel lines are crossed by another line (a transversal), but as their proofs are considered a little "shaky" nowadays we will accept as true without proof the facts about these angles. In the accompanying figure the angles marked X are termed *alternate* angles and the angles marked O are termed *corresponding* angles. Provided that the horizontally drawn lines are parallel, the alternate angles

Old Roman drawing instruments (replicas). The study of mathematics, and especially of geometry, preceded the Christian era first in Greece then in Rome and other centres by many centuries.

(Crown Copyright. From an exhibit in the Science Museum, London, S.W.7.)

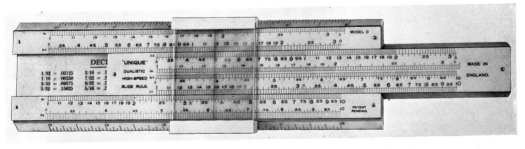

A slide rule in which the scales are arranged to reduce operation of the movable slide to a minimum.

(By courtesy of The Unique Slide Rule Co.)

XY, and N should be somewhere in the space between AB and the parallel line through P that has still to be drawn. You now stretch a third piece of inextensible string straight across from X to Y to find the exact distance. You adjust your loop compass to give you this same distance and, driving a stake into the ground at M for centre, you make the arc FG cutting MN at N′. You join PN′ and prolong it both ways; this is the line required through P parallel to AB, because angle MPN′ = angle YQX. If you cannot do this practical geometry in the open, you should try it on a piece of paper indoors, using ruler and compasses instead of lengths of string. Do not forget how to copy an angle; a protractor can be used for the same purpose, but sometimes no protractor is available.

Triangles.—Copying an angle by the method described above

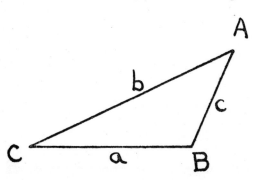

is really equivalent to copying a triangle. Points YQX define a triangle the side XY of which is measured but not drawn. In it side XQ = side YQ. The triangle defined by point MPN′ is made exactly the same in all respects, so that the angle at P shall be the same as the angle at Q.

Suppose now you were sent out to get the measurements of a triangular plot of ground with the idea of making a map or of supplying a land surveyor with data for calculating the area; what measurements would you take? Would you have to measure *all* the sides and *all* the angles? The answer is that you would not.

Imagine the triangle to be lettered ABC at its corners and imagine the sides opposite A, B and C to have lengths *a*, *b* and *c* respectively. To obtain full particulars of the triangle you must measure:

(1) All the sides *a*, *b* and *c*; or

(2) Two of the sides (say *a* and *b*) and the angle included between them (angle C); or

(3) One side (say *a*) and the angles formed with it by the other two sides (angles B and C).

With either of the three sets of data thus obtained you could reconstruct the triangle elsewhere.

Surveyors use a theodolite for measuring angles, but you could make a simpler appliance for this purpose, as shown in the sketch on the next page. The sights S_1 and S_2 are made from one strip of metal which is pivoted are equal to one another (angles marked X are equal) and so are the corresponding angles (angles marked O are equal).

You take it for granted that corresponding angles are equal when you employ ruler and set-square in the usual way to draw one line parallel to another.   Putting the ruler A across the given line BC, you alter its inclination until the set-square S placed against it has one edge coinciding with BC. You then hold A still but slide the set-square into some other position S′, when it will be found that the edge formerly along BC marks out part of another line B′C′ parallel to BC. This is because the angle of the set-square marked O remains the same irrespective of the position of the set-square itself.

How would you draw one line parallel to another on a large stretch of ground, the lines being say 100 ft. apart?

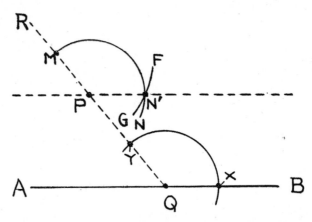

You might be given one line already drawn and be shown a point through which the other must pass. Obviously you could not use a ruler and set-square here. Suppose the given straight line to be AB in the sketch herewith, and suppose P to be the given point. A practical way to draw through P a line parallel to AB is as follows:

Drive a stake into the ground at some point Q along AB. Loop some string round this stake and walk towards P, paying out string as you go. At R, in line with Q and P drive in another stake and secure the string to this, pulling it taut so that it makes a straight line QPR analogous to your ruler A in the previous sketch. You now have to copy at P the angle PQB. To do this use a piece of string 50 to 100 ft. long with its ends tied together to make a loop. The string should be of a kind that does not stretch when pulled, for you are going to use the loop as a "pair of compasses." Looping it round the stake at Q and holding a scriber (a piece of chalk) in the loop at the other end, you draw the arc XY cutting the given line at X and the line QPR at Y. The loop is pulled taut while you draw XY. Now you transfer the loop to P where you must drive in a third stake to serve as anchorage or centre for it. Using the loop as before, but with P as centre instead of Q, you draw the circular arc MN. Obviously the radius of MN is equal to the radius of at its centre C to a board having a circle graduated in degrees. A line scratched under the sight S_1 on the strip forming it serves as a pointer to show how much the sight must be moved when it is turned from one position to another. A spike under the centre of the board would enable you to stick it in the ground exactly in the spot required—say at corner C of a triangle. The angle at C would be determined by sighting first B and then A through S_1 and S_2. To make B and A clearly visible from C you could set up at these points gaily-striped posts such as land surveyors use. A professionally made theodolite is a beautiful scientific instrument; an example is shown in plate facing page 78.

In your drawings the true lengths, as measured in feet or yards, will be too great for full-size reproduction. You might use a scale of 1/12 (1 in. = 1 ft.) for a very small area, but generally it is necessary to resort to such scales as 1 in. = 100 ft. (1/1200), 1 in. = 1 mile (1/63,360) or something even smaller. Maps in a school atlas have to be drawn to a scale of 1 in. = 50 miles for the British Isles and 1 in. = 500 miles for vast land tracks like Siberia or the islands of the Pacific Ocean.

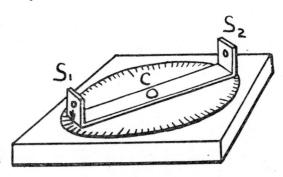

If you have enough data to *draw* a triangle, then you have enough also to be able to measure or calculate every one of its particulars. Thus if you are given the lengths of its three sides, you are able not only to draw it but to find the angles and the area. Given one side and two angles you can find the remaining angle and the other two sides. Given two sides and the included angle you can find the other angles and the remaining side. You should practise drawing triangles from given particulars, doing this until you can be trusted to know what is wanted when you are given an elementary task to perform in land surveying, astronomy or navigation. Without being perfectly familiar with requirements it is possible to come home from an important expedition and then find the whole of the collected data rendered useless for want of a single measurement that could have been and should have been taken. Thus one of the triangles might be found to have its three angles measured instead of its three sides; or two of its sides and one angle but not the included angle. Mistakes of this kind can be tragic when they occur in connection with work that has been very costly to carry out, or in connection with some event—say a transit of Venus across the face of the Sun—that will not occur again for over 100 years.

Problem 30.—When scaled down, a triangle is found to have sides with the following lengths: 2·1 in., 2·7 in. and 2·9 in. Draw this triangle full size and measure all its angles with a protractor. What is the sum of the angles?

To draw this triangle you first of all make a line equal in length to one of the sides—say the side 2·9 in. long. Call this AB. Then with A as centre and radius 2·1 in. draw part of a circle in the region above AB. With B as centre and radius 2·7 in. draw part of another circle, also in the region above AB. The circles will intersect at some point C; join BC and AC. Then ABC is the required triangle.

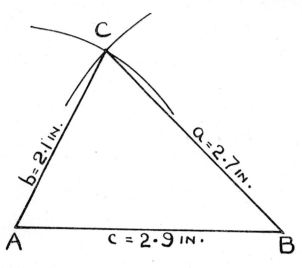

To DRAW A △ GIVEN THREE SIDES

When they are measured and added together the angles of this triangle will be found to amount to 180 degrees.

Set yourself other drawing and measuring exercises of the same kind. You will find that sometimes you give yourself lengths that cannot be used for making a triangle; thus no triangle can be made from lines 2 in., 3 in. and 5½ in. long, because if you start by drawing the side 5½ in. long, the circles of 2 in. and 3 in. radius will not reach one another so as to give a point of intersection. This failure teaches us that of necessity *any two sides of a triangle must together be greater than the third side.* The journey straight from A to B is shorter than the journey via C along AC and CB. In other words, *a straight line is the shortest distance between two points.*

Problem 31.—Draw a triangle in which AB = 3 in., AC = 4 in. and the included angle (at A) = 30 degrees. Measure the remaining angles and add all three angles together; what is their sum?

To draw this triangle make a line AB of 3 in. in length; at A make an angle of 30 degrees by adding to your figure a line AC of 4 in. in length. Join BC; then ABC is the required triangle.

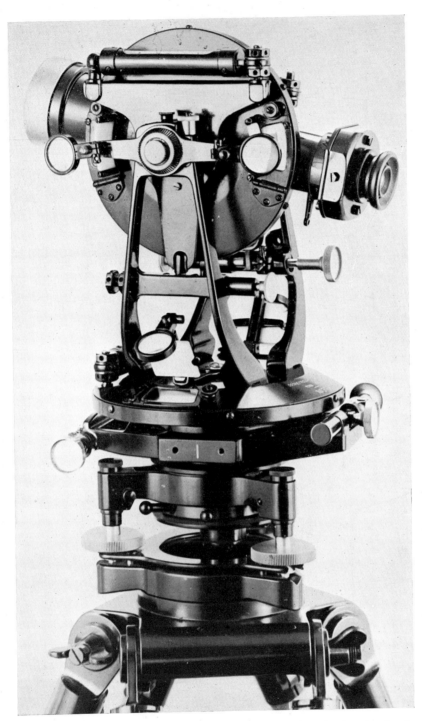

A land surveyor's theodolite. The altitude of the viewed object is given by the tilt of the telescope about the horizontal axis. Its angular displacement relative to other objects in the same horizontal plane is given by the swing of the instrument about the vertical axis. (Altitudes can also be measured by the Sextant, see Volume 1, page 214.)

(By courtesy of Messrs. Cooke, Troughton & Simms, Ltd.)

By measuring angles B and C and then evaluating A + B + C you will obtain a sum which comes to 180 degrees as before.

Set yourself other drawing and measuring exercises of the same kind. You will not get into any difficulties unless you try for angle A an angle exceeding 180 degrees. When angle A is exactly 180 degrees the "triangle" becomes a straight line and angles B and C each become zero. This suggests that angles of any triangle must be limited to a total of 180 degrees.

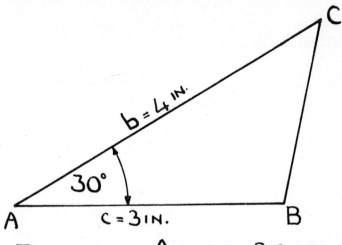

TO DRAW A △ GIVEN 2 SIDES AND THE INCLUDED ANGLE

Problem 32.—Draw the triangle ABC for which AB = 4 in., angle A = 45 degrees and angle B = 60 degrees. Measure angle C and evaluate A + B + C.

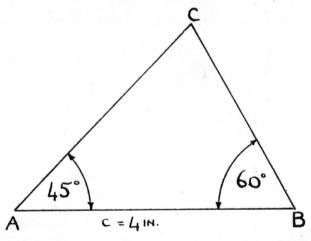

TO DRAW A △ GIVEN ONE SIDE AND ANGLES MADE WITH IT BY OTHER SIDES

To draw this triangle make a line AB of 4 in. in length; from A and B draw lines on the same side of AB, making angles with AB of 45 degrees and 60 degrees respectively. Let C be the point where these lines cut; then ABC is the required triangle.

The third angle of this triangle will be 75 degrees and the sum A + B + C will be 180 degrees as for the other triangles discussed.

Set yourself other drawing and measuring exercises of the same kind. You will find that if the angles given at A and B total 180 degrees or more, you will not get a triangle. If they total 180 degrees exactly, the lines you hoped would meet at C will be parallel and will go on for ever without meeting. Once again your work points to the conclusion that *the sum of the interior angles of any triangle is exactly* 180 degrees. This conclusion is important enough to merit formal proof. Refer now to the diagram on this page.

ABC is *any* triangle and we have to show (if it is true) that angles A, B and C together total two right angles.

Let AB be prolonged to some point D and let BE be drawn parallel to AC.

Because BE and AC are parallel,

∴   angle EBD = angle A....corresponding angles
also   angle EBC = angle C....alternate angles.

Now angle CBD (= angle EBD + angle EBC) is called an *exterior angle* of the triangle and angles A and C are called the interior opposite angles. We have thus shown that the *exterior angle of any triangle is equal to the sum of the interior opposite angles*. To each quantity let us add angle B of the triangle.

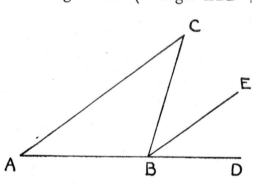

Then angles A, B and C together equal angle B + angle CBD.

But angle B + angle CBD = two right angles.

∴ angle A + angle B + angle C = two right angles.

Since ABC is a triangle of *any* shape, it is universally true that *the sum of the three angles of a triangle equals two right angles*.

Knowing two angles of a triangle, you can find the third angle by subtracting their sum from 180 degrees, *but no engineer or surveyor or mathematician ever does this unless he must.* He works out the third angle independently and keeps the knowledge that all three angles should add up to 180 degrees to serve as a check on all his measurements or calculations.

Here is the difference between being lazy and being conscientious: a boy measured two angles of a triangle, finding them to be 60 degrees and 54 degrees; he saved himself the trouble of measuring the third by mentally doing the sum 180 − 60 − 54 = 66, and he wrote 66 degrees for the third angle. His brother, a more careful worker, measured all three angles, finding them to be 60 degrees, 52 degrees and 68 degrees.

You can see now that the lazy boy got *two* of his answers wrong as the result of making a single slip. Had he *measured* the third angle and found it to be 68 degrees he would have realised that his measure of one of the angles must have been wrong because $60 + 54 + 68 = 182$. He would have gone over his work again and found his mistake.

Problem 33.—In the accompanying diagram A and B are boundary marks on the ground, separated by a building between them. For map-making purposes it was essential to find the distance AB. A land surveyor faced with this problem took his theodolite to a point C such that $AC = 35$ ft. and $BC = 45$ ft. Pointing the theodolite first at A and then at B, he found that the angle $ACB = 29$ degrees. He then went home and ascertained the distance AB; how did he do it, and what was his result?

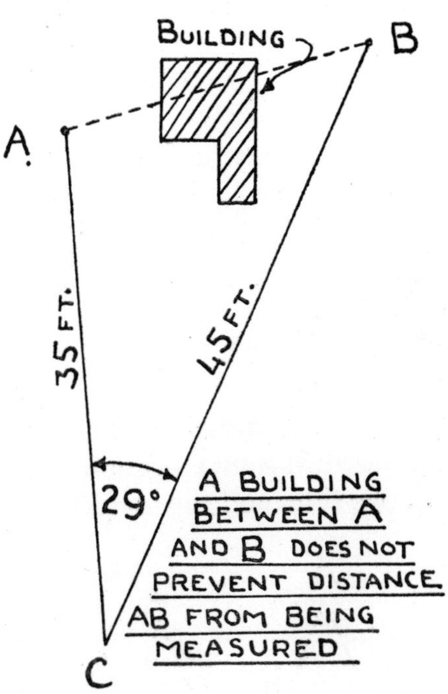

The surveyor drew to scale the triangle ABC for which two sides (AC and BC) and the included angle (ACB) were obtained by actual measurement. He then scaled off on his paper the length AB that he was unable to measure directly on site. It came to 22 ft.; try it for yourself and see if the surveyor was right. (With the help of trigonometry he could have obtained the same result without bothering to *draw* the triangle.)

Problem 34.—To measure the height of a mountain a man walked towards it along the level, stopping at two places A and B 500 yards apart to take the elevation of its summit with a sextant (see Volume I, page 214). At A he found that to view the summit he must look upwards at an angle of 30 degrees to the horizontal, whereas at B he found himself looking up at an angle of 40 degrees. From these particulars he worked out the height of the mountain. How did he do it and what was his result?

Calling the summit of the mountain C, the man drew a triangle ABC in which $AB = 500$ yards (to a scale of 1 in. $= 50$ yards), angle $A = 30$ degrees and angle $B = 180$ degrees $- 40$ degrees $= 140$ degrees. He then measured the height CP of the triangle, finding it to be 930 yards, or 2790 feet.

Already enough practical examples have been worked out for you to make it clear that a knowledge of triangles is really useful. The observers in problems 33 and 34 had certain distances to find and they

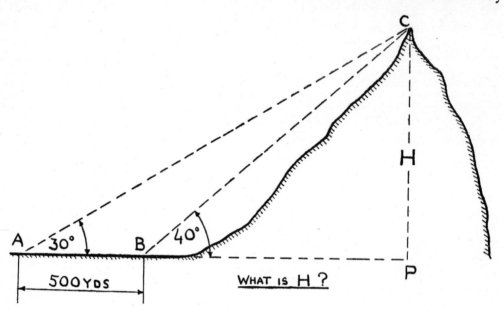

30°   40°

A   B

500 YDS   WHAT IS H ?

set about getting sufficient data for drawing a triangle in which the unknown distance occurred. In problem 33 the man obtained measures for two sides and the included angle; in problem 34 he obtained measures for one side and two angles. The wonderful instruments used by astronomers, surveyors, navigation officers, etc., are solely for the purpose of getting data which will enable triangles to be accurately determined.

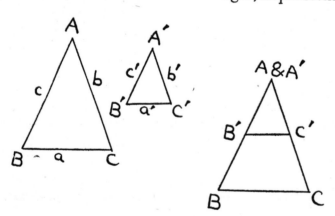

Similar Triangles. —A triangle drawn to scale from an original is of exactly the same shape but every linear dimension in it is a fraction of the corresponding dimension in the original. Thus in a triangle drawn to a scale of one quarter every dimension is a fourth part of what it is in the original. The angles are not affected by this reduction of size.

Triangles which have the same angles as one another and which differ only in the scale of their representation are said to be *similar*. Thus if in the triangles ABC A′B′C′ shown herewith angles A′, B′ and C′ are equal to angles A, B and C respectively, the triangles are similar and the fractions signifying their scale relationship are:

$$\frac{a'}{a} = \frac{b'}{b} = \frac{c'}{c}.$$

Actually they are each equal to $\frac{1}{2}$ in the example given.

If in triangle ABC the side a is, say, $\frac{3}{4}$ of the side b, then it follows that in triangle A′B′C′ the side a' will be $\frac{3}{4}$ of the side b'. Elementary algebra gives us the same result, for if, as shown above,

$$\frac{a'}{a} = \frac{b'}{b}$$

then
$$\frac{a'}{b'} = \frac{a}{b} = \frac{3}{4}.$$

If we fit triangle A′B′C′ over triangle ABC so that A′ falls on A, A′B′ lies along AB and A′C′ lies along AC, we shall get the figure shown on the right and B′C′ will be parallel to BC be-cause the angle AB′C′ = angle ABC (corresponding angles). This suggests a way of dividing up a particular line in a particular ratio. Suppose we have a line PQ in which we wish to find a point R such that PR = $\frac{2}{3}$PQ.

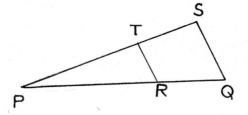

From P we shall draw any other line PS of length 3 in., and along it we shall mark off a distance PT = 2 in. Then we shall join SQ

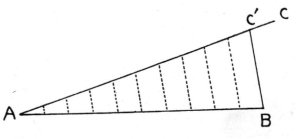

and draw through T a line TR parallel to SQ; this will cut PQ at the required point R because triangles PTR, PSQ are similar and

$$\therefore \qquad \frac{PR}{PQ} = \frac{PT}{PS} = \frac{2}{3}.$$

An extension of the same principle enables us to divide a line quickly into any number of equal parts. Suppose we wish to divide the line AB into ten equal parts, our method will be to draw any other line AC and

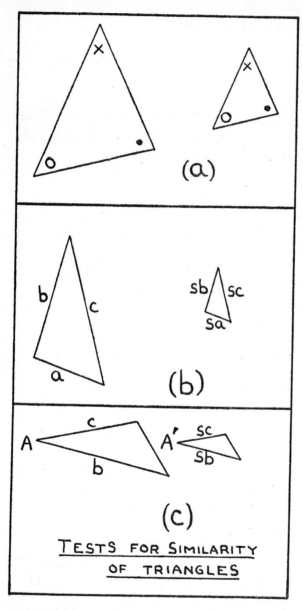

(a)

(b)

(c)

TESTS FOR SIMILARITY
OF TRIANGLES

step off along this with compasses from A ten equal lengths which we *guess* to be about a tenth of AB. Our last mark along AC comes at C' and we join BC'. We then draw lines parallel to C'B through all the compass marks in AC'; these are shown dotted and they divide AB into ten equal parts. All we have done is to make ten similar triangles, the largest of which is ABC'. The other triangles are 1/10 as large, 2/10 as large, 3/10, 4/10, 5/10, and so on.

A knowledge of the properties of similar triangles is indispensable to the engineer and scientist. How can you tell when two triangles are similar? They are similar when:

(1) The angles of the one are equal to the corresponding angles of the other.

(2) The sides of one are the same fraction of the corresponding sides of the other.

(3) Two sides of the one are the same fraction of the corresponding sides of the other and the included angles are equal in the two triangles.

The diagram herewith shows the three tests for similarity applied. In the triangles of sketch (*a*) the angles marked X are equal, those marked O are equal and those marked "." are equal. Equality of the angles marked "." follows from the other equalities because the angles in any triangle make 180 degrees, and if two of them in one triangle are equal to the corresponding two in the other, then of necessity the third angles must be equal.

In the triangles of sketch (*b*) the sides of one triangle are *s* times the sides of the other in length, so that *a, b* and *c* become *sa, sb* and *sc* where *s* is the scale of one triangle in relation to the other.

We see that :

$$\frac{a}{b} = \frac{sa}{sb},$$

$$\frac{a}{c} = \frac{sa}{sc},$$

and

$$\frac{b}{c} = \frac{sb}{sc},$$

the triangles being of the same shape. In the triangles of sketch (*c*) angle A = angle A′, side *b* = *s* times side *b*′, side *c* = *s* times side C′ and the triangles cannot be otherwise than similar, the triangle A′B′C′ being drawn to a scale of *s* times the triangle ABC.

You must remember these tests for similarity because we shall be applying them to a number of triangles presently.

Problem 35.—How would you measure the height of a very tall flagstaff standing on level ground?

The best way to do this is to set up a vertical pole close by and measure the shadows of both pole and flagstaff. If the shadow of the flagstaff is ten times as long as that of the pole, then the flagstaff must be ten times as high as the pole. The reason for this is that the triangles formed by the three lines object, shadow and sunbeam (joining tip of object to end of shadow) are similar, all the angles in the one being equal to all the angles in the other, each to each. About 600 B.C. an ingenious Greek named Thales startled an Egyptian king by measuring the height of a pyramid in this way.

If the Sun had not been shining, Thales could still have earned his reputation for ingenuity by placing his vertical pole at a distance from the pyramid and then stepping back from it until his eye perceived the tops of the pole and the pyramid in one straight line, as shown in the accompanying diagram. From similar triangles we have:

$$\frac{H}{h} = \frac{D}{d}$$

or

$$H = \frac{D}{d}h.$$

Thus if

$$h = 5 \text{ ft.}, \; D = 500 \text{ ft. and}$$
$$d = 10 \text{ ft.}$$

$$H = \frac{500}{10} \times 5 = 250 \text{ ft.}$$

To this figure it is necessary to add the height of the observer himself.

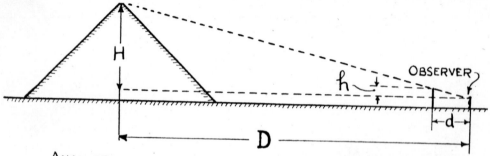

ANOTHER WAY OF FINDING THE HEIGHT OF A TALL OBJECT

Special Triangles.—A triangle having two sides equal is called an *isosceles* triangle; in the example shown below on the left, AB = AC.

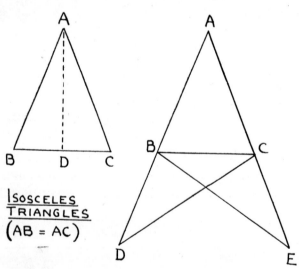

ISOSCELES
TRIANGLES
(AB = AC)

The base angles B and C are equal as we can easily prove by joining A to the mid-point D of BC and comparing the two triangles thus formed. Side AD is common to both, side DB = side DC by construction and side AB = side AC by hypothesis; thus the triangles are equal in every respect and angle B = angle C.

The converse of this proposition is also true. If angle B = angle C, then side AB = side AC. To prove this we must make the figure shown above on the right. Side AB is produced to D making BD = BC, and side AC is produced to E making CE = CB. We then join DC and BE.

In triangles BDC, CEB, BC is common to both.

BD = CE (both equal to BC)

angle CBD = angle BCE (both equal to 180 degrees less a base angle of the triangle ABC).

∴. the triangles are equal in every respect (two sides and included angle of one equal to two sides and included angle of the other).

∴
DC = BE

and angle CDB = angle BEC

and angle DCB = angle CBE.

To each of these latter angles *add* one of the base angles of the triangle ABC. Since these base angles are equal, the sums thus obtained will be equal, that is:

angle ABE = angle ACD.

Then in triangles ACD ABE:

angle ACD = angle ABE (just proved)

angle CDA = angle BEA (proved above)

and
DC = BE (proved above).

∴. the triangles are equal in every respect (two angles and a side of the one equal to two angles and a side of the other).

∴
AC = AB

which was the truth we had to prove.

Although what we have just proved seemed obvious at the outset, obvious things are not always readily demonstrable, and this particular demonstration or proof has been the stumbling-block of so many students of geometry that it has earned the name of "pons asinorum," which is the Latin for "the bridge of asses." If a boy could get no farther in geometry he was dubbed an ass. Once past this proposition a boy was entitled to greater respect.

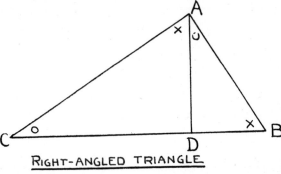

RIGHT-ANGLED TRIANGLE

An *equilateral* triangle is one having all its sides equal. Plainly all the angles must be equal also, and each must be 60 degrees.

A *right-angled* triangle is one having a right-angled vertex. Thus in triangle ABC angle A is a right angle. Obviously the sum of angles B and C must be one right angle.

If a line AD is drawn making the two angles at D equal, then each will be a right angle and

$$\text{angle DAC} = \text{angle B}$$
$$\text{angle DAB} = \text{angle C.}$$

From this it follows that all three triangles ABC, DBA and DAC are equiangular and therefore similar. Many important results can be deduced from this.

In triangles ABC, DBA

$$\frac{BC}{AB} \text{ in one} = \frac{AB}{BD} \text{ in the other.}$$

$$\therefore \qquad\qquad AB^2 = BC \cdot BD \qquad .. \qquad .. \qquad .. \quad (1)$$

(the square on AB is equal in area to the rectangle formed by the lines BC and BD).

In triangles ABC, DAC

$$\frac{BC}{AC} \text{ in one} = \frac{AC}{DC} \text{ in the other.}$$

$$\therefore \qquad\qquad AC^2 = CB \cdot CD \qquad .. \qquad .. \qquad .. \quad (2)$$

(the square on AC is equal in area to the rectangle formed by the lines CB and CD).

Adding results (1) and (2) we get:

$$AB^2 + AC^2 = BC \cdot BD + CB \cdot CD$$
$$= BC(BD + DC)$$
$$= BC^2$$

Thus *the square on the longest side of a right-angled triangle (called the hypotenuse) is equal to the sum of the squares on the other two sides.*

This result was first obtained in the sixth century B.C. by the celebrated Greek geometer Pythagoras, and the theorem takes its name after him. There are scores of ways of proving the same thing.

The Egyptians knew before the time of Pythagoras that a triangle having sides of 3, 4 and 5 units in length gave a right angle between the sides 3 and 4 units long; they made use of this knowledge in order to draw a right angle. Suppose you had a line NS on the ground and through some point P in it you wanted to draw a line EW perpendicular to NS. The Egyptian method would be to mark off a line PQ along PN 4 units long. With a stake at P and a string "compass" 3 units long, the arc A would then be struck. With a stake at Q and a string compass 5 units long, the arc A′ would be struck, cutting A at O. Line PO would be a perpen-

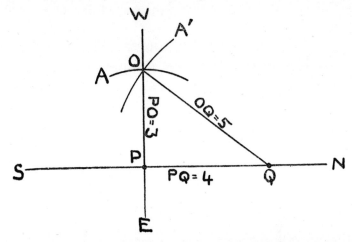

dicular to NS which, being extended in both directions, would give the required line EW.

The Egyptians must also have known from their use of mosaic tiles in the form of isosceles right-angled tri-angles that the square on the hypotenuse of such a triangle was equal to the sum of the squares on the other two sides. Look at the accompanying sketch; it makes this truth quite self-evident.

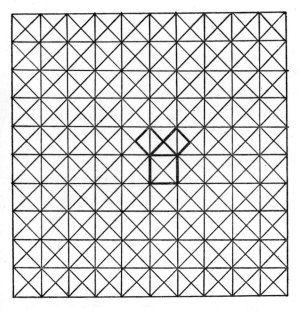

A LESSON YOU CAN LEARN
FROM A MOSAIC FLOOR

Problem 36.—If each side of a square is 4 in. long, what is the length of a diagonal?

The diagonal divides the square into two right-angled triangles each having both of the two shorter sides equal to 4 in.

∴ the square on the diagonal $= 4^2 + 4^2$
$$= 32$$
Length of diagonal
$$= \sqrt{32} = 5.66 \text{ in.}$$

Problem 37.—A kite on a string 100 ft. long appears vertically overhead at a point 75 ft. from the boy who is flying it; how high is the kite if the boy's hand is 4 ft. from the ground?

The kite K, the boy B and the observer O form a right-angled tri-angle KBO with a right angle at O. The string BK is the hypotenuse.

∴ $BK^2 = BO^2 + OK^2$
$OK^2 = BK^2 - BO^2 = 100^2 - 75^2$
$= (100 + 75)(100 - 75)$
$= 175 \times 25 = 4375$
$OK = 66 \cdot 2.$

∴ Height of kite above ground $= 66 \cdot 2 + 4 = 70 \cdot 2$ ft.

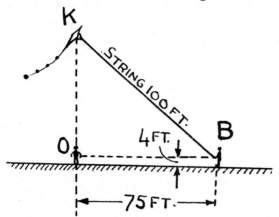

Problem 38.—Find by graphical means the length of a line such that the square on it is equal to the rectangle contained by lines 4 in. and 3 in. long.

There are two constructions for accomplishing this and here is the first: Draw a line AB 4 in. long and mark off along it a length AC = 3in. At C erect a perpendicular to cut at P a semicircle drawn on AB as diameter. Join AP; then AP will be the required length because APB is a right-angled triangle (see page 97) and

$$AP^2 = AC \cdot AB \text{ (see page 88)}.$$

As an exercise you should prove that
$$CP^2 = CA \cdot CB$$
and then use this knowledge to solve problem 38 in the following way: Draw a line $4 + 3 = 7$ in. long and 4 in. from one end erect a perpendicular to cut a semicircle drawn on the whole line as diameter. Then this perpendicular will have the required length. (It should be exactly the same length as AP obtained by the first method.)

Problem 39.—How would you copy exactly twice full size the outline

AB = 4
AC = 3
AP = 3·47 (BY MEASUREMENT)

of a figure such as F in the following diagram?

To do this you must apply your knowledge of the properties of similar triangles.

Take any point O outside the figure and from O draw a number of rays crossing the figure and extending well beyond it. Consider the ray OPQ cutting the figure at P and Q. Span OP with your dividers and

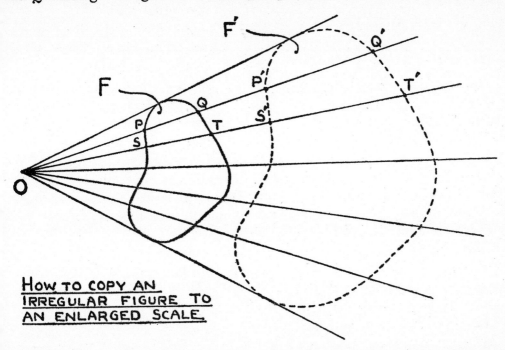

How to copy an
IRREGULAR FIGURE TO
AN ENLARGED SCALE.

then swing the length PO round P to make a mark at P′ in OP produced. Span OQ with your dividers and then swing the length QO round Q to make a mark at Q′ in OP produced. In this way you make OP′ = 2OP and OQ′ = 2OQ. Points P′ and Q′ will be two points in the copy of F that you require to be drawn twice full size. They correspond to points P and Q in the original figure.

Points S′ and T′ along the ray OS produced were obtained from points S and T by repeating the process given for obtaining P′ and Q′. In a similar manner many other points were obtained in the required new outline and finally these points were joined up to form the new figure F′.

Your knowledge should now be sufficient to enable you to prove that triangles OPS, OP′S′ are similar, so that P′S′ = 2PS. In the same way Q′T′ = 2QT. Every dimension in the figure F′ is twice the corresponding dimension in the figure F and it is measured in the same direction, because P′S′ is parallel to PS, Q′T′ is parallel to QT, and the same applies to the joins of any other pairs of corresponding points. The pantograph copying machine works on this principle, and you will find it described in Volume I, page 46, in the article on the steam-engine.

Problem 40.—What is the simplest way to divide a straight line into two equal parts?

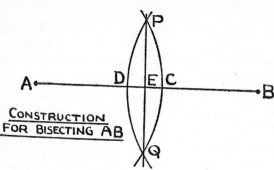

CONSTRUCTION
FOR BISECTING AB

Let AB be the line it is required to bisect. With A as centre and radius AC obviously greater than half of AB, draw a circular arc cutting AB at C. With B as centre and radius BD = AC, draw a circular arc cutting AB at D. Join the points P and Q where these arcs intersect. Let E be the point where PQ crosses AB; then AE = BE, for E is the required middle point of AB.

Proof of this is left as an exercise for the reader.

Problem 41.—What is the simplest way to bisect an angle?

Let the given angle be at A between the lines AB and AC.

With A as centre and any radius AD, draw the circular arc DE cutting AB in D and AC in E.

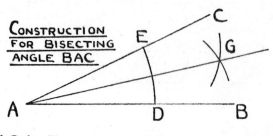

CONSTRUCTION
FOR BISECTING
ANGLE BAC

Using the same or any other radius, strike arcs from D and E as centres; let their cutting point be G. Join GA. Then the angle at A will be bisected by GA.

Proof of this is left as an exercise for the reader.

Problem 42.—From any point C *outside* a line AB draw a perpendicular to AB.

With C as centre and a radius greater than the distance between C and AB, draw an arc cutting AB at P and Q. Bisect the line PQ at at D; join CD. Then CD will be the required perpendicular.

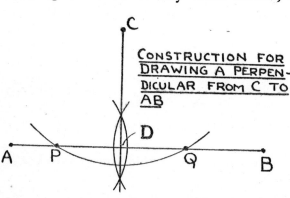

CONSTRUCTION FOR
DRAWING A PERPEN-
DICULAR FROM C TO
AB

Proof of this is left as an exercise for the reader.

Problems that at first sight seem as easy as the above may turn out to be extremely difficult. A deceptive problem of this kind is that of trisecting an angle (dividing it into three equal parts). Another is to find the length of a line whose cube is twice the cube of a given line. These two problems, and one or two more, engaged the attentions of the cleverest geometers of ancient times, and they remained unsolved for many centuries. We shall not attempt to deal with them in this book, as they can be solved easily by non-geometrical methods.

CHAPTER V

MORE ADVANCED GEOMETRY

The triangle is simplest closed figure that can be made with straight sides. No figure can be made with fewer than three sides, and all figures having more than three sides can be divided into two or more triangles by adding diagonal lines to the figure. Thus a four-sided figure can

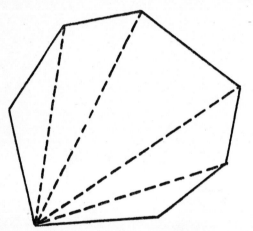

A 7-SIDED FIGURE
MAKES 7-2=5 TRIANGLES

be made into two triangles, a five-sided figure into three triangles, a six-sided figure into four triangles, and so on. If the figure has n sides it will make $n-2$ triangles. In each triangle the sum of the angles is two right angles; consequently the sum of the interior angles of an n-sided figure is $2(n-2) = 2n-4$ right angles.

A triangle is necessarily a plane figure, but figures having four or more sides can be folded along the diagonals without bending any of the sides, and then it no longer remains a plane figure. The ends of chair or table legs define a four-sided figure which is supposed to be a plane figure, but if one leg is slightly longer or shorter than the other it will be impossible to make all four rest on the floor simultaneously; the chair or table will rock in an annoying manner on two of the legs, settling first on one and then on the other remaining leg. Some articles of furniture, notably stools, are made with three legs because then they will stand steadily in all circumstances, even on an uneven floor. Tripods for cameras, theodolites, etc., are, as their name indicates, three-footed stands; they are used to obviate any risk of movement in the instrument supported.

The frame of a motor car is liable to bend or twist slightly on very uneven roads, and to prevent any corresponding distortion of the engine this is invariably attached to the frame at three points only; these points can move up or down relatively to one another but they keep in one plane, albeit a movable plane. The principle of three-point suspension is widely used by engineers in attaching rigid components to flexible frames; the attachments themselves are also flexible, being either of the ball-and-socket or rubber-bushed type.

A plane four-sided figure having its sides and angles unequal is called a quadrilateral. When all its angles are right angles it is called a rectangle; when, in addition, all its sides are equal it is called a square. Plane

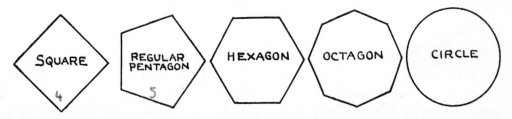

figures having more than four sides are called polygons. A "regular" polygon is one having all its sides and angles equal. A regular pentagon has five sides and a hexagon has six sides. Other special polygons have their own particular names but there is no need to mention them except perhaps the octagon, which is a regular eight-sided figure. Towers are sometimes made octagonal in plan. A circle resembles a regular polygon in which the number of sides has become infinitely great.

However, circles are not made with the help of ruler or set-square, but by means of compasses, and we get our best definition of the circle from considering the method employed in drawing it; a circle is the path (or locus) of a point which moves in a plane so that its distance (called the radius) from a fixed point (called the centre) is constant in amount.

The diameter of a circle is any straight line which passes through its centre and is bounded by the circumference; plainly the diameter is equal in length to twice the radius.

Circles are sometimes made by drawing round coins or the lids of tins, and it may be necessary to find the centre of a circle drawn in this way. The method is to draw two chords from a given point on the circumference and bisect these at right angles. The centre of the circle

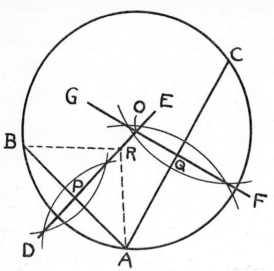

will be at the point of inter-section of the bisectors. A chord is any straight line joining two points on the circumference, and a diameter is a special case, being a chord through the cen-tre and longest of all the chords that can be drawn.

In the diagram given here, AB, AC are chords of the circle; DE and FG are their bisectors making right angles at P and Q respectively. It is easy to show that all points along DE are equidistant from A and B, and that all points along FG are equidistant from A and C. It follows that point O, which is common to both lines, must be equidistant from A, B and C. This, then, can be none other than the centre of the given circle, as not more than *one* circle can be drawn through three points.

To prove that any point along DE is equidistant from A and B all you have to do is select any point on DE—point R, for instance—and join RA, RB. Then in triangles RPA, RPB you have RP common, PA = PB (by construction) and the included angle RPA = the included angle RPB = one right angle (by construction). Therefore the trian-gles are equal in every respect, and so RA = RB. The same argument will serve to show that any point along FG is equidistant from A and C.

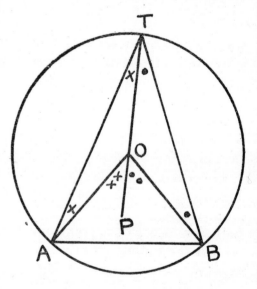

When the extremities A and B of any chord AB are joined to the centre O and also to a point T on the circumference, we discover the remarkable fact that the angle subtended by the chord at O (angle AOB) is twice the angle subtended by the chord at T (angle ATB).

To prove this we join TO and produce to some point P. We then see that triangles TOA and TOB are isosceles triangles with equal angles marked "X" and "." as shown. The exterior angle AOP of triangle ATO must be "XX" (see page 80) and the exterior angle BOP of triangle BTO must be ".." Plainly the angle at O is twice the angle at T.

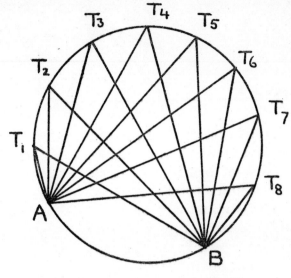

This important relation between the angles at O and T applies irrespective of the position of T, so that if we take several points such as T_1, T_2, T_3, etc., and join all of them to A and B we get at each one an angle equal to half the angle at the centre. All these angles being equal

THE ANGLES AT T_1, T_2, T_3, ETC. ARE ALL EQUAL

to the same thing, they must be equal to one another.

When AB is a diameter of the circle, as shown in the next diagram,

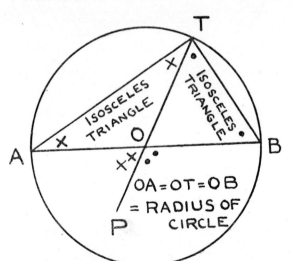

OA = OT = OB = RADIUS OF CIRCLE

the angle at O is two right angles, and consequently the angle at T is one right angle. Use was made of this principle in solving the problem on page 90.

Can a circle be drawn round a right-angled triangle and will its centre be at the midpoint of the hypotenuse?

Let ABC be any right-angled triangle with its right angle at B. From angle B we cut off angle ABP equal to angle A by means of the line BP. The remainder, namely angle CBP, must equal angle C because the two angles at B make a right angle and so do the angles A and C. Triangles BPA and BPC are isosceles triangles because in each there are two equal angles, consequently PA = PB, and PB = PC. Thus all three lines PA, PB and PC are equal, so that a circle drawn from P

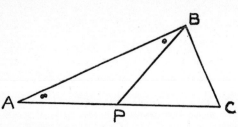

as centre and with radius PA would pass through B and C. The centre of this circle (P) is also the mid-point of the hypotenuse of triangle ABC.

To draw a circle round any triangle whatsoever you must draw the right bisectors of two of the sides; these will intersect at a point equidistant from all three vertices of the triangle so that the centre and radius of the required circle are simultaneously obtained by this construction. The right bisector of the third side must necessarily run through the same point. Because they all meet at a point inside the triangle the right bisectors of its sides are said to be "concurrent."

To draw a circle inside a triangle so that it touches all three sides you must bisect two of the angles; the required circle has its centre where these bisectors meet. The bisector of the third angle must necessarily run through the same point, so that in any triangle the three bisectors of the angles, as well as the right bisectors of the sides, are concurrent.

A line drawn to touch a circle but not to cut it is called a tangent. A line drawn from some point outside a circle to

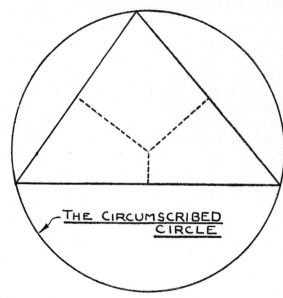

THE CIRCUMSCRIBED CIRCLE

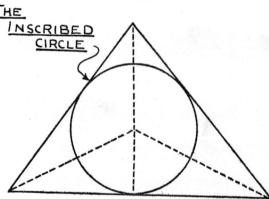

THE INSCRIBED CIRCLE

cut it in two places is called a secant; plainly a tangent is the limiting case of a secant drawn so that the two cutting points are indistinguishable from one another. In the accompanying figure OPQ is a secant (of which PQ is called a chord) and OT is a tangent. If line OPQ is swung

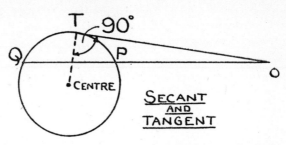

SECANT
AND
TANGENT

clockwise round O the cutting points PQ will approach one another and eventually both will coincide with point T.

The tangent to a circle at any point T is at right angles to the radius drawn to the same point. In order to draw the tangent you must first draw the radius to the given point T, and at T you must draw a line at right angles to this radius. You must not draw a tangent by lining a ruler up against a circle at T in the way you think it should go; if you do this and then test your work by putting in the radius afterwards, you will be almost certain to detect serious inaccuracy.

Problem 43.—To draw a tangent to a circle from a given point outside it.

Let C be the centre of the given circle and O be the given point. On OC as diameter draw a semicircle to cut the given circle at T.

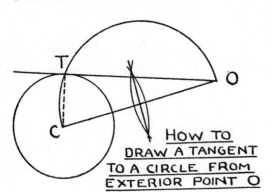

HOW TO
DRAW A TANGENT
TO A CIRCLE FROM
EXTERIOR POINT O

Then triangle OTC will be right angled at T and OT will be the required tangent from O, making a right angle with the radius CT of the given circle at T.

Problem 44.—To draw a circle from a given centre to touch a given line.

Let C be the given centre and AB be the given line (no diagram is shown for this). From C drop a perpendicular on to AB by the construction given in answer to problem 42 on page 92. Let this perpendicular fall on AB at T; then CT is the radius of the required circle.

When drawing a circle to touch the three sides of a triangle you should find its radius by dropping a perpendicular on to one of the sides of the triangle from the meeting-point of the bisectors of the angles. The circle drawn inside a triangle to touch all three sides is called the "inscribed" circle; the circle drawn through the vertices of a triangle is called the "circumscribed" circle.

When a quadrilateral is drawn with all four points on the circumference of a circle it is called a cyclic quadrilateral and the peculiar feature of it is that the sum of opposite interior angles must be two right angles. If you join opposite corners to the centre you will form at this point two angles the sum of which is four right angles. Each, however, is twice an angle at the circumference subtended by the same arc,

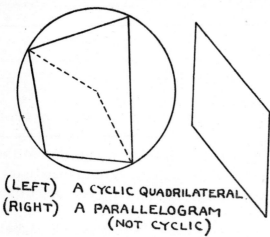

and so the angles at the circumference must together make two right angles.

Not every quadrilateral is a cyclic quadrilateral. A parallelogram, for instance, is not cyclic unless it happens to be a rectangle. In a parallelogram the opposite sides are parallel and consequently the opposite angles are equal. Whether separately less than or greater than a right angle the opposite

(LEFT) A CYCLIC QUADRILATERAL
(RIGHT) A PARALLELOGRAM
(NOT CYCLIC)

angles will differ from two right angles in their sum; only when each individually is a right angle can the two together make two right angles.

The foregoing propositions about circles may not seem to be of much practical importance, but they point the way to some facts having many useful applications.

The first of these facts relates to intersecting chords; the parts of the one contain between them a rectangle equal in area to the parts of the other.

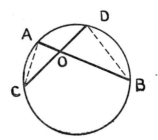
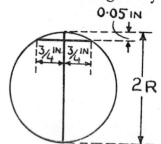

Let AB and CD (left-hand diagram) be chords of a circle intersecting at O; then AO × OB = CO × OD.

To prove this join AC and DB.

In triangles AOC, DOB the angles at O are equal, angle A = angle D (both on arc CB) and angle C = angle B (both on arc AD). Therefore the triangles are equiangular and similar;

∴

$$\frac{AO}{CO} = \frac{OD}{OB}$$

∴

$$AO \cdot OB = CO \cdot OD.$$

Problem 45.—The three legs of a spherometer (see Volume II, page 203) are all ¾ in. distant from the adjustable central leg. When the instrument is stood on a convex lens the central leg has to be raised 0·05 in. relative to the others; what is the radius of curvature of the lens?

From what we have just proved about intersecting chords we know that (see right-hand diagram):

$$(\tfrac{3}{4})^2 = 0{\cdot}05(2R - 0{\cdot}05)$$

∴

$$2R = 20(\tfrac{3}{4})^2 + 0{\cdot}05 = 11{\cdot}3$$

$$R = 5{\cdot}65 \text{ in.}$$

The next proposition relates to secants which, in effect, are chords that meet when produced outside the circle instead of inside the circle.

Let ABO and CDO be the secants under consideration; join AD and CB.

Then in triangles OAD, OCB angle O is common to both and angle A = angle C (both on arc BD); therefore the triangles are equiangular and similar;

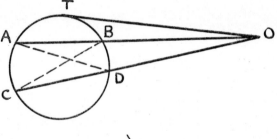

∴

$$\frac{OA}{OD} = \frac{OC}{OB}$$

∴ $OA{\cdot}OB = OC{\cdot}OD.$

This result is important in itself, but in the special case when one of the secants becomes a tangent we get a

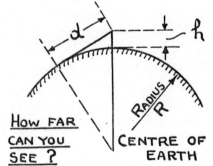

HOW FAR CAN YOU SEE ?

RADIUS R

CENTRE OF EARTH

result that is of daily application in navigation because it is the foundation on which rests the formula for the dip of the horizon as seen from the bridge or deck of a ship (see Volume I, page 216).

In this special case, when the secant becomes the tangent OT,

$$OT^2 = OA{\cdot}OB = OC{\cdot}OD = \text{etc.}$$

Problem 46.—How far can you see across the sea on a clear day when you are standing on a cliff 528 ft. high? Assume that the radius of the earth is 4000 miles.

If we call this distance *d* and put *h* for the height of the cliff, we shall get a formula applicable to any problem of this kind. The accompanying sketch shows that

$$d^2 = h(2R + h)$$

where R is the radius of the Earth,

$$\therefore \quad d = \sqrt{h(2R + h)} = \sqrt{2Rh + h^2}$$
$$= \sqrt{2Rh}$$

since h^2 will always be negligible in comparison with $2Rh$.

In this particular problem we take $R = 4000$ miles and $h = 528$ ft., or $\frac{1}{10}$ mile;

$$\therefore \quad d = \sqrt{2 \times 4000 \times 0 \cdot 1} = 28 \cdot 3 \text{ miles.}$$

When an object is viewed obliquely all its measurements in one direction are foreshortened, though in the direction at right angles they remain unaltered. The sketches below are of a penny. Viewed in a direction perpendicular to one face a penny is circular in outline, as shown on the left. If it is turned 45 degrees round an imaginary axis AB it will have the appearance shown in the middle sketch. All measurements perpendicular to AB are foreshortened,

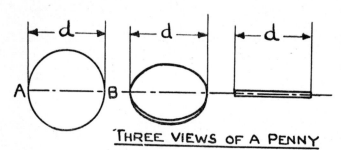

THREE VIEWS OF A PENNY

whereas those parallel to AB remain unaffected. When the penny is turned through 90 degrees we get the edge view shown on the right, and measurements perpendicular to AB in the original view have all become scaled down to nothing. The diameter AB still remains the same length d, however.

How is it possible to draw accurately the shape of a circle seen obliquely? Consider a particular case; the construction will be as shown in the next diagram.

AB is the diameter of the circle forming the axis about which it is imagined to turn. Viewed along this axis from the left the circle becomes a straight line, as shown by CD on the right, and the axis AB becomes the point O. Let the circle be turned round the axis O so that its edge view is now C'D'. Point P on the circle moves to point P'. In the right-hand view we can find P' easily by making OP' = OP (with compasses), we get P' in the left-hand view by drawing the line P'P' parallel to PP (or parallel to ABO). Length PQ in the left-hand view has been foreshortened into the length P'Q, and we see now how to derive length P'Q from length PQ. Applying this construction to a number of lines such

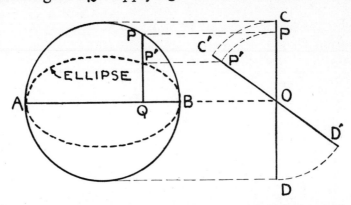

as PQ drawn across the circle perpendicular to AB, we shall get a series of points such as P', and joining all these by a smooth curve we shall obtain the modified or foreshortened figure of the circle. This is shown dotted in the left-hand part of the diagram. The foreshortened view of a circle is called an *ellipse*; it is an important figure which occurs again and again in mathematics and natural science.

A neater way of drawing an ellipse is shown in the next diagram. First of all you decide on the greatest and least dimensions of the ellipse; the dimension corresponding to the unaltered diameter of the circle is called the *major axis* and the dimension corresponding to the diameter at right angles (the most foreshortened diameter) is called the *minor axis*. With O as centre you draw circles having diameters equal to the major and minor axes of the required ellipse. Now draw any line such as ORP cutting the two circles in R and P. If AB is required to be the major axis of the ellipse, you now drop a perpendicular PQ from P

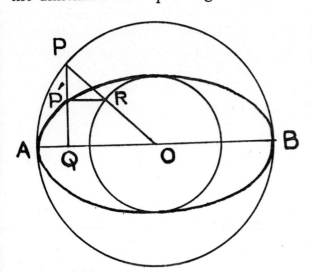

on to AB. Through R you draw a line parallel to AB cutting PQ at P'. Then P' is one point on the required ellipse. Other points are obtained in the same way and then they are joined by a smooth curve.

Another way of describing an ellipse is to say that it is the path of a point which moves so that the *sum* of its distances from two fixed points is constant. Thus F_1 and F_2 are fixed points called foci (plural of focus) and P' is the moving point which traces the ellipse. It moves so that $F_1P' + F_2P' =$ constant. A mechanical way of drawing an ellipse is to set up two pegs at F_1 and F_2 and put a loop of string round them. By means of a pencil P' put within the loop the string is pulled into a triangle F_1F_2P'. If the pencil is moved in the direction of the arrow, keeping the string tight, it will automatically draw an ellipse. The value of the "constant" (equal to $F_1P' + F_2P'$) can be ascertained from con-

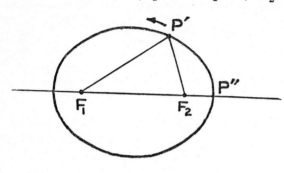

sidering what it must be when the pencil is at P''. The two lengths F_1P'' and F_2P'' add up to make $F_1F_2 + 2F_2P''$ and this is plainly equal to the major axis of the ellipse. Let $2L =$ major axis, $2l =$ minor axis and $2a =$ distance between foci; then it will be clear that

$$L^2 = a^2 + l^2$$

or $$l = \sqrt{L^2 - a^2}.$$

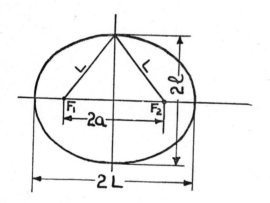

A circle is a special case of the ellipse in which $a = O$ and $l = L$. The two foci have run together and become the centre; the major and minor axes have become equal.

There is another kind of curve having two foci and it is called the hyperbola. This is the path of a point which moves so that the *difference* of its distances from two fixed points is a constant. In the following diagram the difference between F_1P_1 and F_2P_1 is the same as that between F_1P_2 and F_2P_2 or between F_1P_3 and F_2P_3. Distances from F_1 are all greater than those from F_2 so far as curve A is concerned, but another curve can be derived from the same difference of focal distances making the distances from F_2 greater than those from F_1. This explains the derivation of curve B. Both curves are regarded as constituting a single hyperbola— it is a curve with two branches. When the travelling point is very far indeed from F_1 and F_2 its motion is almost but not quite rectilinear, for the hyperbola tends to become a straight line. The two lines ST and

UV which the hyperbola approaches but never quite touches are called the "asymptotes."

In the 1914–18 war British scientists developed a clever method for directing gunfire which depended on knowing the properties of the hyperbola. In the map shown on page 106 A is a gun which is required to shell an invisible enemy position B. Sound-recording stations are installed at points C, D and E. When the shelling starts a note is made of the exact instants when the sound of shell bursts reaches C, D and E. Sound travels at the finite speed of 1100 ft. per second, so that if the report of an exploding shell is heard $\frac{1}{2}$ second earlier at C than at D the observers know that the shell fell at some point closer to C than to D by 550 ft. On the chart a hyperbola H_1 is plotted to join all the points which are 550 ft. closer to C than to D.

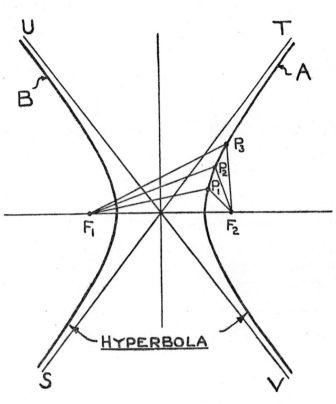

Observation post E may have got the sound a full second later than observation post C, in which case the shell must have burst at some point 1100 ft. farther from E than from C. A hyperbola H_2 drawn with E and C as foci and a common difference of 1100 ft. shows all points where the shell might possibly have fallen so far as the observers at E and C could tell. The two hyperbolic plots cross at point X and plainly the shell must have burst here. Informing the gunner where his shells were falling enabled him constantly to improve his aim until at last the hyperbolic plots showed that point X coincided with the target position B.

This ingenious method of directing gunfire was called "sound ranging," and it was applied also to determining the position of camouflaged

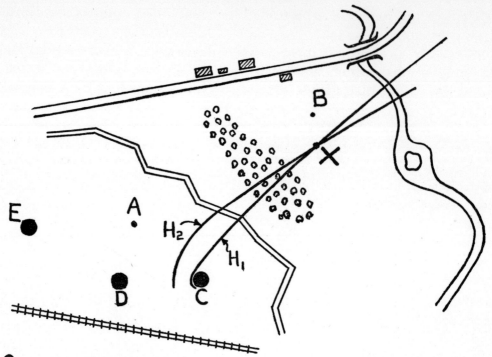

SOUND RANGING

enemy batteries. Listening to the reports of a gun that was harassing our own positions we could obtain intersecting hyperbolic plots on our charts and pinpoint its position. After this we could direct our own guns on to the spot and knock it out of action. This was one of the achievements of British scientists contributing to a victorious issue in the first struggle against Germany. Needless to say, in the next great war both sides were employing sound ranging.

Boyle's Law, connecting the pressure and volume of a given mass of gas at constant temperature (see Volume II, page 143), says that:

Pressure × Volume
= constant.

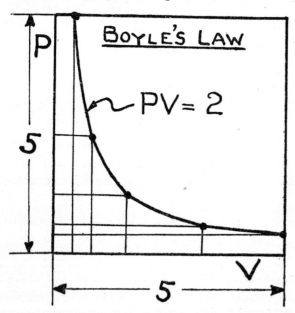

If we make a graph of P (pressure) against V (volume) the resulting curve is hyperbolic and the axes of P and V are the asymptotes. The volume approaches but never quite reaches zero as P is increased; the pressure approaches but never quite reaches zero as V is increased. When the asymptotes are at right angles to one another, as they are here, the curve is called a "rectangular hyperbola."

We could go on making up constructions for strange curves without end and spend a lifetime investigating their properties. Here we must limit ourselves to the consideration of but one more curve, namely the *parabola*. This is the path of a point which moves so that its distance from a fixed point is always equal to its distance from a fixed straight line. The fixed point is called the focus (F in the diagram) and the fixed straight line is called the directrix. The parabola is a most important curve and a

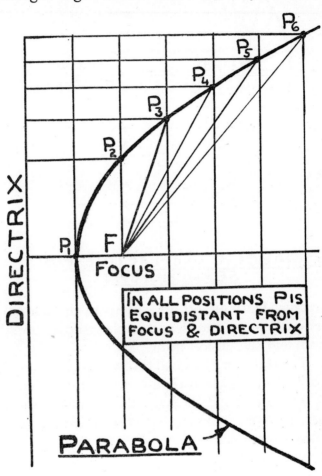

DIRECTRIX

FOCUS

IN ALL POSITIONS P IS EQUIDISTANT FROM FOCUS & DIRECTRIX

PARABOLA

mirror of parabolic form will bring a beam of parallel light to a definite focus, obviating the defect of spherical mirrors known as "spherical aberration" (see Volume II, page 198). The reflectors of searchlights and other powerful projectors are of parabolic cross-section, and a point source of light at the focus provides a truly parallel beam of reflected light. The rays lose nothing of their energy by dispersion as happens when the beam is divergent; consequently a searchlight will illuminate objects a great distance away.

A chain or cable carrying a roadway (as in a suspension bridge)

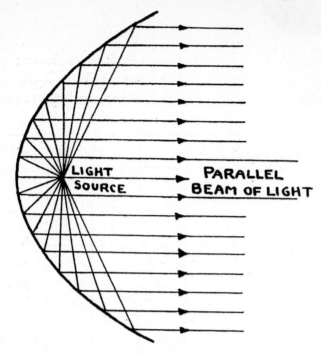

PARABOLIC REFLECTOR FOR SEARCHLIGHT

assumes the form of a parabola, and this is the ideal curve also for the arch of a bridge. The top picture facing this page shows a famous suspension bridge in which the load is supported by the tensile strength of the chains. The arch shown in the bottom picture is, in effect, a suspension bridge inverted and the load is upheld by the compressive strength of the arch members. A splendid modern arch bridge is the Sydney Harbour bridge, shown in the bottom picture facing page 109. The top picture in the same plate shows an older bridge combining the arch and suspension principles.

The trajectory of a ball thrown at a distant object is a parabola; so is the path taken in space of a bomb or any other object dropped from an aeroplane.

The ellipse and the hyperbola assume different forms, but all parabolas are necessarily similar, differing from one another only in the scale of their representation. If you had to draw one through three given points A, B and C the method would be to find the focus F_1 and the line through F_1 parallel to the directrix. Now the required line through F_1 is always four times the

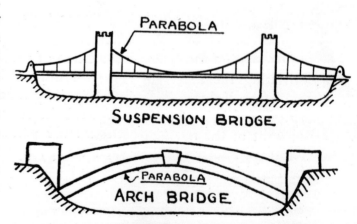

PARABOLA

SUSPENSION BRIDGE

PARABOLA

ARCH BRIDGE

The Menai suspension bridge, built by Thomas Telford, 1819–26. Loaded uniformly across the main span, the supporting chains take up the configuration of a parabola.

(By courtesy of the Director of the Science Museum, London, S.W.7.)

Coalbrookdale cast-iron bridge of 1779, photographed in 1904. Downstream view. An arch bridge like this is in effect a suspension bridge inverted. A uniformly loaded arch must approximate to the parabolic form.

(By courtesy of the Director of the Science Museum, London, S.W.7.)

The Saltash bridge, 1859, in course of construction. Built by Sir Marc Isambard Brunel, this bridge is at the same time a suspension and an arch bridge. Of tubular construction, the arch is above instead of below the railway.

(By courtesy of the Director of the Science Museum, London, S.W.7.)

The Sydney Harbour bridge, completed in 1932, is an arch bridge of great span. On account of the necessarily large rise of the arch the road has to be suspended below it instead of being mounted on top, as is customary with arch bridges.

(By courtesy of Messrs. Dorman Long & Co., Ltd.)

distance from the pole C to the focus F_1 in length, so here is one way of accomplishing your object, though rather a roundabout way.

Draw a parabola using any fixed focus and any fixed line. To do this you must rule lines parallel to the given line at different distances away and then set your compass to these same distances, striking arcs with it from the focus as centre and cutting each line with arcs of the appropriate radius. Beneath your parabola, at A, B and C, are the points through which you wish to draw another parabola. Join C to A and through P in the parabola already constructed draw PQ parallel to CA, cutting the parabola at Q. Draw QR perpendicular to the axis of the parabola, cutting the parabola again at R. Then QPR is the *shape* of the parabola you require through A, B and C, but it is the wrong size. To copy it the right size must be your next task.

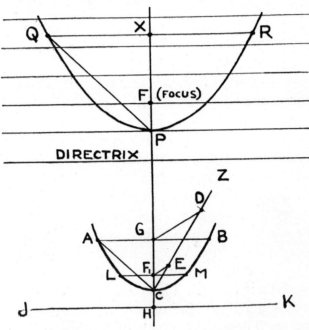

From C draw any line CZ and along it mark off CD = PX and CE = PF. Join D to G and draw EF_1 parallel to DG. Then F_1 is the focus of the parabola we want through A, B and C. Two more points on it can be obtained immediately if we draw LM through F_1 perpendicular to the axis of the required parabola, making $F_1L = F_1M$ = $2F_1C$. Points L and M will both lie on the required parabola. If any more points are required it will be necessary to draw the directrix. This will be the line JK drawn through H, where $CH = CF_1$. The construction of the parabola is then continued as before by finding points equidistant from F_1 and JK.

Clumsy as this method of construction is, it depends on principles already familiar to you, and you are sure that the final result is truly a parabola satisfying the given conditions. On the next page is given a neater construction, but proof that it yields a parabola is too difficult to give here.

Make a rectangle ABDE to include the given points A, B and C. Divide BD into any number of equal parts, say four. Join C to all the

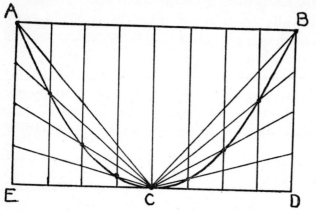

points of division. Now divide CD into the same number of equal parts and through the points of division draw lines parallel to BD. Then the points of intersection between these lines and the rays from C will define the required parabola as shown in the accompanying diagram. The construction shown on the right is repeated on the left in order to obtain the portion CA of the parabola.

The circle, ellipse, parabola and hyperbola can all be obtained from sectioning the surface of a cone. Sections made by planes to which the axis of the cone is perpendicular are circles. If the plane of section is tilted but not so far as to become parallel to the side of the cone, the resulting section of the cone will be an ellipse. When the plane of section is parallel to the side of the cone a parabola is formed. This curve grows ever broader, never closing up to form an ellipse. Tilting the plane of section still more causes it to penetrate both parts of the cone and the intersection of the conical surface with the plane surface is an hyperbola. The last of the diagrams illustrating this chapter shows the relation between the cone and its various sections. The properties of conic sections were investigated very thoroughly by the Greek mathematician Apollonius more than 200 years before the Christian era.

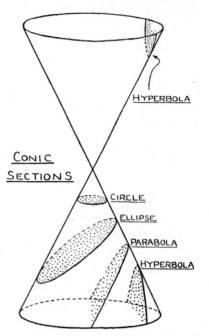

CHAPTER VI

TRIGONOMETRY

In the plans made by engineers and architects it is usual to project images of whatever is being represented on to three planes, as described in Volume I, page 14. Most of the lines in the various views are truly proportional to the corresponding lines in the object drawn; this is the case when the horizontal and vertical lines of a house are shown in ground plan, end elevation and side elevation. The slanting lines of the roof, how-ever, suffer from fore-shortening in two out of the three views. In the diagram on this page a shed is shown in the conventional manner by a side ele-vation (*a*), an end ele-vation (*b*) and a plan (*c*). The sloping line S

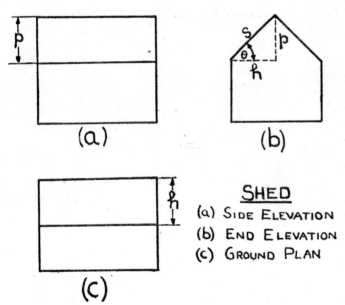

(a)

(b)

SHED

(a) SIDE ELEVATION
(b) END ELEVATION
(c) GROUND PLAN

(c)

is represented in the end elevation to the scale of the whole drawing, but in the side elevation it has its length diminished to p and in the plan it has its length diminished to h. All three lengths s, p and h, are shown forming a right-angled triangle in the end elevation. Plainly the magnitude of the angle θ affects the relations between the three lengths. If θ is small and the roof is approaching flatness, p will be small and h

will be nearly as long as *s*. On the other hand, if θ is large and the roof is of the sharply pointed variety, *p* will be large, approaching *s* in length, whereas *h* will only be a relatively small proportion of *s*.

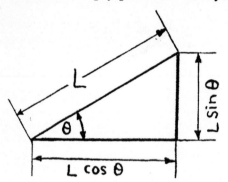

In all cases the ratio of *h* to *s* is called the "cosine" of the angle θ and the ratio of *p* to *s* is called the "sine" of the angle θ. These definitions give us:

$$\frac{h}{s} = \cos \theta$$

$$\frac{p}{s} = \sin \theta.$$

The ratio of *p* to *h* is called the "tangent" of θ and we have:

$$\frac{p}{h} = \tan \theta.$$

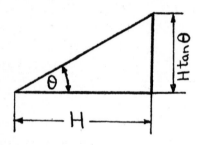

SOME USEFUL RESULTS
TO MEMORISE

Diagrams (*d*), (*e*) and (*f*) show triangles of special shapes that occur often in engineering and constructional work. In diagram (*d*) the angle θ is 45 degrees and so is its complement. In triangle (*e*) the angle θ is 60 degrees and its complement is 30 degrees. This triangle is half of an equilateral triangle just as triangle (*d*) is half of a square. In triangle (*f*)

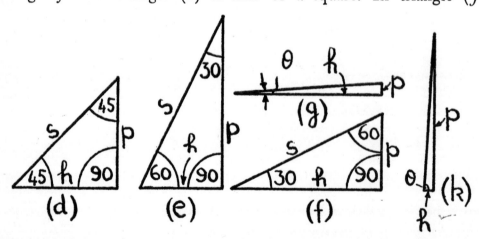

the angle θ is 30 degrees and its complement is 60 degrees. The complement of any angle is the amount by which it falls short of 90 degrees, and in a right-angled triangle the two angles less than right angles are necessarily complementary to one another since they make one right angle between them. (See page 80 for proof of the proposition that all three angles of any triangle are together equal to two right angles.)

In triangle (d) two angles are equal and consequently the triangle is isosceles (see page 86) having $p = h$. If p and h are both of unit length, we have:

$$s^2 = 1^2 + 1^2 = 2 \text{ and } s = \sqrt{2}$$

$\therefore$

$$\sin 45 = \frac{1}{\sqrt{2}} = \frac{1}{1\cdot414} = 0\cdot7071$$

also

$$\cos 45 = \frac{1}{\sqrt{2}} = 0\cdot7071$$

and

$$\tan 45 = \frac{1}{1} = 1.$$

In triangle (e) we know that $h = \frac{1}{2}s$, so that if $h = 1$, $s = 2$ and $p = \sqrt{4-1} = \sqrt{3} = 1\cdot732$

$$\sin 60 = \frac{1\cdot732}{2} = 0\cdot8660$$

$$\cos 60 = \frac{1}{2} = 0\cdot5000$$

$$\tan 60 = \frac{1\cdot732}{1} = 1\cdot7320.$$

Triangle (f) is the same in shape as triangle (e) except that it occupies a different position and has its sides differently named. Here $p = \frac{1}{2}s$; so that if $p = 1$, $s = 2$ and $h = \sqrt{4-1} = \sqrt{3} = 1\cdot732$

$$\sin 30 = \frac{1}{2} = 0\cdot5000$$

$$\cos 30 = \frac{1\cdot732}{2} = 0\cdot8660$$

$$\tan 30 = \frac{1}{1\cdot732} = 0\cdot5774.$$

Triangles (g) and (k) are drawn to have θ very nearly equal to nothing in one case and very nearly equal to 90 degrees in the other. It is evident from these triangles that when in reality $\theta = 0$,

$$\sin \theta = 0, \cos \theta = 1 \text{ and } \tan \theta = 0.$$

When, on the other hand, $\theta = 90$ degrees,

$$\sin \theta = 1, \cos \theta = 0 \text{ and } \tan \theta = \infty.$$

Problem 47.—The gradient on a mountain railway corresponds to a track inclination of 30 degrees to the horizontal. The track speed of the train is 5 miles an hour; what is the rate of its vertical ascent in feet per minute?

The triangle representing this track is similar to triangle (*f*) on page 112. Here we have:

$$\frac{p}{s} = \sin 30 = 0.5000.$$

If the triangle is drawn for a whole hour's travel, $s = 5$ miles and we have:

$$\frac{p}{5} = 0.5000$$

$$p = 5 \times 0.5000 = 2.5 \text{ miles.}$$

Thus the train climbs $2\frac{1}{2}$ miles an hour vertically.

$$2\tfrac{1}{2} \text{ m.p.h.} = 2.5 \times 5280 \div 60 \text{ ft. per min.}$$
$$= 220 \text{ ft. per min.}$$

Horse-power needed to overcome gravity per ton (2240 lb.) of train weight

$$= \frac{220 \times 2240}{33,000} = 14.93.$$

Problem 48.—Observations are taken from points A and B, which are 500 ft. apart, of the summit C of a mountain. The elevation of C from A is 30 degrees and from B 45 degrees. What is the height of the mountain?

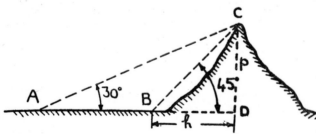

In triangle CDB

$$\frac{p}{h} = \tan 45 = 1.000$$

so

$$h = p \qquad .. \qquad .. \qquad .. \qquad .. \quad (1)$$

In triangle CDA

$$\frac{p}{500 + h} = \tan 30 = 0.5774 \qquad .. \qquad .. \quad (2)$$

Putting p for h in this second equation, we get:

$$\frac{p}{500+p} = 0.5774$$

$$p = 0.5774(500+p) = 288.7 + 0.5774p$$

$$p - 0.5774p = 288.7$$

$$0.4226p = 288.7$$

$$p = \frac{288.7}{0.4226} = 683 \text{ ft.}$$

Problem 49.—A shell is fired at a Velocity of 1600 ft. per second from a gun inclined at 45 degrees to the horizontal. Assuming the acceleration due to gravity to be 32 f.p.s.p.s., what will be the horizontal range of this shell?

To solve this problem we must resolve the velocity of the shell (1600 f.p.s.) into its horizontal and vertical components. These components are denoted by p and h in the accompanying diagram.

$$\frac{p}{1600} = \sin 45 = 0.7071$$

$\therefore$
$$p = 1600 \times 0.7071 = 1131.4 \text{ f.p.s.}$$

Also
$$\frac{h}{1600} = \cos 45 = 0.7071$$

$$h = 1600 \times 0.7071 = 1131.4 \text{ f.p.s.}$$

Now the component p suffers a diminution of 32 f.p.s. in every second, whereas the component h remains constant and equal to 1131.4 f.p.s.; there is no force of gravity to lessen this latter component. Time taken by shell to lose its vertical velocity = $1131.4 \div 32 = 35.4$ seconds. The total time of flight is twice this, or $2 \times 35.4 = 70.8$ seconds. In this time the horizontal travel of the shell will be 70.8×1131.4 ft.

$\therefore$ Range of shell $= \dfrac{70.8 \times 1131.4}{5280} = 15.2$ miles.

The above problems serve to show that much laborious drawing can be saved by a knowledge of trigonometrical ratios.

So far our calculations have related only to angles of the special triangles shown on page 112, but obviously there will be similar ratios for any triangle and it is useful to know what $\sin \theta$, $\cos \theta$ and $\tan \theta$ are for angles such as 15°, 20° 35°, 70° and so on. Given a set of trigonometrical tables (see pages 121, 122 and 123), you can pick out the natural sines, cosines or tangents you require for any calculations whatsoever, but you may not be satisfied to do this unless you know how the values in the tables have been compiled.

For a start you have the following:

θ	$\sin \theta$	$\cos \theta$	$\tan \theta$
0	0	1·0000	0
30°	0·5000	0·8660	0·5774
45°	0·7071	0·7071	1·0000
60°	0·8660	0·5000	1·7321
90°	1·0000	0	∞

For values of θ other than those given above we could refer to graphs of $\sin \theta$, $\cos \theta$ and $\tan \theta$ plotted against θ, using the figures tabulated above for plotting purposes. However, about 150 B.C. the celebrated Greek astronomer Hipparchus (already referred to in the chapters on Astronomy) devised a more accurate procedure. He found out how to evaluate $\cos \frac{1}{2}\theta$ when $\cos \theta$ was known; also $\sin \frac{1}{2}\theta$ when $\sin \theta$ was

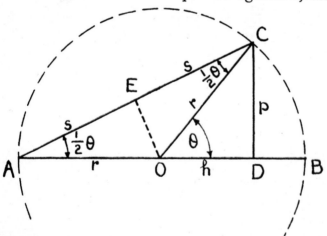

known. This meant that given the cosines and sines of 45 and 30 degrees he could evaluate them for $22\frac{1}{2}$ and 15 degrees; then for $11\frac{1}{4}$ and $7\frac{1}{2}$ degrees, then for $5\frac{5}{8}$ and $3\frac{3}{4}$ degrees, and so on. Obviously he was able to fill in a much bigger table than the one we have given above.

To arrive at the valuable formulæ of Hipparchus we must refer to the above diagram. Here AB is the diameter of a circle having its centre at O, and OC is a radius making an angle of θ with OB. If we join AC we shall get at A an angle of $\frac{1}{2}\theta$. This follows from the fact that in triangle OAC, OA $=$ OC, so that the angles at A and C are separately equal to one another and jointly equal to the exterior angle θ at O.

Dotted line OE drawn perpendicular to AC divides AC into equal parts EA and EC of some length s. Line CD drawn perpendicular to AB has a length p and it makes an intercept OD on AD which we can call h. The radii OA and OC are of length r.

Looking at this diagram, we see that:

$$\cos \theta = \frac{h}{r}$$

$$\cos \frac{\theta}{2} = \frac{r+h}{2s} = \frac{r}{2s} + \frac{h}{2s}$$

$$= \frac{r}{2s} + \frac{h}{r} \cdot \frac{r}{2s}$$

$$= \frac{r}{2s} + \frac{r}{2s} \cos \theta$$

$$= \frac{r}{2s}(1 + \cos \theta).$$

Now in triangle EOC it is evident that $\frac{s}{r} = \cos \frac{\theta}{2}$; consequently:

$$\frac{r}{s} = \frac{1}{\cos \frac{\theta}{2}} \text{ and } \frac{r}{2s} = \frac{1}{2 \cos \frac{\theta}{2}}$$

$$\therefore \qquad \cos \frac{\theta}{2} = \frac{1}{2 \cos \frac{\theta}{2}}(1 + \cos \theta).$$

We multiply both sides by $\cos \frac{\theta}{2}$ and get:

$$\cos^2 \frac{\theta}{2} = \frac{1 + \cos \theta}{2}, \text{ whence}$$

$$\cos \frac{\theta}{2} = \sqrt{\frac{1 + \cos \theta}{2}}$$

This is one of the formulæ of Hipparchus and we can check its correctness by trying $\theta = 90$ degrees; then

$$\cos \frac{90}{2} = \sqrt{\frac{1 + \cos 90}{2}} = \sqrt{\frac{1 + 0}{2}} = \frac{1}{\sqrt{2}}$$

$$= \frac{1}{1 \cdot 414} = 0 \cdot 7071$$

which we know to be the correct result for cos 45.

Again:

$$\cos \frac{60}{2} = \sqrt{\frac{1 + \cos 60}{2}} = \sqrt{\frac{1 + 0 \cdot 500}{2}}$$

$$= \sqrt{\frac{1 \cdot 5}{2}} = \sqrt{\frac{3}{4}} = \frac{\sqrt{3}}{2} = 0 \cdot 8660$$

which we know to be the correct result for cos 30. Having checked this formula, we can apply it with confidence to the determination of the cosines of other half-angles.

When we do this we find that $\cos 22\frac{1}{2} = 0 \cdot 9239$ and $\cos 15 = 0 \cdot 9659$. A study of the triangles on page 112 and of the tabulated figures on page 116 will convince you that the cosine of an angle is equal to the sine of its complement, or vice versa. In symbols,

$$\cos \theta = \sin (90 - \theta)$$
$$\sin \theta = \cos (90 - \theta)$$

∴ $\qquad\qquad \cos 22\frac{1}{2} = \sin (90 - 22\frac{1}{2}) = \sin 67\frac{1}{2}$

so we have $\qquad \sin 67\frac{1}{2} = 0 \cdot 9239.$

Also $\qquad\qquad \cos 15 = \sin (90 - 15) = \sin 75$

so we have $\qquad \sin 75 = 0 \cdot 9659.$

This gives us four more results to include in our table of trigonometrical functions—two additional cosines and two additional sines.

The other formula of Hipparchus can easily be obtained from the one already given. In any of the triangles shown on page 112 we have:

$$p^2 + h^2 = s^2$$

so that:

$$\frac{p^2}{s^2} + \frac{h^2}{s^2} = 1.$$

But $\frac{p}{s} = \sin \theta$ and $\frac{h}{s} = \cos \theta$ and consequently the above relation is the same as

$$\sin^2 \theta + \cos^2 \theta = 1.$$

From this we get:

$$\sin^2 \theta = 1 - \cos^2 \theta.$$

It is equally true that:

$$\sin^2 \frac{\theta}{2} = 1 - \cos^2 \frac{\theta}{2}.$$

On page 117 it was stated that:

$$\cos^2 \frac{\theta}{2} = \frac{1 + \cos \theta}{2}$$

$$\therefore \quad \sin^2 \frac{\theta}{2} = 1 - \frac{1 + \cos \theta}{2} = \frac{2 - 1 - \cos \theta}{2} = \frac{1 - \cos \theta}{2}$$

$$\therefore \quad \sin \frac{\theta}{2} = \sqrt{\frac{1 - \cos \theta}{2}}.$$

This is the other formula of Hipparchus. Let us test it before using it. If $\theta = 90$,

$$\sin \frac{90}{2} = \sqrt{\frac{1 - 0}{2}} = \sqrt{\frac{1}{2}} = \frac{1}{\sqrt{2}} = \frac{1}{1 \cdot 414} = 0 \cdot 7071$$

which we know to be correct for sin 45. Again, if $\theta = 60$,

$$\sin \frac{60}{2} = \sqrt{\frac{1 - 0 \cdot 5}{2}} = \sqrt{\frac{1}{4}} = 0 \cdot 500$$

which we know to be correct for sin 30. Having checked this formula, we can apply it with confidence to the determination of the sines of other half-angles. When we do this we find that sin $22\frac{1}{2}$ = 0·3827 and sin 15 = 0·2588. It is therefore true also that cos $67\frac{1}{2}$ = 0·3827 and cos 75 = 0·2588.

At this stage we can rewrite our table, putting in the newly evaluated results:

θ	$sin \, \theta$	$cos \, \theta$	$tan \, \theta$
0	0	1·0000	0
15	0·2588	0·9659	0·2679
$22\frac{1}{2}$	0·3827	0·9239	0·4142
30	0·5000	0·8660	0·5774
45	0·7071	0·7071	1·0000
60	0·8660	0·5000	1·7321
$67\frac{1}{2}$	0·9239	0·3827	2·4142
75	0·9659	0·2588	3·7321
90	1·0000	0	∞

The formula for the tangents is a very simple one; since $\sin\theta = \dfrac{p}{s}$ and $\cos\theta = \dfrac{h}{s}$, we have:

$$\tan\theta = \frac{p}{h} = \frac{p}{s}\times\frac{s}{h} = \frac{p}{s}\div\frac{h}{s} = \frac{\sin\theta}{\cos\theta}.$$

We obtain sines and cosines from the formulæ of Hipparchus and then perform simple divisions of sines by cosines in order to evaluate the tangents.

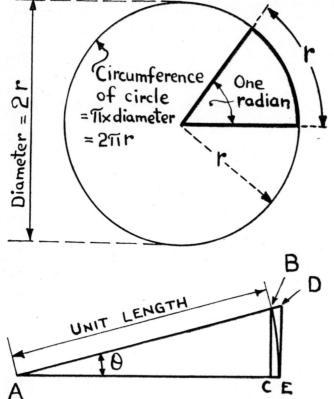

The table given above can be extended by evaluating sines and cosines for $\dfrac{75}{2} = 37\frac{1}{2}$, $\dfrac{67\frac{1}{2}}{2} = 33\frac{3}{4}$, $\dfrac{22\frac{1}{2}}{2} = 11\frac{1}{4}$ and $\dfrac{15}{2} = 7\frac{1}{2}$, also for the complementary angles. After this certain of the angles could be halved again. Eventually we could by this method arrive at a table for a great number of closely spaced angles, but there is no need for us to go through the work here because reliable printed tables can be procured very cheaply. The table which follows is for angles between o and 90 in degree steps. In the second column the radian measure of each angle is given; this is the measure in degrees divided by 360 and multiplied by 2π. A radian is the angle subtended at the centre of a circle by an arc equal to the radius in length; since the circumference of the circle contains the radius 2π times, there must be 2π radians in 360 degrees and this explains why the radian measure of θ degrees is $\dfrac{\theta}{360}\times 2\pi$.

The diagram on this page shows two radii, AB and AE, of a circular arc BE drawn with centre A. The angle between these two radii is θ and each radius is assumed to be of unit length. We see that:

$$\sin \theta = \frac{BC}{AB} = BC, \text{ since } AB = 1$$

$$\theta = \frac{\text{arc BE}}{AB} = BE \text{ radians, since } AB = 1$$

$$\tan \theta = \frac{DE}{AE} = DE, \text{ since } AE = 1.$$

From the diagram it can be seen that for any angle θ, $\sin \theta < \theta$ and $\theta < \tan \theta$ where the symbol $<$ stands for "is less than." For very small values of θ the sine and the tangent are very nearly equal to the radian measure and this fact is made apparent by the table below. Putting θ for $\sin \theta$ or $\tan \theta$ is a very usual approximation to make when θ is small, and in the limit, as θ approaches zero the ratios $\dfrac{\sin \theta}{\theta}$ and $\dfrac{\tan \theta}{\theta}$ both become unity:

θ (deg.)	θ (rad.)	sin θ	cos θ	tan θ
0	0	0	1	0
1	0·0175	0·0175	0·9998	0·0175
2	0·0349	0·0349	0·9994	0·0349
3	0·0524	0·0523	0·9986	0·0524
4	0·0698	0·0698	0·9976	0·0699
5	0·0873	0·0872	0·9962	0·0875
6	0·1047	0·1045	0·9945	0·1051
7	0·1222	0·1219	0·9925	0·1228
8	0·1396	0·1392	0·9903	0·1405
9	0·1571	0·1564	0·9877	0·1584
10	0·1745	0·1736	0·9848	0·1763
11	0·1920	0·1908	0·9816	0·1944
12	0·2094	0·2079	0·9781	0·2126
13	0·2269	0·2250	0·9744	0·2309
14	0·2443	0·2419	0·9703	0·2493
15	0·2618	0·2588	0·9659	0·2679
16	0·2793	0·2756	0·9613	0·2867
17	0·2967	0·2924	0·9563	0·3057
18	0·3142	0·3090	0·9511	0·3249
19	0·3316	0·3256	0·9455	0·3443
20	0·3491	0·3420	0·9397	0·3640

θ (deg.)	θ (rad.)	sin θ	cos θ	tan θ
21	0·3665	0·3584	0·9336	0·3839
22	0·3840	0·3746	0·9272	0·4040
23	0·4014	0·0397	0·9205	0·4245
24	0·4189	0·4067	0·9135	0·4452
25	0·4363	0·4226	0·9063	0·4663
26	0·4538	0·4384	0·8988	0·4877
27	0·4712	0·4540	0·8910	0·5095
28	0·4887	0·4695	0·8829	0·5317
29	0·5061	0·4848	0·8746	0·5543
30	0·5236	0·5000	0·8660	0·5774
31	0·5411	0·5150	0·8572	0·6009
32	0·5585	0·5299	0·8480	0·6249
33	0·5760	0·5446	0·8387	0·6494
34	0·5934	0·5592	0·8290	0·6745
35	0·6109	0·5736	0·8192	0·7002
36	0·6283	0·5878	0·8090	0·7265
37	0·6458	0·6018	0·7986	0·7536
38	0·6632	0·6157	0·7880	0·7813
39	0·6807	0·6293	0·7771	0·8098
40	0·6981	0·6428	0·7660	0·8391
41	0·7156	0·6561	0·7547	0·8693
42	0·7330	0·6691	0·7431	0·9004
43	0·7505	0·6820	0·7314	0·9325
44	0·7679	0·6947	0·7193	0·9657
45	0·7854	0·7071	0·7071	1·0000
46	0·8029	0·7193	0·6947	1·0355
47	0·8203	0·7314	0·6820	1·0724
48	0·8378	0·7431	0·6691	1·1106
49	0·8552	0·7547	0·6561	1·1504
50	0·8727	0·7660	0·6428	1·1918
51	0·8901	0·7771	0·6293	1·2349
52	0·9076	0·7880	0·6157	1·2799
53	0·9250	0·7986	0·6018	1·3270
54	0·9425	0·8090	0·5878	1·3764
55	0·9599	0·8192	0·5736	1·4281
56	0·9774	0·8290	0·5592	1·4826
57	0·9948	0·8387	0·5446	1·5399
58	1·0123	0·8480	0·5299	1·6003
59	1·0297	0·8572	0·5150	1·6643
60	1·0472	0·8660	0·5000	1·7321

θ (deg.)	θ (rad.)	sin θ	cos θ	tan θ
61	1·0647	0·8746	0·4848	1·8040
62	1·0821	0·8829	0·4695	1·8807
63	1·0996	0·8910	0·4540	1·9626
64	1·1170	0·8988	0·4384	2·0503
65	1·1345	0·9063	0·4226	2·1445
66	1·1519	0·9135	0·4067	2·2460
67	1·1694	0·9205	0·3907	2·3559
68	1·1868	0·9272	0·3746	2·4751
69	1·2043	0·9336	0·3584	2·6051
70	1·2217	0·9397	0·3420	2·7475
71	1·2392	0·9455	0·3256	2·9042
72	1·2566	0·9511	0·3090	3·0777
73	1·2741	0·9563	0·2924	3·2709
74	1·2915	0·9613	0·2756	3·4874
75	1·3090	0·9659	0·2588	3·7321
76	1·3265	0·9703	0·2419	4·0108
77	1·3439	0·9744	0·2250	4·3315
78	1·3614	0·9781	0·2079	4·7046
79	1·3788	0·9816	0·1908	5·1446
80	1·3963	0·9848	0·1736	5·6713
81	1·4137	0·9877	0·1564	6·3138
82	1·4312	0·9903	0·1392	7·1154
83	1·4486	0·9925	0·1219	8·1443
84	1·4661	0·9945	0·1045	9·5144
85	1·4835	0·9962	0·0872	11·4301
86	1·5010	0·9976	0·0698	14·3006
87	1·5184	0·9986	0·0523	19·0811
88	1·5359	0·9994	0·0349	28·6363
89	1·5533	0·9998	0·0175	57·2900
90	1·5708	1	0	∞

Graphs of θ in radians, sin θ, cos θ and tan θ plotted against θ in degrees are shown on page 124. The graph for tan θ runs off the diagram a little beyond θ = 45 degrees as the vertical scale is not carried far past 1.

The well-known sine curve or sine wave is obtained by plotting sin θ for an angle that grows indefinitely. The ratio p/s rises to unity as θ reaches 90 degrees; after this it falls again until when θ = 180 degrees $p/s = 0$. Beyond θ = 180 the magnitude p becomes negative as it is measured downwards. The length s is assumed to remain the same and

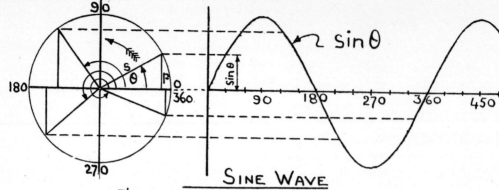

$\sim \sin \theta$

SINE WAVE

The graph of sinθ for ever increasing θ
has the form of an endlessly repeating wave.

its sign is always taken as positive. Thus, between $\theta = 180$ and $\theta = 360$ the ratio p/s is negative. When $\theta = 270$ degrees (3 right angles),

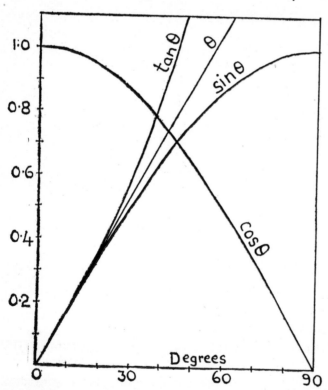

$\sin \theta = -1$ because p is then equal in length to s but is measured in a negative direction. When θ passes 360 degrees a new "cycle" of changes in $\sin \theta$ commences.

To gain facility in the use of trigonometrical functions we must do many exercises involving an acquaintance with them. Some examples follow:

Problem 50.—The crank of a steam-engine is 1 ft. long and the connecting-rod is 5 ft. long. When the crank and connecting-rod are at right angles to one another the thrust of the steam on the piston is 15 tons; what is then the turning effort (in tons-ft.) on the crank?

The following sketch shows the piston-rod, connecting-rod and crank in the attitude described, with crank and connecting-rod making an angle of 90 degrees between them. The thrust of 15 tons in the piston-rod is responsible for two additional thrusts, namely P in the connecting-rod and Q in the crosshead. The gudgeon-pin is at the meeting-point of these three forces and is held in equilibrium by them. Below the main diagram is shown the triangle of forces (see Volume II, page 35) for this pin. The sides of this are drawn parallel to the piston-rod (15 tons), perpendicular to the piston-rod (Q tons) and parallel to the connecting-rod (P tons). The directions of all sides are known and the magnitude of one side (15 tons) is also known, so that the triangle is unambiguously defined (see page 76) and we can evaluate P and Q.

Clearly $Q = 15 \tan \theta = 15 \times \frac{1}{5} = 3$ tons.

From the tables we see that the angle whose tangent is $\frac{1}{5}$ (sometimes written $\tan^{-1} 0\cdot200$) is between 11 degrees and 12 degrees.

tan 11 degrees $= 0\cdot1944$
tan 12 degrees $= 0\cdot2126$
   difference $= 0\cdot0182$.

Between $0\cdot1944$ and $0\cdot2000$ the difference is $0\cdot0056$, so if we assume that over the small interval 11 degrees to 12 degrees the angle grows in proportion to its tangent, the angle we are seeking is $11\frac{56}{182}$ degrees $= 11\cdot308$ degrees.

Referring again to the triangle of forces, we see that:

$$\frac{15}{P} = \cos 11\cdot308$$

$$\therefore \quad P = \frac{15}{\cos 11\cdot308}$$

now $\qquad \cos 11 = 0\cdot9816$
and $\qquad \cos 12 = 0\cdot9781$
   difference $= 0\cdot0035$.

To find cos $11\cdot308$ we must take $0\cdot308$ of this difference (namely $0\cdot308 \times 0\cdot0035 = 0\cdot0011$) from cos 11. The result is $0\cdot9816 - 0\cdot0011 = 0\cdot9805$.

$$P = \frac{15}{0\cdot9805} = 15\cdot33 \text{ (by slide rule)}$$

$\therefore$ Turning effort on crank $= 15\cdot33 \times 1$
$\qquad\qquad\qquad\qquad = 15\cdot33$ tons-ft.

This calculation shows a weakness in our table—it goes from angle to angle in steps that are too large, so that we have to waste time applying the rule of proportional parts. A really good set of tables occupies a great deal of space and it sets out the values of θ, sin θ, cos θ and tan θ for every sixtieth part of a degree increase in θ. A sixtieth of a degree is called a "minute of angle," so that we should read 30° 14′ as "thirty degrees fourteen minutes." In astronomical work angles must be measured to sixtieths of sixtieths of a degree, namely to "seconds." Thus, for astronomical work there should be no less than 3600 values of θ,

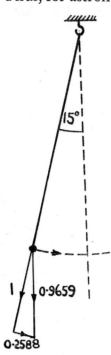

sin θ, cos θ and tan θ between $\theta = $ 1° and $\theta = $ 2°, between $\theta = $ 2° and $\theta = $ 3°, and so on. An angle of 13 degrees 14 minutes 12 seconds is written 13° 14′ 12″. In astronomy the accuracy of measuring is such that fractions of seconds can be taken into account—they are usually shown as decimal fractions, so that 2 seconds and 85 hundredths of a second would be shown as 2″·85.

Our own table is seen to be rather a rough or coarsely divided one, but it is sufficiently accurate for most practical purposes and we can make it take care of fractions of degrees if we do not mind stopping to apply the rule of proportional parts.

Problem 51.—A weight of 1 ton hangs on a long rope and swings to and fro, the greatest angle the rope makes with the vertical being 15 degrees. What is the tension in the rope when it is in its extreme position, and what is then the momentary acceleration of the weight?

The downward force of 1 ton can be resolved into two component forces one of which, namely 1 × cos 15 = 0·9659 ton, is taken care of by the rope and the other, namely 1 × sin 15 = 0·2588 ton, is available for accelerating the weight along its circular path towards its lowest position.

Acceleration of weight $= \dfrac{0\cdot2588}{1} \times g$ where g is the acceleration of a freely falling body (see Volume II, page 5). If we assume that $g = $ 32 f.p.s.p.s.

Acceleration of weight = 0·2588 × 32
= 8·28 f.p.s.p.s.

Problem 52.—The refractive index of glass is $\frac{3}{2}$. At what angle will light proceed through a slab of glass if the incident light makes an angle of 30 degrees to the normal?

We are told that $a^\mu g = \dfrac{\sin i}{\sin r} = \tfrac{3}{2}$; also that $i = 30$ degrees. From this it follows that

$$\frac{\sin 30}{\sin r} = \frac{3}{2}.$$

But $\sin 30 = 0\cdot500$

∴ $\dfrac{0\cdot500}{\sin r} = \dfrac{3}{2}$

$$3 \sin r = 2 \times 0\cdot500 = 1\cdot000$$
$$\sin r = \tfrac{1}{3}$$
$$r = 19 \text{ degrees (very nearly).}$$

To find r more accurately we have to apply the rule of proportional parts (or use a more complete set of tables).

$$\sin 19 = 0\cdot3256$$
$$\sin 20 = 0\cdot3420$$
$$\text{difference} = 0\cdot164$$
$$\text{difference that interests us} = 0\cdot333 - 0\cdot3256$$
$$= 0\cdot0077$$

∴ $r = 19\tfrac{77}{164} = 19\cdot468$ degrees.

We can convert decimal fractions of a degree into minutes, if we wish, by multiplying by 60. Thus, $0\cdot468$ degree $= 0\cdot468 \times 60$ minutes $= 28\cdot08$ minutes.

Similarly we can convert decimal fractions of a minute into seconds by multiplying by 60. Thus, $0\cdot08$ second $= 0\cdot08 \times 60$ seconds $= 4\cdot8$ seconds.

Finally, then,
$$r = 19° \ 28' \ 4''\cdot8.$$

It is really rather doubtful whether we ought to express our result as accurately as this; the rule of proportional parts is based on the assumption that over a very short length (say between $19°$ and $20°$) we can take the

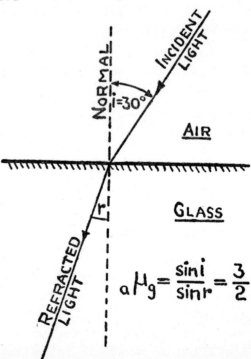

graph of sin θ to be a straight line. This assumption enables us to get a *rough* estimate of fractional parts of a degree when we refer to our table, so that we are justified in writing $r = 19°\ 28'$ but behave rather presumptuously in affirming that $r = 19°\ 28'\ 4''\cdot8$.

Referring to some very good five-figure tables, I find:

$$\sin 19°\ 28' = 0\cdot33326$$
$$\sin 19°\ 29' = 0\cdot33353$$
$$\text{difference} = 0\cdot00037.$$

The difference we are interested in is $0\cdot33333 - 0\cdot33326 = 0\cdot00007$; consequently,

$$r = 19°\ 28\tfrac{7}{37}\ \text{min.} = 19°\ 28'\cdot189$$
$$= 19°\ 28'\ 11''\cdot34.$$

Plainly this result is more dependable than the one got with our rough four-figure tables. So it shows us the folly of striving after too great an accuracy in our answer when the data we have to work with is not in itself of that degree of accuracy. Our rough table will generally give us angles correct to the nearest minute, but there are places where the rule of proportional parts fails us very badly—for instance, we could never depend on it for the tangents of angles beyond 80 degrees or so.

In tables of four-figure logarithms it is expected that the fourth figure will be got by applying the rule of proportional parts, and the figures tabulated to the right of the main table are, in fact, differences calculated in accordance with this rule.

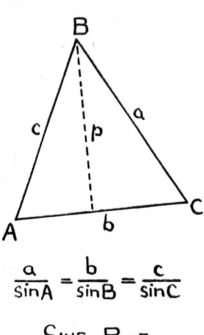

$$\frac{a}{\sin A} = \frac{b}{\sin B} = \frac{c}{\sin C}$$

SINE RULE

So far we have discussed only right-angled triangles, but for these trigonometry is not always really essential as many of the results obtained by it could be equally well obtained by applying the principle of Pythagoras. Where trigonometry is of immense value is in dealing with triangles that are *not* right-angled. To such triangles two rules apply: The first of these is the SINE RULE, which states that the sides of any triangle are proportional to the sines of the opposite angles. That this must be so will be evident from the accompanying diagram of triangle ABC in which the angles are A, B and C and the sides opposite these angles are *a*, *b* and *c* respectively. The line of length *p* is a perpendicular dropped from B on to the side *b*. We have:

$$\frac{p}{c} = \sin A \text{ and } \frac{p}{a} = \sin C$$

∴

$$\frac{\sin A}{\sin C} = \frac{p}{c} \times \frac{a}{p} = \frac{a}{c}.$$

In the same way, by dropping a perpendicular from A on to side *a*, we could prove that:

$$\frac{\sin B}{\sin C} = \frac{b}{c}.$$

The results of this investigation are best summarised by saying:

$$\frac{a}{\sin A} = \frac{b}{\sin B} = \frac{c}{\sin C}$$

and it is in this form that the SINE RULE is generally memorised.

The other rule of general application is the COSINE RULE which states that the square on the side of any triangle is equal to the sum of the squares on the other two sides less twice the rectangle contained by one of these other sides and the projection of the second side upon it.

This complicated statement is best expressed symbolically in reference to a diagram such as that shown here, in which ABC is any triangle and CD is a perpendicular drawn from C to AB. The COSINE RULE is equivalent to the statement:

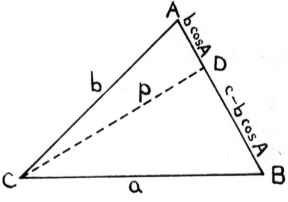

$$a^2 = b^2 + c^2 - 2bc \cos A$$

COSINE RULE

$$BC^2 = AB^2 + AC^2 - 2AB \cdot AD,$$

or

$$a^2 = c^2 + b^2 - 2cb \cos A.$$

The length AD which equals *b* cos A is called the "projection" of *b* on to *c*. The projected length of a line is the length it has when viewed obliquely. Thus, in the diagram on page 111 we saw that the line of length s had a projected length of $s \cos \theta$ in the plan and $s \sin \theta$ in the side elevation.

Proof of the CosINE RULE is quite easy. We must first of all observe that the perpendicular CD (of length p) divides AB into two lengths that we can call $b \cos A$ and $c - b \cos A$, the whole of AB being c.

By applying the principle of Pythagoras to the right-angled triangle CDB we get:

$$a^2 = p^2 + (c - b \cos A)^2$$
$$= p^2 + c^2 - 2cb \cos A + b^2 \cos^2 A \text{ .. \quad .. (1)}$$

Now p is one side of the right-angled triangle ACD,

$\therefore$

$$p^2 = b^2 - (b \cos A)^2 = b^2 - b^2 \cos^2 A \text{.. \quad .. (2)}$$

Combining equations (1) and (2) we get:

$$a^2 = b^2 - b^2 \cos^2 A + c^2 - 2cb \cos A + b^2 \cos^2 A$$
$$= b^2 + c^2 - 2cb \cos A$$

which was the result we had to prove.

Equally true are the statements:

$$b^2 = a^2 + c^2 - 2ac \cos B$$

and
$$c^2 = a^2 + b^2 - 2ab \cos C.$$

The CosINE RULE is of particular value in finding the third side of a triangle when two sides and the included angle are given. The SINE RULE helps us to evaluate the other angles very quickly.

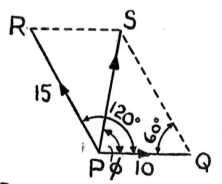

Problem 53.—Forces of 10 lb. and 15 lb. act simultaneously at a given point on a body, the angle between their lines of action being 120 degrees. Find the magnitude and direction of the resultant force.

PARALLELOGRAM OF FORCES

In the accompanying diagram the two forces are shown by PQ = 10 and PR = 15, the angle RPQ being 120 degrees. The resultant force is represented in magnitude and direction by the diagonal PS of the parallelogram PRSQ. In triangle PQS angle $Q = 60$ degrees and $QS = 15$. Applying the CosINE RULE, we have:

$$PS^2 = 10^2 + 15^2 - 2 \times 10 \times 15 \cos 60$$
$$= 100 + 225 - 300 \times 0 \cdot 5000$$
$$= 325 - 150 = 175$$
$$PS = \sqrt{175} = 13 \cdot 23 \text{ (by slide rule).}$$

To enable us to specify the direction of PS we will evaluate the angle φ. By the SINE RULE we have:

$$\frac{15}{\sin \varphi} = \frac{13 \cdot 23}{\sin 60}$$

$$\therefore \quad \sin \varphi = \frac{15 \sin 60}{13 \cdot 23} = \frac{15 \times 0 \cdot 8660}{13 \cdot 23} = 0 \cdot 9870 \text{ (by slide rule)}$$

$$\therefore \qquad \varphi = 81 \text{ degrees (to the nearest degree).}$$

The above example is typical of thousands that are worked out daily in connection with parallelograms of vector quantities such as forces, alternating electric currents, voltages, etc., etc. For such computations a rough table and a slide rule generally suffice. Similar calculations are performed by land surveyors, but here very great accuracy is required and such helps as the slide rule and the rule of proportional parts must be used with discrimination.

The sine, cosine and tangent have reciprocal values the use of which is sometimes an economy in time and labour. The reciprocal of $\sin \theta$ is called cosecant θ, so we have (see the diagram on page 111):

$$\frac{1}{\sin \theta} = \frac{s}{p} = \text{cosec } \theta.$$

The reciprocal of cosine θ is called secant θ, so we have:

$$\frac{1}{\cos \theta} = \frac{s}{h} = \text{sec } \theta.$$

Finally, the reciprocal of tangent θ is called cotangent θ, so we have:

$$\frac{1}{\tan \theta} = \frac{h}{p} = \text{cot } \theta.$$

We have seen that $\cos \theta = \sin (90 - \theta)$ and is called the *cosine* because it is the sine of the complementary angle. The same principle accounts for the names *co*secant and *co*tangent, for:

$$\operatorname{cosec} \theta = \sec (90 - \theta)$$
and
$$\operatorname{cotan} \theta = \tan (90 - \theta).$$

There are not more than six trigonometrical ratios because it is not possible to pair the three sides of a triangle in more than six ways.

CHAPTER VII

MENSURATION

The value or utility of a piece of land, or of a piece of cloth, is dependent upon several factors, but most important of these is its *area*. The sides or edges form a closed figure and the amount of the surface contained within this figure must be estimated in units of area before we can say how much land or cloth is involved. If one field has twice the area of another but is the same in other respects, it will grow twice as much foodstuff and therefore it will be twice as valuable. And, assuming cloth to be cut into reasonable shapes, the number of useful garments that can be made from a given piece will be in direct proportion to its area.

In the accompanying diagram you can see a rectangular area the long side of which is of 6 length units and the short side of 4 length units. This can be divided into four strips of unit width and 6 units long. Each strip can be divided into six squares of unit length and breadth. Thus the whole area is equivalent to $6 \times 4 = 24$ such unit squares.

All areas are measured in unit squares as described here; the square inch is an area in the form of a square having all its sides 1 inch long. Square feet, square yards and square centimetres are other square units of area, the sides being the foot, the yard and the centimetre respectively. Evidently the area of a rectangle of length l units and of breadth b units will be lb square units.

Problem 54.—An acre is equivalent to 4840 sq. yds. A rectangular area of 1 acre is twice as long as it is broad; what is its length?

Suppose that the length in question is l yards; then the breadth will be $\frac{1}{2}l$ and the area will be $l \times \frac{1}{2}l = \frac{1}{2}l^2$ sq. yds.

But we are told that the area is 4840 sq. yds.

∴
$$\tfrac{1}{2}l^2 = 4840$$
$$l = \sqrt{2 \times 4840} = 98{\cdot}4 \text{ yds.}$$

The breadth will be $\tfrac{1}{2} \times 98{\cdot}4 = 49{\cdot}2$ yds. You can see from this calculation that an acre of ground in the form of a rectangle twice as long as it is broad will be roughly 100 paces by 50 paces.

Problem 55.—A chest 6 ft. long by 4 ft. wide by 3 ft. deep is to be lined top, bottom and sides with lead foil weighing 0·5 lb. per sq. ft. What weight of foil will be needed?

Area of top and bottom surfaces	$= 6 \times 4$ sq. ft. each.
∴ combined area of these surfaces	$= 2 \times 6 \times 4 = 48$ sq. ft.
Area of end surfaces	$= 4 \times 3$ sq. ft. each.
∴ combined area of these surfaces	$= 2 \times 3 \times 4 = 24$ sq. ft.
Area of side surfaces	$= 6 \times 3$ sq. ft. each.
∴ combined area of these surfaces	$= 2 \times 6 \times 3 = 36$ sq. ft.
Total area to be lined	$= 48 + 24 + 36 = 108$ sq. ft.
Weight of foil required	$= 0{\cdot}5 \times 108 = 54$ lb.

When a rectangular area of length l and breadth b is drawn to a scale of one-half full size its area is *not* reduced to one-half but to one-quarter. The original area of lb is reduced to $\tfrac{1}{2}l \times \tfrac{1}{2}b$ and plainly this is $\tfrac{1}{4}lb$.

We shall see presently that whenever any figure, no matter what its shape, is reproduced to an nth part of its original size as regards its lengths, the area will be diminished in the proportion n^2 to 1. Thus, if we have a model of any engine, aeroplane or building to a scale of $\tfrac{1}{12}$, the paint needed to cover it will not be a twelfth of that required to cover the original but a hundred and forty-fourth part $\left(\tfrac{1}{144}\right)$.

The same rule applies to enlargements as well as to reductions. If a model ship requires 2 square yards of sail, the same design built 20 times larger will need 20×20 or 400 times as much, namely 800 square yards of sail.

The truth of these assertions will be evident when we have before us all the formulæ for the areas of different figures. In each formula there appears a product of *two* lengths, so that the area is obviously affected *twice* by a change of scale. Each length being, say, n times what it was before, the area must be $n \times n = n^2$ times what it was before, no matter whether n is less than 1 (for a reduction of scale) or greater than 1 (for an enlargement of scale).

From what has been written here you may think that the area of a figure is related to its perimeter (the distance round its outline), but in reality there is no simple connection applicable to all figures. In the accompanying diagram you can see a figure ABCD made by distorting the rectangle A'B'CD. Originally the area was $l \times b$, but in the distorted figure it is considerably less; actually it is $l \times b \cos \theta$, where θ is the angular measure of the distortion. Thus a change of area has occurred without there being any change of perimeter; plainly there can be no connection between the two when we can alter one at our pleasure while keeping the other invariable.

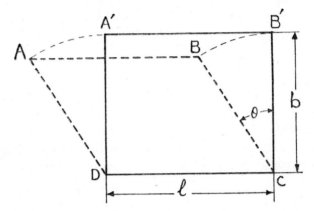

Problem 56.—A square of given area is turned into a rhombus by being distorted until its originally vertical sides make an angle of θ with the vertical. If the area of the rhombus is one-half of that of the original square, what is θ in degrees?

If the side of the square is s, its area is s^2.

Area of rhombus $\quad = s \times s \cos \theta = s^2 \cos \theta$.

Now $\qquad s^2 \cos \theta = \tfrac{1}{2}s^2$

∴ $\qquad\qquad \cos \theta = \tfrac{1}{2}$

$\qquad\qquad \theta = 60$ degrees.

A rectangle distorted into a lozenge-shaped figure is called a parallelogram, and we have just affirmed (without proof) that the area of such a figure is given by the length of its base (l) times the vertical height ($b \cos \theta$). It is usual to express this truth in words as follows:

"Parallelograms standing on the same base and between the same parallels are equal in area, this area being the product of the base length and the perpendicular distance between the parallels."

In the following diagram parallelogram ABCD is plainly equal in area to rectangle A'B'CD. The figure AB'CD is common to both, and whereas the rectangle is this figure plus the triangle A'AD, the parallelogram is this same figure plus the equal triangle B'BC. Both parallelogram and rectangle have the area "base length × vertical height."

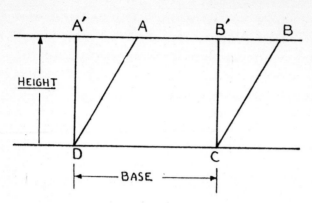

Any triangle can be turned into a parallelogram by having an equal triangle added to it, as shown by the dotted lines in the following diagram. The area of this parallelogram is $b \times h$ and consequently the area of the triangle is $\frac{1}{2}b \times h$; in words, one-half of the base multiplied by the height.

A trapezium is a quadrilateral figure having two of its sides parallel. In the accompanying figure you can see a trapezium in which the parallel sides are of lengths p and q while the distance between them is h. The dotted line divides the figure into triangles having the areas $\frac{1}{2}ph$ and $\frac{1}{2}qh$. Thus the total area of the trapezium is:

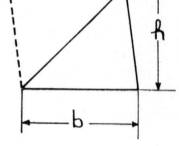

$$\tfrac{1}{2}ph + \tfrac{1}{2}qh = h\left(\frac{p+q}{2}\right)$$

or, in words, the average of the parallel sides multiplied by the distance between them.

Very often the area of an irregular figure must be computed. Thus, in finding the work done by a steam-engine we use an indicator (see Volume I, page 46) which makes diagrams showing the pressure variation in the cylinder in relation to the piston position, and the area of these diagrams is a direct measure of what we are seeking to know.

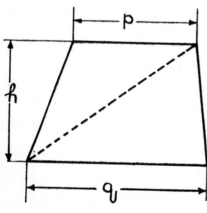

In the diagram on the next page (*a*), ABCD, etc., is a curve traced by an indicator; the base line of "zero" pressure is PQ. We are required to measure the shaded area shown between the curve and the base line. To do this accurately and quickly we might use an instrument called a "planimeter," but if we do not possess such an instrument we must be content to get an approximate result by dividing our diagram into any number n of narrow strips all of the same width and then adding up the areas of all the strips.

According to what is called the "Mid-Ordinate Rule" we treat the strips as rectangles of width w and heights equal to the dotted centre lines. If these heights are h_1, h_2, h_3, etc., then we have (see diagram (b)):

$$\text{Total area} = w(h_1 + h_2 + h_3 + \ldots . h_n)$$

$$= b \left(\frac{h_1 + h_2 + h_3 + \ldots . h_n}{n} \right)$$

$$= \text{base length} \times \text{average height of figure.}$$

In reality we are evaluating the area bounded by the stepped line, but this scarcely differs from the area bounded by the original curve

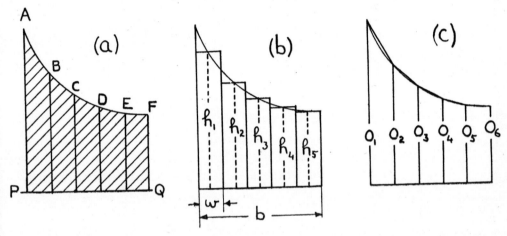

when a sufficiently large number of strips is taken. The tiny areas added above the curve are nullified more or less exactly by those subtracted where the steps fall below the curve.

Another and even simpler rule for evaluating this kind of area is the "Trapezoidal Rule," according to which we regard each strip as a trapezium (see diagram (c)). Using this rule we are saved the trouble of drawing mid-ordinates, for we measure the boundary lines of the strips instead. If these are of lengths o_1, o_2, o_3, o_4, etc., then:

$$\text{Total area} = \left(\frac{o_1 + o_2}{2} \right) w + \left(\frac{o_2 + o_3}{2} \right) w + \left(\frac{o_3 + o_4}{2} \right) w + \ldots$$

$$= \frac{w}{2} (o_1 + 2o_2 + 2o_3 + 2o_4 + \ldots o_{n+1}).$$

The last ordinate is called o_{n+1} here: it will be the 6th if there are five strips and so it will be the $n + 1$th if there are n strips.

The trapezoidal rule over-estimates the area beneath a hollow curve such as that shown and it under-estimates the area beneath a convex curve. It may give a close result for a "lumpy" curve that consists of both humps and hollows.

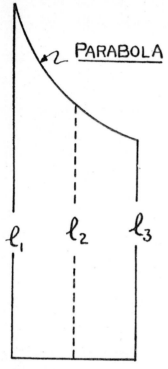

PARABOLA

ℓ_1 ℓ_2 ℓ_3

Perhaps the best rule of all is Simpson's Rule, according to which each strip is treated as though it were bounded at the top by a short length of a parabola (see page 107). The diagram here shows a strip to an enlarged scale; its end ordinates are l_1 and l_3 in length and its mid-ordinate is l_2 in length. If the curve limiting the area at the top is truly parabolic, then the average height of the strip is given *exactly* by the quantity $\dfrac{l_1 + 4l_2 + l_3}{6}$, so that its exact area is this same quantity multiplied by w.

In applying Simpson's Rule to a curve of some extent we must set up evenly spaced ordinates dividing the given area into an *even* number of strips $(2n)$. The mean height of the whole area is then found by evaluating

$$\tfrac{1}{6n}(o_1 + 4o_2 + 2o_3 + 4o_4 + 2o_5 + 4o_6 + \ldots o_{2n+1})$$

AVERAGE HEIGHT

$= \dfrac{1}{6}\left(\ell_1 + 4\ell_2 + \ell_3\right)$

where o_{2n+1} is the length of the last ordinate. Inside the brackets is a sum comprising the first and last ordinates together with twice all the other odd ordinates and four times all the even ordinates.

Problem 57.—One strip of an irregular figure is bounded by ordinates 6 and 7 in. long. The mid-ordinate is 6·25 in. long. Evaluate the average height of this strip by the three rules given above.

According to the mid-ordinate rule the average height is 6·25 in.

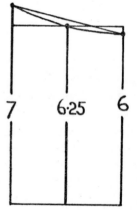

7   6·25   6

According to the trapezoidal rule it is $\dfrac{6 + 7}{2} = 6\cdot 5$ in.

According to Simpson's Rule it is $\tfrac{1}{6}(6 + 4 \times 6\cdot 25 + 7) = \tfrac{38}{6} = 6\tfrac{1}{3}$ in. Here the mid-ordinate and trapezoidal rules obviously introduce appreciable error, but of course they are not intended to be applied to diagrams of only one strip. Simpson's Rule gives a result which is likely to be very near the truth, being exactly right for a parabolic curve passing through the three points defined by the heights 6, 6·25 and 7. Such a curve may be almost indistinguishable from the actual curve. Proof of the exactness of Simpson's Rule for parabolic curves is too advanced to be given here.

If you mark with pencil or chalk that point on a wheel which touches the ground, and then roll the wheel along in a straight course until the same mark touches the ground again, you will get a straight line marked out on the ground exactly equal in length to the circumference or periphery of the wheel. You can measure this line and compare its length with the diameter of the wheel. You will find in this way that the circumference of any circle is rather more than three times its diameter. A useful approximation to the true figure is $3\frac{1}{7}$; a nearer approximation is 3·142. For more accurate calculations you can use 3·1416 or even 3·141593. The true figure usually denoted by π (pī) cannot be precisely expressed in any notation, for it is not a whole number of any other quantity however small that other quantity might be.

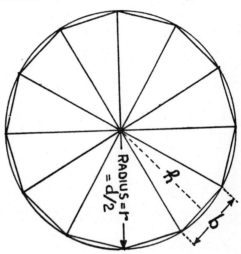

To find the area of a circle we can imagine it to consist of many narrow sectors and add up their several areas to get the total area. The accompanying diagram shows a circle divided into twelve sectors. Each sector consists of a triangle and a segment. The "height" of each triangle is nearly equal to the radius of the circle, which we denote by r, and the "base" of each triangle is a chord of the circle very nearly equal in length to the circumference it cuts off. If the actual dimensions are h and b as shown, then the area of the triangle is $\frac{1}{2}hb$. This area differs from the area of the whole sector by the area of the segment and the difference can be made as small as we please by taking the sector sufficiently narrow. When there is no sensible difference between the area of the triangle and that of the sector, we can put r for h and c for b, where c is circular arc bounding the sector, now indistinguishable from the chord.

If we imagine the circle to consist of an indefinitely large number of such narrow sectors, we get for its area the following:

$$\text{Total area} = \tfrac{1}{2}rc + \tfrac{1}{2}rc + \tfrac{1}{2}rc + \ldots$$
$$= \tfrac{1}{2}r(c + c + c + c + \ldots)$$
$$= \tfrac{1}{2}r \times \pi d = \tfrac{1}{2}r \times 2\pi r = \pi r^2.$$

Thus the area of a circle is π times the square made with the radius for its side, or $\dfrac{\pi}{4}$ times the square made with the diameter for its side. The expression

$$\text{area of circle} = 0\cdot 7854 d_2$$

shows you that for a *rough* mental approximation you can take a circle to be three-quarters of the area of the square drawn round it ($0\cdot 75 d^2$). The area of any sector including an angle of θ will be $\dfrac{\theta}{360}$ times the area of the whole circle.

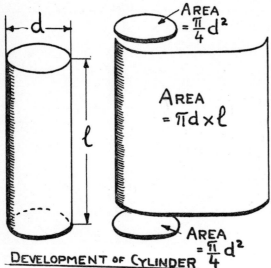

AREA $= \dfrac{\pi}{4} d^2$

AREA $= \pi d \times l$

AREA $= \dfrac{\pi}{4} d^2$

DEVELOPMENT OF CYLINDER

The area of a segment is the area of the corresponding sector less a triangular part.

The surface areas of solid or three-dimensional bodies must sometimes be calculated. Suppose you had to make cylindrical floats of diameter d and length l, using tinplate weighing w lb. per unit area, what would be the buoyancy of such floats? It would be equal to the weight of water displaced less the weight of the float itself (see page 150). To calculate the weight of the float you would need to estimate the area of tinplate used in its construction. For each of the two ends you would equire a disc of area $\dfrac{\pi}{4} d_2$. For the cylindrical surface you would need a ectangular piece of length πd and breadth l. Thus, not allowing for overlap at joints, the area of the tinplate required would be:

$$2 \times \dfrac{\pi}{4} d^2 + \pi d \times l = \pi \left(\dfrac{d^2}{2} + dl\right)$$

and the weight would be this quantity multiplied by w. In practice you would need to add on a small percentage for additional material at the joints, not forgetting any solder used.

To find the amount of material required to make a cone or funnel you must imagine the conical surface to be flattened or "developed." It will then represent the sector of a circle of radius equal to the slant side s of the arc drawn with this the cone. The length of base is πd, where d is

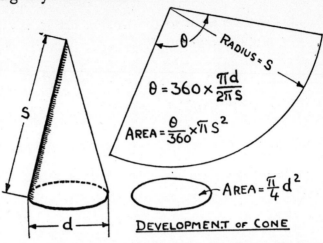

$$\theta = 360 \times \frac{\pi d}{2\pi s}$$

$$AREA = \frac{\theta}{360} \times \pi s^2$$

$$AREA = \frac{\pi}{4} d^2$$

DEVELOPMENT OF CONE

the base diameter of the cone. The angle of the sector is θ and in degrees:

$$\theta = \frac{\pi d}{2\pi s} \times 360 = 180\frac{d}{s} = 360\frac{r}{s}, \text{ where } r = \frac{d}{2}.$$

The area of the material used is $\frac{r}{s} \times \pi s^2 = \pi r s$.

Problem 58.—A conical lampshade is to have a top opening 6 in. in diameter and a bottom opening 12 in. in diameter. The height is to be 5 in. Make a scale plan of the development of this lampshade and estimate the area of the material used.

The cone is one which tapers $12 - 6 = 6$ in. in a height of 5 in. Thus it will taper to a point in a height of $\frac{12}{6} \times 5 = 10$ in.

LAMP-SHADE

The slant side of the complete cone is given by:

$$s = \sqrt{10^2 + 6^2} = \sqrt{136} = 11 \cdot 65 \text{ in.}$$

This is the radius of the larger arc in the development diagram (*b*).

The slant side of the cone shown dotted in diagram (a) is given by:

$$s' = \sqrt{5^2 + 3^2} = \sqrt{34} = 5{\cdot}83 \text{ in.}$$

This is the radius of the smaller arc in the development diagram (b). The angle θ is given by:

$$\theta = \frac{\pi \times 12}{2\pi \times 11{\cdot}65} \times 360 \text{ degrees} = 185 \text{ degrees.}$$

The area of material used is:

$$\frac{185}{360} \times \pi \times 11{\cdot}65^2 = 218 \text{ sq. in.}$$

Areas of spherical surfaces are to be found by imagining a cylinder to contain the whole sphere of which the given surface or surfaces form a

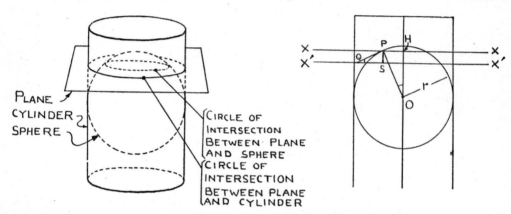

PLANE
CYLINDER
SPHERE
CIRCLE OF
INTERSECTION
BETWEEN PLANE
AND SPHERE
CIRCLE OF
INTERSECTION
BETWEEN PLANE
AND CYLINDER

part. In the accompanying diagram a sphere with centre o and radius r is shown inside a cylindrical tube that exactly fits it. Lines xx and $x'x'$ represent parallel planes cutting both sphere and cylinder, making circular intersections in both. PQ, at right angles to OP, is part of a tangent drawn to the sphere at P.

Between planes xx and $x'x'$ lie narrow zones or belts of both cylinder and sphere. The width of the cylindrical belt is PS and its length is $2\pi r$, consequently its area is $2\pi r \times \text{PS}$.

The width of the spherical belt is very nearly equal to PQ, and if planes xx, $x'x'$ were very close together, we could say without scruple: area of the spherical belt $= 2\pi \cdot \text{PH} \cdot \text{PQ}$.

In triangles OHP, QSP

$$\text{angle H} = \text{angle S} = \text{one right angle,}$$
and
$$\text{angle O} = \text{angle Q}$$

$\therefore$ triangles are equiangular and similar.

$$\therefore \qquad \frac{PS}{PQ} = \frac{PH}{PO}$$

$$\therefore \qquad PH \cdot PQ = PS \cdot PO = r \times PS$$

$$\therefore \qquad 2\pi \cdot PH \cdot PQ = 2\pi r \times PS.$$

But the quantities equated here are the two zonal areas already discussed above and consequently it follows that when two parallel planes simultaneously make intercepts on a cylinder and a sphere as shown, the surface areas of these intercepts are equal.

We have proved the above result for planes extremely close together, but it is true for planes a considerable distance apart, since an infinite number of planes could be inserted between, making an infinite number of paired though very narrow and cylindrical spherical zones the sum of which for the cylinder would be equal to the sum for the sphere.

The above proof is the best that can be given here, though the more critical mathematician will want (and deduce) a better proof, getting an identical result. From this result we see that if we cut a sphere into slices of equal thickness by parallel planes, the zonal areas will be the same for all slices. The equatorial slice will have the same spherical area as either of the polar caps and the surface area of a whole hemisphere will be equal to the area of its containing cylinder, which is $2\pi r \times r$, or $2\pi r^2$. The latter result is of particular interest because it shows us that *the surface area of a hemispherical dome is exactly twice the area of its circular plan*. The area of the whole sphere is four times area of one of the great circles.

Problem 59.—A spherical buoy 4 ft. in diameter is made of material weighing 0·05 lb. per sq. in. What is the finished weight?

Surface area of buoy $= 4 \times$ area of great circle

$$= 4 \times \pi r^2 = 4 \times \pi \times 24^2$$
$$= 7240 \text{ sq. in.}$$

Weight of buoy $\qquad = 0 \cdot 05 \times 7240$
$$= 362 \text{ lb.}$$

Problem 60.—A concave spherical reflector is 12 in. in diameter and the concavity is 1 in. deep. Calculate the area inside this reflector and find out how it compares with the area of a flat disc of the same diameter.

To find the diameter d of the whole sphere which the reflector surface forms a part, we have (see page 100):

$$6 \times 6 = 1(d - 1) = d - 1$$
$$d = 36 + 1 = 37.$$

Area of reflector = area of 1 in., belt of cylinder 37 in. in diameter
= π × 37 × 1 = 116 sq. in.

$$\text{Area of 12 in. disc} = \frac{\pi}{4} \times 144 = 112\cdot5 \text{ sq. in.}$$

$$\frac{\text{Area of reflector}}{\text{Area of disc}} = 1\cdot031.$$

Any algebraic quantity, such as xyz, involving the multiplication of three factors together is equivalent to the volume of a rectangular block of length x, breadth y and depth z. The unit of volume is a cube having all its edges of unit length and all its faces of unit area. The above-mentioned rectangular block has a base area of xy so that xy unit cubes could stand upon it, taking up all the available area. To fill the block, however, the unit cubes would have to be piled on the base to a height of z; consequently, z unit cubes would be piled on each unit square of the base. There being xy such unit squares, there must be xyz unit cubes in all, and consequently the volume of the block is equal to xyz volume units.

Consider now a cube having its edges 1 ft. (or 12 in.) long. The base area is 12 × 12 = 144 sq. in. and the volume = 144 × 12 = 1728 cub. in.

Builders' merchants sell sand by the "yard," meaning the cubic yard or a measure equal to a cube having all its edges 1 yd. (or 3 ft.) long. The base area of such a cube is 3 × 3 = 9 sq. ft. and the volume is 9 × 3 = 27 cub. ft. A large bucket might contain a cub. ft. of sand but a cub. yd. is equivalent to no less than twenty-seven such buckets.

Models representing solid objects to a reduced scale are less bulky than the original (and less weighty) and the diminution is in accordance with the third power (the cube) of the scale. Thus a model made $\frac{1}{2}$ full size will be $(\frac{1}{2})^3 = \frac{1}{8}$ as bulky as the original. An engine made to a scale of 1 in. = 1 ft. will have a bulk of only $(\frac{1}{12})^3 = \frac{1}{1728}$ of the original. The material of its construction being the same it will weigh only $\frac{1}{1728}$ of the original. Thus, if the original weighed 100 tons, the model would weigh only $\dfrac{100 \times 2240}{1728} = 129$ lb.

Problem 61.—To what depth in feet will 3 cub. yds. of sand fill a pit 5 ft. square?

Volume of sand used = 3 × 27 = 81 cub. ft.
Area of base of pit   = 5 × 5 = 25 sq. ft.
∴ Depth of sand in pit = $\frac{81}{25}$ = 3·24 ft.

In all branches of engineering it is necessary to compute volumes and weights of component parts of machines and structures. Their cost and functional suitability are related to these quantities. Occasionally a part is in the form of a cube or a rectangular block, but cylinders, cones, spheres and other solid figures are met with and so it is necessary to be able to evaluate the volume of objects of any shape.

The volume of a cylinder is calculated in the same way as that of a rectangular block: its base area is found and this is multiplied by the height or length.

Problem 62.—How much steam is required to fill a locomotive cylinder 2 ft. in diameter and 2 ft. 6 in. long?

Cross-sectional area of cylinder $= \dfrac{\pi}{4} \times 2 \times 2$ sq. ft.

Volume of cylinder $= 2 \cdot 5 \times \dfrac{\pi}{4} \times 2 \times 2 = 2 \cdot 5\pi = 7 \cdot 854$ cub. ft.

This, then, is the volume of steam required.

Problem 63.—What weight of iron is used in making an engine flywheel 3 ft. in diameter if this is in the form of a solid disc 3 in. thick? Take 1 cub. ft. of iron as 430 lb.

Area of disc $\quad = \dfrac{\pi}{4} \times 3 \times 3$ sq. ft.

Volume of disc $\quad = \dfrac{\pi}{4} \times 3 \times 3 \times 0 \cdot 25$ cub. ft.

Since 3 in. $\quad = 0 \cdot 25$ ft.

Weight of disc $\quad = 430 \times \dfrac{\pi}{4} \times 3 \times 3 \times 0 \cdot 25$

$\qquad\qquad\qquad = \dfrac{430 \times \pi \times 9}{16} = 760$ lb.

Problem 64.—Obtain a formula for the volume of a circular ring of rectangular cross-section, taking the inside radius as r, the outside radius as R and the thickness as t. Apply the formula to the determination of the volume of a ring of 4 ft. outside diameter, 3 ft. inside diameter and 6 in. thick.

A ring is the difference of two cylinders.

Vol. of outer cylinder $= \pi R^2 t$
Vol. of inner cylinder $= \pi r^2 t$
$\qquad$ Vol. of ring $= \pi R^2 t - \pi r^2 t = \pi t (R^2 - r^2)$
$\qquad\qquad$ or $\pi t (R + r)(R - r)$.

Applying this to the numerical example, we have:

Vol. of ring $= \pi \times 0.5(2 + 1.5)(2 - 1.5)$

$= \pi \times 0.5 \times 3.5 \times 0.5 = 2.74$ cub. ft.

Sometimes the volume of a circular hoop is evaluated by taking its cross-sectional area, in this case $t(R - r)$, and multiplying by the mean circumference, in this case $2\pi \dfrac{(R + r)}{2}$. The result, namely $\pi t(R + r)$ $(R - r)$, is the same as we had above. The method is applicable to rings of circular or any other cross-section symmetrical about a centre.

Problem 65.—A ring of 3 in. diameter circular cross-section has an inside diameter of 2 ft. What is the volume of the metal in this ring?

Mean diameter $\qquad = 2$ ft. 3 in. $= 2.25$ ft.

Cross-sectional area $\qquad = \dfrac{\pi}{4}(0.25)^2 = \dfrac{\pi}{64}$ sq. ft.

Volume of ring $\qquad = \dfrac{\pi}{64} \times \pi \times 2.25 = 0.347$ cub. ft.

The volume of a cone can be found by using Simpson's Rule (see page 138) to evaluate its average cross-section. This decreases from a maximum at the base to zero at the apex. The diameter d at any distance y from the apex can be expressed by the relation:

$$d = ay$$

where a is some numerical constant. Thus we have:

Cross-sectional area $\quad = A = \dfrac{\pi}{4}d^2 = \dfrac{\pi a^2}{4}.y^2.$

If we plotted A against y, the resultant graph would be a parabola and this is why we can apply Simpson's Rule to the determination of the mean value of A.

In a given case suppose that the base area $= B$. Then, half-way between base and vertex the diameter will be half the base diameter, so that the cross-sectional area will be $\dfrac{B}{4}$. At the apex the cross-sectional area $= O$.

The mean or average cross-section by Simpson's Rule $= \dfrac{B + 4 \times \frac{B}{4} + o}{6}$

$= \dfrac{2B}{6} = \frac{1}{3}B.$

Volume of cone $=$ average cross-section $\times$ height

$= \dfrac{B}{3} \times h.$

It is thus one-third of the volume of a cylinder of equal height standing on the same base.

The formula above is true of a pyramid standing on a base of *any* shape so long as the base area is B and the height is *h*.

A truncated cone or pyramid (called a frustum) is the difference between the whole and the part cut away, so that you can easily calculate its volume. An easier method, however, is to apply Simpson's Rule, as explained in the next example.

Problem 66.—A truncated pyramid has a height of 2 ft. Its base area is 6 sq. ft. and its top area is 3 sq. ft. What is its volume?

We must find the sectional area half-way between the top and the bottom before we can use Simpson's Rule. Any linear dimension of the base is to the corresponding linear dimension of the top as $\sqrt{6}$ is to $\sqrt{3}$.

To the same scale this dimension at mid-height will be $\dfrac{\sqrt{6}+\sqrt{3}}{2}$

and therefore the cross-sectional area at mid-height $= \left(\dfrac{\sqrt{6}+\sqrt{3}}{2}\right)^2$

$$= \tfrac{1}{4}(6 + 2\sqrt{6 \times 3} + 3)$$
$$= \tfrac{1}{4}(6 + 8 \cdot 5 + 3) = \tfrac{17 \cdot 5}{4} = 4 \cdot 375 \text{ sq. ft.}$$

Average cross-section (by Simpson's Rule)

$$= \frac{6 + 4 \times 4 \cdot 375 + 3}{6} = \frac{26 \cdot 5}{6} = 4 \cdot 425.$$

$\therefore$ Volume of frustum $= 2 \times 4 \cdot 425 = 8 \cdot 85$ cub. ft.

Let us see if the alternative method of working is better.

The pyramid decreases dimensionally at the rate of $\sqrt{6}$ to $\sqrt{3}$ in 2 ft. This represents a diminution of $2 \cdot 45 - 1 \cdot 73 = 0 \cdot 72$ in 2 ft. For a diminution of $2 \cdot 45$ we need to ascend $2 \times \frac{2 \cdot 45}{0 \cdot 72} = 6 \cdot 81$ ft. Thus the height of the complete pyramid is $6 \cdot 81$ ft. and of the part cut off $6 \cdot 81 - 2 = 4 \cdot 81$ ft.

Volume of whole pyramid $= \tfrac{6}{3} \times 6 \cdot 81 = 13 \cdot 62$ cub. ft.

Volume of part cut off $= \tfrac{3}{3} \times 4 \cdot 81 = 4 \cdot 81$ cub. ft.

Volume of frustum $= 13 \cdot 62 - 4 \cdot 81 = 8 \cdot 81$ cub. ft.

Problem 67.—What is the cubical capacity of a pan 1 ft. 6 in. deep if it tapers from a diameter of 3 ft. at the top to 2 ft. at the bottom?

Radius at middle height　　　$= \dfrac{1 \cdot 5 + 1}{2} = 1 \cdot 25$ ft.

Mean cross-section of pan　　$= \frac{1}{6}(\pi \times 1^2 + 4\pi \times 1 \cdot 25^2 + \pi \times 1 \cdot 5^2)$

$$= \frac{\pi}{6}(1 + 6 \cdot 25 + 2 \cdot 25)$$

$$= \frac{\pi}{6} \times 9 \cdot 5 = 4 \cdot 97 \text{ sq. ft.}$$

Cubic capacity of pan　　　$= 1 \cdot 5 \times 4 \cdot 97 = 7 \cdot 45$ cub. ft.

The volume of a sphere can be regarded as being made up of innumerable slender pyramids with their bases forming the outside surface of the sphere and their common apex at the centre of the sphere. Let the radius of the sphere be r and the base areas of these pyramids be a. Then,

$$\text{Volume of sphere} = \frac{a}{3} \times r + \frac{a}{3} \times r + \frac{a}{3} \times r + \ldots$$

$$= \frac{r}{3}(a + a + a + \ldots)$$

$$= \frac{r}{3} \times \text{surface of area whole sphere}$$

$$= \frac{r}{3} \times 4\pi r^2 = \frac{4}{3}\pi r^3 = 4 \cdot 18 r^3.$$

A cubical box into which the sphere fitted exactly would have a volume of $(2r)^3 = 8r^3$, so that the sphere fills $4 \cdot 18/8 = 0 \cdot 523$ of the box. To evaluate the volume of a spherical cap we must first evaluate the spherical surface, then multiply by $r/3$ and finally take away the volume of an unwanted conical part.

Problem 68.—A plano-convex lens is 18 in. in diameter and its thickness varies from 2 in. at the centre to nothing at the edges. What volume of glass is contained in it?

Let r be the radius of the sphere of which the lens forms a part. Then (see page 100):

$$9 \times 9 = 2(2r - 2) = 4r - 4$$

$$r = \frac{81 + 4}{4} = 21 \cdot 25 \text{ in.}$$

Area of spherical surface $= 2 \times 2\pi \times 21 \cdot 25$

$$= 267 \text{ sq. in.}$$

Between this surface and the centre of the sphere is a volume of

$$\frac{21 \cdot 25}{3} \times 267 = 1910 \text{ cub. in.}$$

There is a conical part having a circular base of 18 in. diameter and a height of $21 \cdot 25 - 2 = 19 \cdot 25$ in.

$$\text{Volume of this part} = \frac{\pi}{4} \times 18^2 \times \frac{21 \cdot 25}{3} = \pi \times 27 \times 21 \cdot 25$$
$$= 1470 \text{ cub. in.}$$

Volume of lens $= 1910 - 1470 = 440$ cub. in.

The volume of irregularly shaped spaces (e.g. the combustion chambers of petrol or Diesel engines) is often found by pouring oil into them until they are filled, noting how much must be put in. A graduated measuring vessel is used for this purpose.

The volume of an irregularly shaped lump of iron could be measured by dropping it into a vessel containing liquid and noting how much the liquid level rises. If a graduated measuring vessel is used, the volumetric displacement of the mass can be read off directly. The more usual way of measuring the volume of an irregular mass is to weigh it in air and again in water. The difference (for it weighs less in water) will be equal to the weight of water displaced (the Principle of Archimedes), and knowing the weight of unit volume of water it is possible to estimate the total volume.

Problem 69.—A body weighing 10 lb. in air is found to have a weight of 8 lb. when wholly immersed in a liquid weighing 0·03 lb. per cub. in. What is the volume of the body and what is its weight per cub. in.?

The body loses $10 - 8 = 2$ lb. when it is immersed. The weight of liquid displaced = 2 lb.

Volume of liquid displaced $= \frac{2}{0 \cdot 03} = 66 \cdot 7$ cub. in.

∴ Volume of body $= 66 \cdot 7$ cub. in.

It weighs 10 lb. in air or $\frac{10}{66 \cdot 7} = 0 \cdot 15$ lb. per cub. in.

The weight of unit volume of a substance is called its *density*, so that in the above problem the densities of liquid and solid body are 0·03 and 0·15 lb. per cub. in. respectively.

The ratio of the density of a substance to the density of water is called its Specific Gravity. Thus, an oil having a specific gravity of 0·85, is one weighing volume for volume 0·85 times as much as water.

Problem 70.—A rectangular block of some light material is floated in water. The depth of the block is 3 in. and when it is in the water 1 in. shows above the surface. What is the specific gravity of the material comprising the block?

The block is $\frac{2}{3}$ submerged so that it displaces $\frac{2}{3}$ of its own volume of water. This water has the same weight as the whole block has in air. Thus, if the volume of the block is V, V unit volumes of the substance comprising it weigh as much as $\frac{2}{3}$V unit volumes of water. One unit volume weighs $\dfrac{\frac{2}{3}V}{V} = \frac{2}{3}$ unit volumes of water. Thus the specific gravity of the substance is $\frac{2}{3}$.

The depth to which a spherical buoy of given diameter and weight

Volume of displaced water

PRINCIPLE OF ARCHIMEDES

A floating body receives support equal to the weight of displaced liquid.

will submerge is something we could calculate if we knew the density of sea water. The displacement of the buoy (as for ships) is a body of water equal to itself in weight; dividing that weight by the density we get the volume displaced. The problem then resolves itself into finding the diameter (or the depth) of the spherical cap which possesses the volume in question. Calculations of this kind may lead to quite complicated equations, but if these cannot be solved analytically, they can always be solved by making a graph (see page 59). The practical man does not mind how he solves problems so long as they *are* solved.

In addition to calculating areas, volumes and weights we may be called upon to locate centres of gravity. The centre of gravity (C.G.) of a body is the point at which, for certain purposes, we may regard the whole of its mass as concentrated. Thus, if you had to lift with one hand a bar 4 ft. long loaded at the ends with masses weighing 10 and 30 lb., you would be interested to know where to grip the bar so as to have the masses balance. As a matter of fact you would have to grip it at the centre of gravity of the system. Mechanics teaches us (see Volume II, page 57) that you would have to grip the bar at a distance of 1 ft. from the 30-lb. mass. The turning action of this mass around this point would be 30 × 1 and it would be exactly counterbalanced by the turning action exerted by the 10-lb. mass, this being 10 × 3. Turning actions are called "moments."

So far as your hand is concerned the two masses 4 ft. apart are equivalent to a combined mass of 40 lb. situated 1 ft. from the 30-lb. mass.

Where is the balancing point of a square sheet of iron? The answer is "at its geometrical centre." For a circular plate it is also at the centre; for a parallelogram it is at the point of intersection of the diagonals. These are easy cases because the figures are perfectly symmetrical, but a triangle is not so easy.

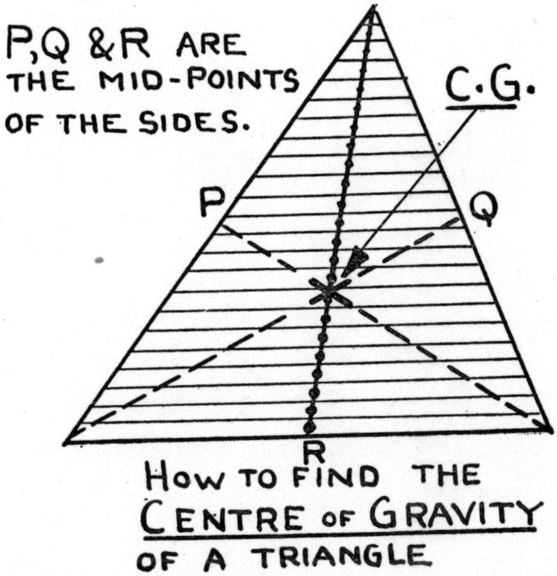

In the accompanying figure a triangle is shown divided up into narrow strips by lines drawn parallel to the base. The C.G. of each strip is at its central point and the central points of all the strips lie on a straight line. This line is called the median of the triangle and it runs from the vertex to the mid-point R of the base.

Now if the C.G.s of all strips lie on the median, it means that the whole mass of the triangle can be regarded

P, Q & R ARE THE MID-POINTS OF THE SIDES.

C.G.

P

Q

R

HOW TO FIND THE CENTRE OF GRAVITY OF A TRIANGLE

as concentrated on this same line. It can equally well be regarded as concentrated on either of the other medians (shown dotted). Consequently it must have the meeting-point of the three medians for its ultimate centre of gravity. By applying what you know about similar triangles (see page 82) you can prove that the C.G. lies at a point one-third of the way from the base to the vertex.

To find the C.G. of a quadrilateral figure you can divide it into two triangles and find the C.G. of both. Against the two C.G.s you must write the corresponding areas, for the masses will be proportional to these. Finally, you must divide the line joining the C.G.s inversely as the two masses; this will give you the ultimate C.G. or balancing-point for the whole figure.

Polygonal figures can be divided into three or more triangles and what you do here is find the common C.G. of two; join this common C.G. to the C.G. of a third and find the common C.G. of all three. This common C.G. of all three can be joined to the C.G. of a fourth and then the common C.G. of all four can be found. There is no limit to the number of times this process can be repeated. It will give you confidence in the methods of calculation described here if you will ascertain the C.G.s of triangles, quadrilaterals and five-sided figures and then check your results by drawing the figures to scale, cutting them out and then seeing if they will balance on a pin at the calculated point.

A quick way of finding the C.G. of *any* figure (including irregular ones) is to draw the figure accurately, cut it out and hang it up by a thread from successive points on its periphery. While it is hanging you must continue the line of the thread downwards by drawing its prolongation on the figure as shown by the dotted lines in the accompanying sketch. The meeting-point of all these dotted lines is the C.G. required.

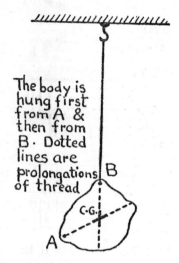

The body is hung first from A & then from B. Dotted lines are prolongations of thread

TO FIND THE C.G. OF AN IRREGULAR BODY

The picture facing this page shows how to find the height above the ground of the centre of gravity of an omnibus. At the angle when overturning becomes a possibility the centre of gravity must be somewhere in the vertical plane through the contact between the ground and the wheels bearing the weight. It must also be somewhere in the longitudinal centre plane of the bus, as the bus is symmetrical in construction. Finally, then, it must be in the line of intersection between the two planes. Not every massive body or assemblage of bodies can be so readily tilted as an omnibus and consequently you should become familiar with the calculation method of finding centres of gravity. A practical example of its utility is given below.

Problem 71.—Machines weighing 3, 4, 5 and 7 tons are located on a factory floor at points forming a square the sides of which are 20 ft. long. It is decided to provide an additional column below the floor to support the additional weight. Where must this column be placed if it is to be under the common C.G. of the four machines?

To find the common C.G. of the machines weighing 3 and 4 tons we must divide the 20 ft. between them into 3 + 4 = 7 equal lengths of

Tilting a bus to ascertain at what angle the vertical pull of its weight, acting through the centre of gravity, will fall outside the wheelbase and cause overturning.

(*By courtesy of London Transport Executive.*)

$\frac{20}{7}$ ft. each. The common C.G. will be 4 of these lengths from the 3-ton machine. Thus, in the diagram shown here,

$$AG_1 = \frac{4 \times 20}{7} = 11\cdot43 \text{ ft.}$$

To find the common C.G. of the machines weighing 5 and 7 tons we must divide the 20 ft. between them into $5 + 7 = 12$ equal lengths of $\frac{20}{12}$ ft. each.

The common C.G. will be 5 of these lengths from the 7-ton machine. Thus, in the diagram shown here,

$$DG_2 = \frac{5 \times 20}{12} = 8\cdot33 \text{ ft.}$$

At G_1 there is concentrated 7 tons and at G_2 12 tons. The common C.G. of these two aggregates is at G_3 in the line $G_1\ G_2$. Point G_3 divides the distance between AB and DC in the ratio:

$$\frac{G_1G_3}{G_2G_3} = \frac{12}{7}.$$

A line drawn through G_3 parallel to AB and DC cuts the lines AD and CB in the same ratio. This line is shown dotted. It lies $\frac{12}{19} \times 20 = 12\cdot65$ ft. below AB and cuts AD at a point P which is $12\cdot65$ ft. below A. The distance

$$PG_3 = 11\cdot43 - \frac{12\cdot65}{20}(11\cdot43 - 8\cdot33)$$

$$= 11\cdot43 - 1\cdot96 = 9\cdot47.$$

Thus to find G_3 it is only necessary to go $12\cdot65$ ft. along the line from A to D and then go $9\cdot47$ ft. at right angles to AD within the square.

Point G_3 is nearer to AD than to BC and this is as it should be because $3 + 7 = 10$, whereas $4 + 5 = 9$. Distance PG_3 should be $\frac{9}{19} \times 20 = 9\cdot47$ ft., which is what we have already found it to be by another method.

Wherever possible, final results should be checked in this way by some alternative method of calculation. If no alternative working suggests itself, an important result should be worked out by two or more people independently of one another and their results compared. *The best of us makes a mistake sometimes and mistakes in engineering calculations can lead to disastrous consequences.*

CHAPTER I

DIFFERENT KINDS OF MATTER

Most fascinating of all studies to both young and old is Chemistry, which has to do with the transformation of different substances one into another. The origins of chemistry go back many centuries to the time when men hoped, by its aid, to turn base substances into Gold or Silver. They hoped for other things as well—the Elixir of Youth, for instance; this was an imaginary medicine that was to keep its discoverer perpetually young and even transform already old people back into young ones.

The history of chemistry is too tedious to be worth retelling in any great detail here. Its real discoveries were nearly all made by accident. Pursuing researches that were doomed to failure, the alchemists nevertheless stumbled on transformations of a mundane kind so that practical knowledge of real value accumulated through the ages. Less than 200 years ago all this knowledge remained unsystemised—it was just a collection of unrelated recipes.

By the beginning of the nineteenth century attempts had been made to bring about some sort of scientific order to relate the known facts to one another. Many cherished delusions had to be scrapped before there could be a satisfactory theoretical basis for chemistry. One of the last and greatest hindrances to rational development of the science was the belief in an imaginary element called "phlogiston," the supposed presence of which in bodies was held to make them combustible. A body consumed by fire was said to give up its phlogiston and thus become lighter. Alas for this theory, the test of experience showed that many bodies became heavier as a result of combustion. To keep track of changes in weight the chemical balance was introduced; the plate opposite shows a modern example. Another type can be seen in the picture facing page 156, showing part of a chemical laboratory. The experiments to

High-precision analytical balance.   Accuracy in weighing is the basis of scientific chemistry and with this balance a difference of $\frac{1}{20}$ milligram can be discerned with 200 grams in each pan.

(By courtesy of Messrs. Baird & Tatlock (London), Ltd.)

make gold and other things men did when they were looking for some fancied and non-existent good need not now concern us, though mention will be made of several discoveries arising out of these early researches. The first truly scientific work was done by John Dalton in the early years of the nineteenth century. By Dalton and his successors many old experiments were repeated under close scientific scrutiny, and in that way they were made to reveal hitherto unsuspected truths of general application throughout the material universe.

One of the conclusions reached in the nineteenth century was that all material substances could be resolved into certain simpler substances called "elements" if they were not already elementary in their nature. An element was defined as a substance that had never been resolved into anything else and that experimenters believed to be permanently unresolvable.

Some familiar substances of an elementary nature will now be described. There are many more, but since they are not often encountered in everyday life a discussion of them will be deferred until later. In their pure form the common metals are elements, though for engineering purposes mixtures of metals or alloys are widely used. Brief accounts will be given of Iron, Copper, Zinc, Lead, Tin, Aluminium, Nickel, Mercury, Platinum, Silver and Gold.

Common non-metals of great familiarity are Carbon and Sulphur.

Elements which are very widely distributed in Nature in combination with other elements (but known by hardly anybody except the chemist in their elementary form) are Calcium, Sodium, Silicon, Potassium, Magnesium, Phosphorus, Iodine and Manganese. With the exception of Silicon, Phosphorus and Iodine these are classed as metals.

The most common gaseous elements are Oxygen, Nitrogen, Hydrogen and Chlorine.

Iron is the most useful of all metals and it has been employed by mankind for a great variety of purposes since remote times (see Volume I, Chapter I). It readily combines with atmospheric oxygen in the presence of moisture to form the oxide we call rust, and for this reason no great quantity of metallic iron occurs in Nature. Such fragments as are found of more or less pure metallic composition are meteoric in origin, and it is believed that the inaccessible central core of our own planet consists of an alloy of metallic iron and nickel.

In combination with oxygen, or with oxygen and carbon, iron forms rocky or earthy ores the extraction of which from the ground forms a major industry in many parts of the world. When the ore is mixed with coke or charcoal (forms of carbon) and heated in a furnace, the iron is liberated because carbon has a greater affinity for the oxygen, causing it to combine with itself and form the invisible gas known as carbon dioxide. The process of reducing iron ore to metallic iron is termed "smelting" and was formerly confined to forest districts where charcoal could be made in abundance. This accounted for the existence of the industry in Sussex and other sylvan districts many centuries ago.

Nowadays the iron industry is located in coal-mining areas, its carbon requirement being met by converting coal into coke in special "coke ovens." Great Britain, Germany and the United States manufacture large quantities of iron from native and imported ores. Sweden and Spain produce more ore than they can smelt economically, and for this reason they export a great deal to Britain and Germany. In association with controlled amounts of carbon, nickel, tungsten and other elements, iron can be made into a variety of different steels. In the last 100 years the use of more or less pure iron (and of crude cast iron) has been to a large extent given up, steel in one form or another having taken its place. For this reason the present has sometimes been termed the "steel age," thus bringing up to date the chronological sequence: Stone Age, Bronze Age and Iron Age.

Copper is a valuable metal, reddish in colour, which has a fair degree of strength and great ductility. As a conductor of electricity it is surpassed only by silver, but being much cheaper it is practically unrivalled for the manufacture of electric wires and cables. Alloyed with tin copper makes the metal bronze that did duty for iron and steel for many centuries before iron was discovered. Bronze is still widely used, and the name is given to many relatively new alloys as well as to alloys of ancient origin. Alloyed with zinc copper gives us brass, which is inferior to bronze and cheaper. Bronze retains something of the reddish colour of copper but brass is yellow.

Copper has been found in metallic form, particularly in the neighbourhood of Lake Superior, but the bulk of the world's needs must be extracted from ores, in the best of which the copper is found united with sulphur. North America, South America, Australia and Siberia all yield ores sufficiently rich to repay extraction. Spain is well supplied with copper and at one time copper ore was worked in Cornwall.

Zinc does not occur free in Nature, and consequently it was not discovered until comparatively recent times. It was first produced in England in 1730; on the continent its manufacture was delayed until 1807. Suitable ores are found in Britain, Belgium, Germany, Spain and

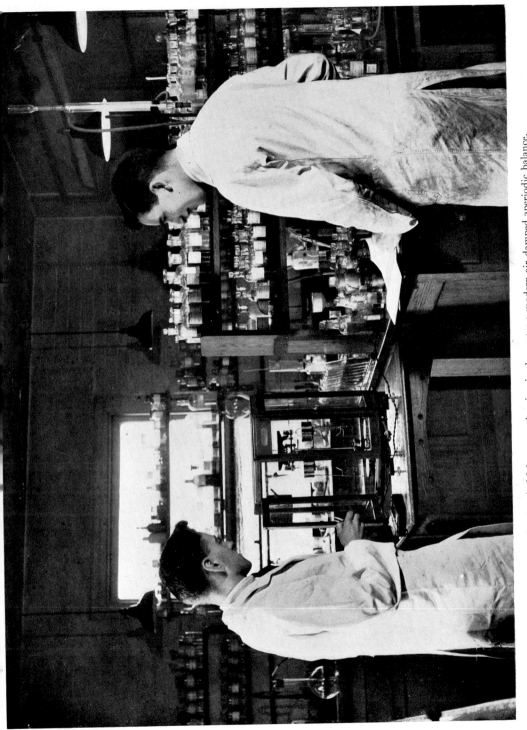

A corner of a chemical laboratory showing in the centre a modern air-damped aperiodic balance.

(By courtesy of Messrs. Baird & Tatlock (London), Ltd.)

the United States. Besides being useful as a component of brass, zinc is employed as a protective coating on iron wires and sheets, the coating process being called "galvanising." Zinc sulphate is the benign substance in a variety of medicinal ointments.

Lead is a soft and very heavy metal that is easily melted. Its rather lustreless silvery appearance is soon lost on exposure to the atmosphere, due to the formation of an oxide film. This, however, affords ample protection against further corrosion, so that lead has been favoured for many centuries for the manufacture of pipes and receptacles to resist the chemical action of water, acids, etc., etc. Britain is well provided with lead ore, one form of which, containing sulphur and called galena, is found chiefly in Derbyshire. Wales, Cornwall, Cumberland, Northumberland and Durham are other British sources of lead. Much imported ore has come from Southern Spain.

Tin is the silvery and easily melted metal used as a rust-proof coating on the sheet iron known as "tinplate." Wire made of tin serves as an excellent electric fuse. In ancient times tin was valued as an ingredient of bronze, and Cornwall was the first known source of supply. The ore, called tin-stone, is an oxide; its ancient name was "cassiterite." It is treated in much the same way as iron ore to liberate the tin from the oxygen. Tin is also obtained from South America and Australia.

Aluminium, next to magnesium, is the lightest of the metals; it is silvery in appearance and rather soft, but alloyed with other metals it possesses good structural properties. Not occurring free in Nature or in any readily worked combination, it remained undiscovered until 1827. It is widely distributed as a silicate in clays, slate and felspar, but it is extracted chiefly from an impure hydrated oxide known as bauxite. This is an earthy mineral, white to red in colour, found at Baux near Arles in France. Bauxite is also found in the United States. The process of extraction has been made economically possible by supplies of very cheap electricity, and extraction plant is located close to the Niagara Falls and at other places where electricity from water power is abundant.

Nickel is a hard white metal not unlike iron. It is even slightly magnetic. It makes a durable coinage and alloyed with iron it enters into the composition of some valuable steels. Nickel is present in the sun's atmosphere and in meteoric iron. It was discovered as the ingredient of a deceptive-looking ore in the earth's crust by Cronsted in 1751. This particular ore had acquired the name of "kupfer-nickel" or "goblin copper" because, although it appeared to promise copper, nobody had found the way to extract that metal from it. Actually no copper was present and it fell to the lot of Cronsted to show that an entirely different metal was forthcoming. He gave to this metal the name of "nickel," borrowing part of the name already assigned to the ore. The first considerable source of supply of nickel ore was New Caledonia, an island in the Pacific Ocean about a thousand miles east of Australia.

In recent times Canada has become the chief nickel-producing region of the world.

Platinum is a soft white metal having a high melting-point. Being somewhat rare, it is expensive and it has been used to make jewellery. Having the same coefficient of thermal expansion as glass, it was formerly used for the current leading-in wires in electric lamps. In this application it has now been superseded by a cheaper substitute metal alloy. Being highly resistant to temperature and corrosion effects, it is employed to make crucibles and retorts for the use of chemists. Metallic platinum occurs as small grains in alluvial deposits in the Ural Mountains. It is commonly alloyed with other rare metals and is greatly hardened by admixture with iridium. Electric make-and-break contacts are sometimes tipped with platinum to resist the heat and oxidising effect of sparks.

Mercury, or quicksilver, is the only metal that is liquid at normal atmospheric temperature and pressure. It is silvery in appearance and exceedingly heavy. The alchemists thought that it was an essence of all metals, giving them their lustrous appearance. It is familiar as the backing of mirrors and as the expanding substance in thermometers. It is able to dissolve other metals, thus forming a liquid or pasty mixture called an amalgam. In Nature it occurs chiefly as a sulphide called cinnabar; this is found at Almaden in Spain and also in the Balkan peninsula. A rich source of cinnabar more recently discovered in California has been named New Almaden.

Silver occurs in metallic form, more or less pure, and also as an alloy, but principally in chemical combination with other elements. It is a soft metal, nearly as malleable as gold, and it is not tarnished by exposure to ordinary atmospheric conditions. In the presence of sulphur, however, it turns black. This explains the discoloration of silver egg-spoons.

In 1557 Bartolomeo de Medina devised a method for extracting silver from its ores. This was put into use in Mexico in 1566 and in Peru in 1574 and the same method is still employed in these regions to-day. The ore is powdered and spread with common salt and moisture on a mixing floor, where mules tramp round and produce an intimate mixture.

Metallic mercury is then added and the mixing process continued for 15 to 45 days. Some of the mercury replaces the silver in the original compound of silver, and the liberated silver is dissolved by the surplus mercury. Eventually this amalgam of mercury and silver is subjected to a distillation process, the mercury is evaporated and silver is left. The mercury is recovered in a condenser. At various times silver has ranked equal to gold for making coins and ornaments. Compounds of silver sensitive to the influence of light have been in great demand for photographic purposes since the middle of the nineteenth century.

Gold is the only naturally yellow metal, and because it occurs in Nature unmixed or uncombined with other substances, it has been known and esteemed from remote times. Fragments varying from large nuggets to microscopic particles are found in alluvial deposits arising from the erosion of gold-bearing rocks; these rocks may be many miles distant. Most of the alluvial deposits have now been discovered and thoroughly sifted by fortune seekers; these have flocked in their thousands to the remote places where gold finds have been reported. The recovery of gold from the original rock beds is an expensive mining process beyond the resources of individual pioneers, and it is being carried out by mining companies in Africa, Australia, California and elsewhere, often at a loss. When the rock has been pulverised and sifted, the average yield of gold may be no more than a twentieth to a fortieth of an ounce per ton handled. The gold is sometimes dissolved out of the surrounding rubbish by passing the whole through metallic mercury. Primitive and modern methods of obtaining gold are shown in the pictures facing page 162.

A peculiarity of gold is that it can be welded in the cold state; thus small particles can be amalgamated and formed into coins or ornaments of considerable size by the application of pressure alone. Such is the ductility of the metal that a single grain of it can be drawn into a wire 500 ft. long or be beaten into 56 square inches of flat leaf only $\frac{1}{282000}$ inch thick. When it is as thin as this, gold will permit the passage of a little light. Held up to the sun it appears green by transmitted light.

Carbon is normally a black combustible solid; it is the main ingredient of such substances as coke, soot and lamp-black. Compressed in the presence of great heat it assumes the form of graphite (the so-called black-lead in pencils) and under extremes of pressure and temperature it yields the hard and transparent diamond. Carbon has a much stronger affinity for oxygen than the metals, and one of its chief uses is in the smelting of metallic ores. Metal in combination with oxygen is released from its bondage by the union of this oxygen with the carbon. Animal and human foodstuffs, like the fuel supplied to engines, are rich in carbon, the combustion (i.e. chemical conversion to carbon dioxide) of which provides heat energy. Breathed out by ourselves and by animals, carbon-dioxide gas forms an invisible impurity in the air. Plants are enabled by sunlight to absorb carbon dioxide, building the carbon into their own tissues and restoring the oxygen to the atmosphere.

Sulphur in the form of fine powder is an odourless lemon-yellow substance. It burns sluggishly with a blue flame, giving off a pungent gas having disinfectant and fumigating properties. It exists the world over in all kinds of mineral compounds, and in volcanic areas it is found in its elementary form. Vast amounts of it have been taken up without any difficulty in Sicily and Italy. So ready is it to combine with metals that iron and many more will burn brightly in its vapour. Ordinary black gunpowder contains 10 per cent. of sulphur, 15 per cent. of charcoal and 75 per cent. of potassium nitrate.

Calcium is a light, white, hard metal that rapidly tarnishes to a yellow colour in air. It is not found in Nature in its elementary form, and it can only be extracted from its compounds with difficulty by an electrolytic process. Nevertheless, it is one of the most widely distributed of metals, since chalk, marble and limestone consist almost wholly of calcium carbonate. Sea-shells and egg-shells consist largely of the same substance, and calcium phosphate is the main inorganic constituent of bones. Calcium chloride is commonly used for drying air as it has an affinity for moisture, and calcium carbide, when wetted, produces acetylene gas, a valuable illuminant and also a convenient source of heat for oxy-acetylene welding. The oceans of the world are estimated to contain 1800 billion tons of calcium compounds. The top picture facing page 163 shows chalk being quarried for use in making Portland cement.

Sodium is a silvery-white metal soft enough to be moulded to shape in the fingers. It melts at the low temperature of 60° C., and is so ready to combine with water that it cannot exist in a free state in Nature. The bulk of the world's sodium exists as sodium chloride (common salt) in sea water. There is estimated to be sodium chloride amounting to 36,000 billion tons in the world's oceans. Great deposits of this and other soluble salts from the sea are found in areas where sea water has undergone ceaseless evaporation in the remote past. The bottom picture facing page 163 shows a deposit in Cheshire. Sodium nitrate obtained from Chili is a valuable mineral fertiliser; it is known as Chili Saltpetre.

Silicon is as widely distributed among the inorganic constituents of the earth's crust as carbon is among the organic materials comprising vegetables and animals. It never occurs in the free state and is very difficult to obtain even in the laboratory, though there it may be seen either as a black solid or a brown powder. Combined with oxygen it forms silica, the main ingredient of flint, granite, sandstone, sand, etc., etc. Quartz is silica in crystalline form. Silica is also found in combination with metallic oxides as "silicates." Clay and slate consist of aluminium silicate.

Potassium closely resembles sodium in its characteristics and chemical affinities. It is a soft, easily fusible white metal that combines too readily with water ever to be discovered in the free state. The water of the world's oceans is estimated to contain 1141 billion tons of potassium sulphate. In one form or another it is present in most rocks and fertile soils. Salts of potassium are invaluable to plants, and potassium is always present in the ash obtained by burning vegetable remains. Potassium nitrate (common nitre), which forms 75 per cent. by weight of common black gunpowder, is found in India, but a good deal of this valuable nitrogenous compound is made from Chili saltpetre (sodium nitrate) and used as a fertiliser. The saltpetre is decomposed with caustic potash, carbonate of potash or chloride of potassium, and the by-product is caustic soda, carbonate of soda or sodium chloride (common salt) respectively, depending on the process used.

Magnesium is a silvery-white metal which is even lighter than aluminium. An immensely powerful white light can be obtained by burning magnesium in air, and powdered magnesium is the principle ingredient of photographer's flash-powder. An alloy of magnesium called electron metal possesses good structural qualities and is invaluable for aircraft components on account of its lightness. Though not occurring free in Nature, magnesium is very widely distributed in different minerals. It is a constituent of talc, asbestos and Epsom Salts. The oceans of the world are estimated to contain 7300 billion tons of magnesium compounds.

Phosphorus is a waxy substance that must be kept under water to prevent it from igniting spontaneously. Being so readily oxidised, it cannot exist naturally in the free state. It was discovered by an alchemist named Brand, of Hamburg, in the seventeenth century. It can be obtained by distilling bone-ash acid and charcoal at a high temperature. A more modern method of production is to heat the calcium phosphate from bones with coke and sand in an electric furnace, which excludes air. Slag of calcium silicate is drawn off and new material is put in to take its place. In this way phosphorus can be made continuously. Phosphorus is very poisonous, and burns caused by it are troublesome to heal.

Iodine is a lustrous black crystalline solid which turns readily into a blue-violet vapour under ordinary atmospheric conditions. Its name is derived from the Greek word meaning violet-coloured. Under a pressure of rather more than one atmosphere it melts before vaporising. It will not dissolve to any great extent in water but it forms a brown solution in alcohol, and in this form it has medicinal uses. Seaweed absorbs iodine from its ocean environment, and this iodine can be recovered. However, the world's needs for iodine can be met and even exceeded by suitably treating the mineral called sodium iodate, which occurs in South American beds of caliche (saltpetre).

Manganese is a very hard and brittle metal resembling grey iron. Being easily oxidised, it does not occur as a metal in Nature but as a black oxide named pyrolusite. As a constituent of manganese steel it provides an invaluable material for making railway points and crossings that have to withstand much battering and wear. The ore is found in central Europe and Spain, and its reduction can be accomplished by the use of aluminium. "Reduction" is the term used to describe the removal of oxygen from a compound by any substance having a chemical affinity for it.

Oxygen, discovered by Priestley in 1774, is the first element so far considered which is of a gaseous nature at normal temperature and pressure. It can be liquefied and even solidified if the temperature be reduced low enough, and if pressure be applied. This is true of the other so-called "permanent" gases, and reference to the fact will not be made again, though it applies to Hydrogen, Nitrogen and Chlorine. Oxygen comprises about a fourth part by weight of the earth's atmosphere. Combined with hydrogen it forms water and it represents eight-ninths of the weight of pure water. It is also present in many of the mineral constituents of the earth's crust; for example, in chalk, limestone and metallic oxides. All ordinary combustible substances take oxygen from the air when they burn, and many substances which can scarcely be induced to burn in air will flare up energetically in an atmosphere of pure oxygen. A common test for oxygen is to insert a smouldering splint of wood into the jar where its existence is suspected. The splint will burst into flame if, in fact, undiluted oxygen is present. Oxygen is the atmospheric constituent demanded by ourselves when we breathe. In our lungs it is transferred to our blood, by which it is carried to our

Gold prospecting in the simplest and oldest way. The dirt suspected of bearing gold is simultaneously shaken up and subjected to an air current. Light particles are blown away and the heavy gold particles (if any) remain.

There is no more gold to be won by simple methods. Gold-bearing lodes have to be mined as shown here and subjected to elaborate processes.

(Both by courtesy of the Editor of " Mine and Quarry Engineering." Australian Official Photographs.)

Chalk (or limestone) consisting mainly of calcium carbonate, is quarried as shown here. Mixed with clay and water to form a slurry it comprises the raw material from which Portland cement is made. Portland cement was invented in England in 1824. By 1939 some ten million tons a year were being produced in this country—about a tenth of the total world production.

(By courtesy of the Cement and Concrete Association.)

Salt (sodium chloride) deposited by evaporation occurring over millions of years forms layers many yards thick. Here is a salt mine in Cheshire.

(By courtesy of the Editor of " Mine and Quarry Engineering." Sport and General Press Agency Photograph.)

muscles. Here carbon is oxidised into carbon dioxide to produce energy, and blood made impure by this gas is conveyed back to our lungs, where fresh oxygen is caused to replace the impurity.

Hydrogen is gaseous and is the lightest of all the elements. Volume for volume it weighs only a sixteenth as much as oxygen and for this reason it is used as a filling for balloons and airships. It burns readily in air, combining with oxygen to form water. Though two volumes of hydrogen combine with but a single volume of oxygen to form water, in the final result the hydrogen represents only a ninth part of the total weight. Cavendish is credited with having discovered hydrogen in 1766.

A cheap way of making hydrogen is to pass steam over red-hot iron, since the iron oxidises (or rusts) and thereby reduces some of the steam to hydrogen. Hydrogen can be used to perform the reverse operation of converting iron oxide to metallic iron. In a heated retort containing iron oxide, a copious stream of hydrogen will appropriate the oxygen so as to leave metallic iron and become partially converted to steam in the process. It will take up chlorine in the same way from any compounds containing it, and the combination of hydrogen with chlorine gives hydrochloric acid gas. Dissolved in water this forms the solution familiarly known as Spirits of Salt.

Nitrogen is the relatively inactive gas serving to dilute the oxygen in our atmosphere. It is not quite so heavy as oxygen, volume for volume, but it represents about three-fourths of the total weight of air. We should rapidly become ill if the air consisted wholly of oxygen. Minerals containing nitrogen are scarce, the only ones of importance being Chili saltpetre and native nitre. Compounds of nitrogen are essential to vegetable and animal life, which explains why nitrogenous minerals are used as fertilisers. Ammonium chloride (sal-ammoniac) is another such compound; it is an invaluable by-product of the gas industry. Ammonia gas, familiar to all on account of its peculiar pungency, is a compound of hydrogen and nitrogen and it can be derived from urine. Nitric acid, which combines hydrogen, oxygen and nitrogen, is another well-known substance embodying nitrogen. Atmospheric electricity is able to combine small quantities of nitrogen with other gaseous components of air to form substances which mingle with rain water, to the great benefit of plant life. Soil bacteria associated with certain root crops are, however, the principal restorers of nitrogenous compounds to soil which has become impoverished by the growing of cereals.

Chlorine is a heavy greenish-yellow gas causing very painful effects if accidentally inhaled. It abounds in Nature as one of the constituents of sodium chloride (common salt), but it was not isolated and studied until 1774. It can be produced by heating a mixture of sulphuric acid and common salt. The gas is useful for industrial bleaching purposes and, combined with hydrogen to form hydrochloric acid, it provides an agent for "pickling" castings and forgings, i.e. for cleaning their outside surfaces in preparation for workshop operations. Hydrogen and chlorine can be mixed together in the dark (in equal volumes) and no reaction takes place. A violent explosion occurs, however, if the mixture is exposed to the bright light of the sun or to a magnesium flare. In diffused daylight the combination takes place gradually.

In all there are more than 90 elements, but much of the chemistry of everyday life can be explained with reference to the 25 commoner elements described in this chapter.

CHAPTER II

CHEMICAL COMBINATION

In their rather haphazard experiments of long ago the alchemists mixed different elements and compounds while hopefully looking to produce gold or silver, and many a valuable lesson they might have learnt was lost because they did not study chemical changes quantitatively. When Dalton and others started to keep account of the weights and measures involved, some very interesting and important facts were noticed. For instance, it was found that in any compound of elementary substances the proportions of these substances by weight was always the same. Thus, although you could *mix* hydrogen and oxygen in any proportions you liked, their *combination* to produce water is invariably in the ratio of one part hydrogen (by weight) to eight parts of oxygen. Similarly, in the production of a gas by burning carbon in air you will find that the carbon takes up oxygen in the ratio of three parts carbon to eight of oxygen. When carbon unites with hydrogen to form benzene, the proportions are twelve of carbon to one of hydrogen.

Dalton noticed another thing, which was that the same elements might combine in two or more differing proportions to form distinct and very different compounds. Thus three units by weight of carbon might combine with four units by weight of oxygen instead of with eight units, and then an entirely different gas would be formed—a poisonous and inflammable gas. Carbon and hydrogen were also observed to combine in different proportions (always quite definite and invariable proportions) to form distinct compounds. Comparing the formulæ (or recipes) for all the innumerable compounds it was possible to make, Dalton concluded that the combining weights of the elements at their lowest could be expressed in terms of the unit of hydrogen. Thus, if hydrogen appeared in amounts designated as 1, 2, 3, 4, etc., then oxygen appeared in amounts 16, 32, 48, 64, etc., and carbon in amounts 12, 24, 36, 48, etc. For sulphur the corresponding figures were 32, 64, 96, 128, etc., for iron the figures were 56, 132, 168, 224, etc. Dalton inferred from these interesting figures that all substances might be regarded as assemblages of indivisible atoms, the atom being the smallest imaginable particle of a substance that could enter into combination with any other substance. It was clear from many experiments that the atom of oxygen must be sixteen times as heavy as the atom of hydrogen, and so it could be concluded that in the formation of water each atom of oxygen must combine with two atoms of hydrogen. Similarly, in the burning of carbon it could be inferred from a knowledge of the atomic-weight ratios, that an atom of carbon combined with either one or two atoms of oxygen, the gas formed in the first instance being the poisonous and inflammable carbon monoxide and the relatively harmless inert and heavy-gas carbon dioxide in the second instance.

We regard this matter of chemical combination to-day in much the same way as Dalton taught his contemporaries to regard it. A certain amount of confusion was caused at first by the failure of experimenters to realise that the atoms of gases in the free state went about in linked pairs, but now that this fact is known and taken into account, chemical changes are easy to follow and conflicting appearances do not arise.

The smallest imaginable quantity of any compound substance is called the "molecule," so that a molecule of water (steam) consists of an atom of oxygen linked with two atoms of hydrogen. Hydrogen and oxygen exist in the free state not as separate atoms but as linked pairs of atoms, and so we say that the gas is made up of molecules too. The transformation:

$$\text{Hydrogen} + \text{Oxygen} = \text{Water}$$

is expressed symbolically as:

$$2H_2 + O_2 = 2H_2O.$$

Here the substances Hydrogen and Oxygen are represented symbolically by their initial letters H and O. By themselves, however, the letters stand for individual atoms and we are dealing with molecules. The molecule of Hydrogen consists of two atoms, and so we write it H_2. Similarly the molecule of Oxygen is O_2. When the gases unite the *proportion* is an atom of oxygen to two of hydrogen, but the *reality* is a molecule of oxygen to two of hydrogen, and that is why the formula is written in the manner given above and not as:

$$H_2 + O = H_2O.$$

Calculations in chemistry involve a knowledge of the relative weights of the atoms of the elements (more briefly called "atomic weights"), and the figures for the commoner elements should be memorised. The table below gives the atomic symbol and the atomic weight for all the substances described in Chapter I.

Iron	..	..	Fe	..	..	56
Copper	..	..	Cu	..	..	63·5
Zinc	..	..	Zn	..	..	65
Lead	..	..	Pb	..	..	207
Tin	..	..	Sn	..	..	119
Aluminium	..	..	Al	..	..	27
Nickel	..	..	Ni	..	..	59
Mercury	..	..	Hg	..	..	200
Platinum	..	..	Pt	..	..	195
Silver	..	..	Ag	..	..	108
Gold	..	..	Au	..	..	197
Carbon	..	..	C	..	..	12
Sulphur	..	..	S	..	..	32
Calcium	..	..	Ca	..	..	40
Sodium	..	..	Na	..	..	23
Silicon	..	..	Si	..	..	28·5
Potassium	..	..	K	..	..	39
Magnesium	..	..	Mg	..	..	24·5
Phosphorus	..	..	P	..	..	31
Iodine	..	..	I	..	..	127
Manganese	..	..	Mn	..	..	55
Oxygen	..	..	O	..	..	16
Nitrogen	..	..	N	..	..	14
Hydrogen	..	..	H	..	..	1
Chlorine	..	..	Cl	..	..	35·5

When gases combine with one another they do so in very simple proportions, and the volume of the compound (if also a gas) bears a very simple relation to the volumes of the original constituents. Thus, when hydrogen and chlorine unite according to the formula:

$$H_2 + Cl_2 = 2HCl,$$

one volume of hydrogen unites with one volume of chlorine to produce two volumes of hydrogen chloride (hydrochloric acid gas).

Likewise at a high temperature hydrogen and oxygen unite to form steam, and the formula given on page 166 shows that two volumes of hydrogen unite with one of oxygen to form two of steam.

That the volumetric proportions are as simple as this indicates that the volume of a gas per molecule must be the same for all gases. In other words, equal volumes of different gases, *under identical conditions as to temperature and pressure*, contain equal numbers of molecules. This is called the Law of Avogadro, after the Italian scientist who first enunciated it early in the nineteenth century.

It follows from the Law of Avogadro that the densities of two gases under identical conditions will bear the same ratio to one another as their atomic weights. Thus at any specified temperature and pressure oxygen will have a density 16 times that of hydrogen, 16/14 times that of nitrogen, 16/35·5 times that of chlorine, and so on.

The comparison here is between atomic weights, and this is correct only because all the gases mentioned are "diatomic," having molecules of two atoms each. In comparing the densities of oxygen and, say, carbon dioxide (CO_2) we must be more careful. The molecular weight of oxygen is $16 + 16 = 32$, while that of carbon is $12 + 16 + 16 = 44$. It follows that carbon dioxide is denser than oxygen in the ratio 44/32.

Pure oxygen is denser than air, as air consists mainly of nitrogen, which has a molecular weight of 28; consequently, carbon dioxide is heavier by comparison with air than the above ratio suggests. If you have a jar of carbon dioxide, you can pour this into a jar of air, just as though it were a visible fluid, and it will drive out the air. If carbon dioxide is resting in a wide shallow basin, you can cause a soap bubble filled with air to float upon it without any visible means of support. If you wish to try these experiments for yourself, you can make carbon dioxide by pouring some hydrochloric acid (HCl dissolved in water) over crushed chalk. The latter consists of calcium carbonate ($CaCO_3$) and the resulting chemical reaction is as follows:

$$CaCO_3 + 2HCl = CaCl_2 + H_2O + CO_2.$$

Observe that on each side of this equation there appear *one* atom of calcium, *one* atom of carbon, *two* atoms of chlorine, *two* atoms of hydrogen and *three* atoms of oxygen. There must always be this kind of balance because material substances can never be destroyed or augmented as the result of a chemical change. Every chemical equation you make to represent what happens in an experiment must be true to this law, which is called the Conservation of Matter. It must also show products that are true to nature on the right-hand side. You *could* equate the left-hand side to $CaH_2 + OCl_2 + CO_2$ but this would be wrong, as no such substances as CaH_2 and OCl_2 result from the chemical interaction.

Besides obtaining the CO_2 gas we want we obtain calcium chloride ($CaCl_2$) mixed with water (H_2O). We can heat the mixture in a crucible until the water is evaporated and then we shall have the well-known crystalline substance that is so valuable as an absorbent of moisture in a desiccator (see Volume II, page 169).

Glassware in great variety is made for laboratory use; samples can be seen in plate facing page 170. Apparatus for preparing CO_2 is sketched below. At A is the flask in which the chalk lumps are placed with enough water to cover them. Strong hydrochloric acid is poured a little at a time into the thistle funnel. The CO_2 from A is passed through the wash-bottle B in order to remove any HCl gas which may try to pass over into the collecting jar C. The water in B will absorb this highly soluble impurity, and it will absorb a small quantity of CO_2 as well; but enough of the latter will pass over to fill several jars. Because CO_2 is so much heavier than air, the collecting jar can be stood the right way up. The carbon

dioxide will flow into it until all the air is pushed out; then there will be an overflow of carbon dioxide. To tell when a jar is full you can hold a lighted match at its mouth; this will be extinguished when it is enveloped in CO_2 to the exclusion of atmospheric oxygen.

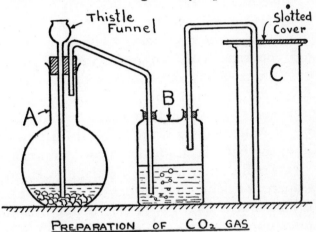

PREPARATION OF CO₂ GAS

Carbon dioxide in quantity will extinguish any fire, and in unattended electric power stations or switch-rooms there are cylinders of compressed CO_2 which are automatically opened by a thermostatic device if a fire occurs.

Carbon dioxide can also be made by simply *heating* chalk in a hot flame. The chalk residue is a valuable substance called quicklime. The reaction is as follows:

(Chalk)   (Quicklime)   (Carbon Dioxide)

$$CaCO_3 = CaO + CO_2.$$

In volcanic districts limestone rock containing much $CaCO_3$ is decomposed by heat, and the resulting CO_2 is apt to collect in gulleys and ravines making them dangerous to human and animal life. In one such place near Naples (close to the volcano Vesuvius) the gas forms a not very thick layer close to the ground. A man may safely enter this place but his dog is quickly suffocated. The local name for this place is Grotto del Cane (Dog's Grotto).

The most reliable test for the presence of CO_2 gas is to introduce a drop of lime water on a stick into a jar suspected of containing it; the clear droplet turns milky.

Lime water is made by shaking up some slaked lime in water, allowing it to settle and then pouring off the clear solution. Slaked lime is the material formed when water is poured over quicklime (CaO). The resulting reaction, which leads to the evolution of much heat, is given by the equation :

$$CaO + H_2O = Ca(OH)_2.$$

The substance $Ca(OH)_2$, commonly known as slaked lime, also bears the more precise title of calcium hydroxide.

Quicklime (CaO) is obtained on a commercial scale by heating chalk to redness in kilns of the kind shown in the pictures facing page 171. Quicklime is the essential ingredient in the making of cements, mortars and concrete. You can make mortar yourself by mixing a paste of freshly slaked lime and water with three times its own weight of sand. The sand increases the bulk and prevents shrinkage, which might otherwise cause the mass to crack and crumble. The mixture hardens by loss of water, but principally by the action of atmospheric CO_2 on the lime; the latter is gradually turned into calcium carbonate (limestone).

Hydraulic mortar (or Portland Cement) possesses the valuable property of being able to harden under water. In its preparation chalk or limestone is mixed with clay before it is burnt in kilns. The resulting quicklime is, of course, mixed with impurities, but it is these which confer such valuable properties on it.

That the human breath is impregnated with carbon dioxide you can easily prove by blowing through a straw into a tumbler containing clear lime water; your breath will make it cloudy. The effect of CO_2 on the slaked lime in lime water is to convert it back into plain water and chalky calcium carbonate, which last makes its appearance as an insoluble white precipitate. The equation for this change is :

$$Ca(OH)_2 + CO_2 = CaCO_3 + H_2O.$$

You may now wish to become acquainted with the important and easily prepared gases hydrogen and oxygen.

The apparatus for preparing hydrogen is shown in the sketch on the next page. Flask A contains shavings of zinc which have been covered with water. Strong hydrochloric acid is poured a little at a time into the thistle funnel and the resulting hydrogen is collected in the inverted jar B, as it is much lighter than air and must be permitted to displace the

Apart from common test tubes, glassware of every description finds application in the chemical laboratory.

(By courtesy of Messrs. Baird & Tatlock (London), Ltd.)

Rotary cement kiln, showing the driving machinery. A slurry consisting of ground-up chalk (or limestone) and clay, mixed with water, is fed into one end of the long tubular kiln, which is inclined slightly. It is dried and chemically transformed as it passes down the kiln, there being a fire fed with pulverised coal at the far (or lower) end.

Two rotary cement kilns producing a clinker which, with a small addition of gypsum, is ground to form Portland cement. A kiln may be 10–12 ft. in diameter and 500 ft. long. Such a kiln will weigh 1,000 tons and will rotate at a speed of about 1 r.p.m.

(Both by courtesy of the Cement and Concrete Association.)

latter *downwards*. To avoid any risk of collecting an explosive mixture of hydrogen and air you would do well to exclude all air from the jar by collecting under water as shown, also you must not start collecting until all the air has been driven out of the apparatus. The gaseous emission from your collecting tube should be allowed to pass into a small inverted test-tube until a flame test shows that you are obtaining almost pure hydrogen. The test-tube with its sample of gas is closed by the thumb and then brought close to a naked flame at a safe distance from the apparatus. On removal of the thumb the tube is presented to the flame, and if hydrogen is present there will be a slight "pop" as this is ignited and burnt to form water. You can start collecting in earnest when this test yields a positive result.

You can pour the hydrogen in an inverted gas jar *upwards* into another inverted gas jar.

A lighted taper plunged into a jar of hydrogen will be extinguished for want of oxygen, but the hydrogen itself is likely to be set aflame at the mouth of the jar where it has access to atmospheric oxygen.

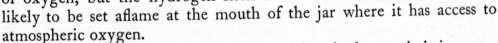

PREPARATION OF HYDROGEN

The chemical reaction in the flask A when hydrogen is being produced is given by the equation :

(Zinc)   (Hydrochloric Acid)   (Zinc Chloride)   (Hydrogen)
$$Zn + 2HCl = ZnCl_2 + H_2$$

Oxygen can be prepared by strongly heating native nitre or pyrolusite (manganese dioxide), and this was the method employed by chemists long ago. A more convenient substance, artificially prepared for the purpose, is chlorate of potash, which does not need such an intense heat. The presence of a little powdered manganese dioxide (about a fifth part of the mixture by weight) makes the liberation of oxygen much more brisk.

The flask in which the heating is done should be of good heat-resisting glass, and it is best held on its side so that any moisture condensing in the neck remains there and does not trickle back on to the heated part of the flask and crack it. The oxygen should be collected by the water-displacement method, as shown. To test for an issue of oxygen from the collecting pipe you can hold a smouldering splint of wood at its orifice.

So long as air is being driven from the apparatus nothing noteworthy occurs, but when oxygen issues forth the smouldering splint will burst into flame.

Substances having an affinity for oxygen are said to be combustible, and the process of their oxidation always produces heat. If the process is sufficiently rapid (and in the presence of pure oxygen it may be very rapid indeed), this heat causes a temperature rise we can observe by the incandescence of the oxidising material. We say that it is *burning*, and if it is volatilised by the heat there will be a *flame*. Iron, which normally

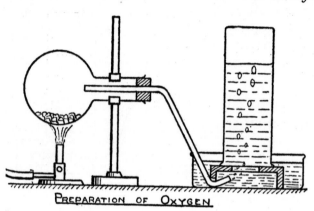

PREPARATION OF OXYGEN

oxidises very slowly by rusting, thereby giving out heat imperceptibly, will burn vigorously in pure oxygen, and the heat generated is then made plainly evident to our senses of touch and sight.

The most important combustion processes we have to deal with are those affecting carbon and hydrogen. Carbon burns completely in accordance with the equation :

$$C + O_2 = CO_2$$

and the product is carbon dioxide. The heat released by this complete combustion of carbon amounts to 8130 Centigrade Heat Units per pound of carbon consumed (see Volume II, page 131). If there is not an adequate supply of oxygen, the carbon will burn to a half-way stage, forming an inflammable and highly poisonous gas called carbon monoxide in accordance with the equation :

$$2C + O_2 = 2CO.$$

The heat produced in this way per pound of carbon is only 2450 C.H.U., but the remainder (5680 C.H.U.) can be obtained by burning the carbon monoxide gas.

Carbon monoxide is poisonous, and it is particularly dangerous because it is odourless and invisible, so escaping detection. It is given off by a coke stove when the draught of air is insufficient, and it is also produced by the engine of a motor car when the strangler is in use to limit the intake of air. That is why it is inadvisable to start any engine from cold in a closed garage.

The combustion of hydrogen in accordance with the equation

$$2H_2 + O_2 = 2H_2O$$

results in a heat release of 29,100 C.H.U. per pound of hydrogen burnt. This gas will combine with eight times its own weight of oxygen to form 9 pounds of water vapour.

Explosives such as gunpowder, dynamite, etc., etc., are of interest because they do not require atmospheric oxygen for their combustion. The process of decomposition liberates precisely the amount of oxygen needed to make the reaction self-supporting. This explains how these unpleasant substances will undergo combustion in the confined space of a bomb, or shell case or cartridge. The danger arises from the extreme rapidity with which the heat is released. Before there is any chance for it to escape the gaseous products of combustion are elevated to an enormously high temperature and pressure so that the expansive force is wellnigh irresistible. The difference between explosion and ordinary combustion is only in this matter of rapidity. Actually, pound for pound, coal possesses far more energy than gunpowder or any other explosive. The explosive is saddled with the weight of the oxygen it needs for its combustion, whereas the coal is not. Coal consists in the main of combustible carbon and hydrogen, and so do fuel oil and its derivatives. The oxygen for combustion must come from the atmosphere.

CHAPTER III

CHEMISTRY IN ENGINEERING

In all branches engineering depends for its success very largely on the correct management of chemical processes. To extract iron, copper, tin and other useful metals from their crude ores is essentially a task for the chemist, and chemists again play a large part in producing the steels, bronzes and other composite materials which have so largely superseded Nature's elementary substances in engineering construction.

Power is sometimes derived from falling water, but in the main it is obtained from engines which burn fuel, and this burning is a chemical process that repays scientific study and control, so that nowadays every large-scale consumer of fuel keeps a chemist on the premises. His main duty will be to analyse samples of fuel to be sure that they contain an agreed amount of combustible material. Also he will calculate the amount of air needed to effect complete combustion of this fuel and he will analyse samples of the gaseous combustion products (flue gases) to ascertain whether the boilers are being managed economically. If too little air is being supplied, some of the carbon in the fuel will be burned to CO instead of to CO_2, and this will entail great loss because CO is an inflammable gas that should not be allowed to pass unconsumed up the chimney. If too much air is being supplied, the combustion will be complete but the excess air will rob the fire of heat that should pass into the water of the boiler, carrying it to waste up the chimney instead. A plant engineer can tell, merely by noting the amount of CO_2 in the combustion products, whether the quantity of air going to the fire is correct in relation to the amount of fuel being burned. For his guidance every furnace will be fitted with a dial gauge to record automatically the percentage of CO_2 in the flue gases.

When dry coal is analysed it should show a carbon content of more than 80 per cent. by weight and a hydrogen content of 4 to 5 per cent. The balance will consist mainly of such incombustible materials as go to form clinker and ash in the furnace, but there may be traces of phosphorus and sulphur. The latter substance is most unwelcome, as its combustion gives rise to the gas sulphur dioxide (SO_2), which may react with water vapour to form a corrosive acid. Besides being injurious to parts of the boiler plant, this acid can be a nuisance to the entire neighbourhood. Contained in the smoke from the power-house chimney it poisons the atmosphere, making it harmful to buildings, vegetation and even human beings. Nowadays all big power stations must be equipped with apparatus for removing sulphur products from chimney gases.

In analysing coal it is important to take a dry sample because a mois sample will show an unduly high content of hydrogen and, so far from being an asset, any hydrogen in the form of water will be a liability. Combustion of moist coal results in the formation of steam, and useful heat arising from the fire will be wasted in forming this steam—more than 500 Centigrade heat units for every pound of it. Hydrogen shown in the analysis of a *dry* sample of coal will be a useful heat-producing ingredient of the coal.

To evaluate the weight of air theoretically needed for the combustion of a pound of coal, it will be best to take a numerical example.

Problem 1.—A dry sample of coal is found to give the following analysis : carbon 85 per cent., hydrogen 4 per cent., sulphur 1 per cent., ash 10 per cent. How many pounds of air will be needed for the complete combustion of one pound of this coal? What results would you expect from the analysis of the flue gases?

Assume that air is 23 parts of oxygen to 77 of nitrogen by weight (21 parts oxygen to 79 of nitrogen by volume).

When carbon burns to carbon dioxide the chemical reaction is as follows:

$$C + O_2 = CO_2.$$

The proportional weights are:

$$12 + 32 = 44.$$

Actually we have 0·85 lb. of carbon (not 12 lb.), so that the oxygen required will be $\frac{0·85}{12} \times 32 = 2·26$ lb., and the quantity of CO_2 formed will weigh $2·26 + 0·85 = 3·11$ lb.

The hydrogen combines to form water in accordance with the formula:

$$2H_2 + O_2 = 2H_2O.$$

The proportional weights are

$$4 + 32 = 36.$$

Actually we have 0·04 lb. of hydrogen (not 4 lb.), so that the oxygen needed will be $\frac{0·04}{4} \times 32 = 0·32$ lb., and the quantity of H_2O formed will weigh $0·32 + 0·04 = 0·36$ lb.

The sulphur combines to form sulphur dioxide in accordance with the formula:

$$2S + O_2 = 2SO_2.$$

The proportional weights are

$$64 + 32 = 96.$$

Actually we have 0·01 lb. of sulphur (not 64 lb.), so that the oxygen fequired will be $\frac{0·01}{64} \times 32 = 0·005$ lb., and the quantity of SO_2 rormed will weigh $0·005 + 0·01 = 0·015$ lb.

Collecting up the amounts of oxygen required, we have for the grand total :

$$2·26 + 0·32 + 0·005 = 2·585 \text{ lb.}$$

Associated with this will be $\frac{77}{23} \times 2·585$ lb. of nitrogen, i.e. 8·66 lb. of nitrogen. Consequently the weight of air needed per pound of coal is $8·66 + 2·585 = 11·245$ lb.

The total weight of flue gases will be made up as follows:

CO_2	3·11 lb.
H_2O	0·36 ,,
SO_2	0·015 ,,
N_2	8·66 ,,
Total	12·145 lb.

A sample of flue gas taken for analysis is usually cooled to a point below which any steam will have condensed, so that it is what is termed a "dry" sample. In general the SO_2 will have become associated with this condensed water vapour, so that this will be missing also. The tests made during the analysis will be for free oxygen, carbon monoxide and carbon dioxide. Whatever is left will be assumed to be nitrogen. Here we have :

CO_2	3·11 lb.
N_2	8·66 lb.
CO	nil
O_2	nil
Total	11·77 lb.

In percentages the analysis (by weight) will give:

CO_2	26·4
N_2	73·6
CO	nil
O_2	nil
Total	100·0

The relative volumes of the CO_2 and the N_2 must be computed from the formula:

$$\text{Volume} = \frac{\text{weight}}{\text{density}}.$$

The densities of CO_2 and N_2 are proportional to their molecular weights of 44 and 28, so that the relative volumes will be:

$$CO_2 \quad \quad \quad \quad \quad \frac{3\cdot11}{44} = 0\cdot071$$

$$N_2 \quad \quad \quad \quad \quad \frac{8\cdot66}{28} = 0\cdot310$$

Total ..   ..   .. $0\cdot381$

In percentages the analysis by volume will give:

CO_2	18·6
N_2	81·4
CO	nil
O_2	nil
Total	100·0

The practical method of flue-gas analysis is an analysis by *volume* and not by weight. A sample of gas is drawn into a calibrated glass vessel by allowing water to pass out. The calibrated vessel is then put into communication with a second vessel containing a caustic potash solution, and the flue-gas sample is driven over into this by readmitting water into the first vessel. The caustic potash absorbs any CO_2 present and the amount of this becomes evident when the flue-gas sample is drawn back again into its original calibrated container. As compared with its original volume V_1, the flue-gas sample now has some reduced volume V_2, and the difference $V_1 - V_2$ represents the volume of CO_2 originally present. Thus the percentage of CO_2 in the flue gas must have been:

$$\frac{V_1 - V_2}{V_1} \times 100.$$

To test for CO the process is repeated, but the absorbent chemical in the second vessel must now be acid cuprous chloride. In testing for oxygen the absorbent chemical is alkaline pyrogallol.

Since CO_2 is soluble in pure water, the liquid used for suction of the sample into the calibrated vessel, and for its repeated displacement into other vessels containing chemical reagents, should be a saturated solution of common salt. This will not take up enough CO_2 seriously to vitiate the accuracy of the test.

The presence of CO in the flue gas is an indication of incomplete combustion and is usually associated with a lack of O_2. On the other hand, an absence of CO coupled with the presence of much O_2 shows that there is an excess of air going to the fire. If the excess air is extravagant in amount, the fire will be wasting its heat very largely in heating the atmosphere. A satisfactory state of affairs is attained when the test shows no CO and only a small amount of O_2. The single indication which is most informative to the boiler operative is the percentage of CO_2, and as mentioned above, it is usual to fit a CO_2 recorder to all boilers to serve as a guide to the operative. If the indication of this instrument is too high, he admits more air to his fire; if it is too low, he restricts the supply. A figure of 15 per cent., corresponding to the supply of about 25 per cent. more air than is theoretically necessary, is usually regarded as the optimum.

Coal can be turned into a liquid fuel closely resembling the natural oils from which petrol is derived. The process is difficult and costly, however. In principle it is simple enough and the method might occur to you at once if you were to compare the chemical analysis of natural petroleum with that of coal. The principal difference between these two substances lies in the greater hydrogen content of the liquid. Whereas coal contains (by weight) only 4 to 5 per cent. of hydrogen, oil fuels contain 10 to 12 per cent. Under certain conditions of temperature and pressure the coal can be persuaded to take up more hydrogen and then it becomes converted into a liquid which may be processed just like a natural oil for high-grade petrol and other valuable spirits. The conversion of coal to oil is termed "hydrogenation," and it has been performed on a commercial scale at Billingham by the Imperial Chemical Industries. The various retorts necessary are costly and short-lived because the reactions occur under destructively high temperatures and pressures. So far, there remains little prospect of oil being produced from coal at a competitive price.

To convert coal into a gas which can be transmitted through pipes for domestic and factory consumption is much easier, and the ingenious engineer, William Murdoch, was lighting his house and office at Redruth, Cornwall, with coal gas in 1792. The first process in the gasification of coal is to distil it, that is, to heat it in an air-tight oven or retort. This process "cooks" or "cokes" it. Natural gases and vapours are driven off, and although some of these condense subsequently to form substances like tar and pitch, there will remain a gaseous mixture rich in heat which can be stored in great gasholders and distributed therefrom to an underground network of pipes supplying shops, houses and factories.

The residue from the retorts, known as coke, consists of free carbon and the valueless rubbish that makes ash or clinker in a fire. The coke itself can be gasified to a large extent, though, of course, the rubbish is bound to remain. The gas derived from coke, called "water-gas," is rather poor stuff and it is devoid of illuminating properties. However, in every modern gasworks some of this gas from coke is mixed with the main product from the retorts, and what we call town's gas is the rich distillate diluted with an agreed percentage of water-gas. The heating value of the latter (per cubic foot) is about a quarter to a fifth of the heating value of the former.

In a water-gas plant steam and air are passed through a thick bed of hot coke. The air supply is insufficient to cause the coke to burn to CO_2—it burns to the half-way stage of CO, releasing enough heat to turn water into steam and then assist the steam to combine with the coke in accordance with the relation:

$$H_2O + C = CO + H_2.$$

The net result is to form a gas consisting partly of CO and partly of H_2, but also very largely of atmospheric nitrogen. As a rule some of the carbon in the coke is converted to CO_2, which further dilutes the useful constituents CO and H_2. A typical volumetric analysis of water-gas is given below:

CO	19·8 per cent.
CO_2	14·4 ,, ,,
H_2	28·8 ,, ,,
N_2	37·0 ,, ,,
Total	100·0 per cent.

In a modern gasworks the limit placed on water-gas generation causes a glut of coke, and at one time this was difficult to dispose of. To-day, however, there are many domestic hot-water and central-heating boilers designed to consume coke, and consequently the present demand for coke enables the gas companies to sell their surplus at a good price.

Some of the materials removed from coal gas in the process of its purification are extremely valuable to other branches of industry. Most familiar to us are tar and pitch, but there are others. Furthermore, tar and pitch can themselves be treated so as to yield more valuable chemical substances. On the whole the gas enthusiasts are right when they affirm that the mere burning of coal is a deplorable waste. The gasworks processes enable nearly as much heat to be derived from the coal ultimately, yet they ensure that there are saved from the flames many precious chemical compounds that would otherwise be lost to industry.

Much coal is burned in power stations with the object of generating electricity. The heat of combustion is taken up by water which becomes converted into steam at a high pressure. This steam passes to turbines where it performs the mechanical work of turning a bladed rotor at high speed. Coupled to this rotor is an electrical generator. The electrical equivalent of 1 horse-power for an hour is produced by approximately a pound of coal burnt in the furnace. This electricity is a valuable return for the coal when it is utilised to drive electric motors, work X-ray apparatus or do other specialised forms of work. However, much electricity is merely turned back into heat again in electric cookers and radiators. It then returns only about a third of the heat that the coal released in order to produce it, as the overall efficiency of the generating process—coal to electricity—is not much above 30 per cent. even in the best and biggest power stations. Consuming electricity for heating purposes is as wasteful as consuming any other manufactured article by fire—books, for instance, or woven fabrics. It is excused only because it is convenient and because we are rich enough to permit ourselves some extravagance. In times when fuel or electric plant is in short-supply, the enormity of using electricity for heating purposes becomes glaringly apparent, and we are asked not to do it.

Can electricity be obtained from chemical processes more directly than by evolving heat chemically, turning this heat into mechanical work as far as possible and then turning the work into electricity? So roundabout a process seems hardly necessary. It is known to be very wasteful and, requiring so much complicated machinery, it is expensive on other counts. Alas, the alternatives are not promising. From our little torch batteries we obtain electricity by direct chemical action, but not any more cheaply. The fuel used in a torch battery is metallic zinc, and this is dearer in first cost than coal. Per kilowatt hour generated electricity from chemical batteries costs several shillings instead of a penny or two, so that there is a loss and not a saving. The great convenience of a generator that can be pocketed makes a battery tolerable in small sizes, but nobody could afford to light his house or cook his dinner by using electricity from batteries of chemical cells.

ELECTRO-CHEMISTRY

Before considering the production of electricity by chemical means we ought to notice the simpler chemical effects that may result from a flow of electricity. An experiment of particular interest in this connection is the electrolysis of water. When it is made conducting by the addition of a small quantity of acid, water can be electrolysed, or resolved into its constituent gases, oxygen and hydrogen, by the passage through it of a current of electricity. Bare wires or plates connected to the poles of a battery are inserted in a bowl of the slightly acid water, as shown in the accompanying sketch, and instantly bubbles of gas are seen to arise therefrom. The bubbles are seen to be more numerous at the negative electrode, and if gas jars are inverted over the two electrodes the water will be displaced twice as fast from one as from the other, showing that twice as much gas is formed at the negative electrode as at the positive electrode. Tests will show that the most freely formed gas is hydrogen, whereas the gas formed at the slower rate is oxygen. To every volume of the latter there are two of the former, as might be expected from the formula:

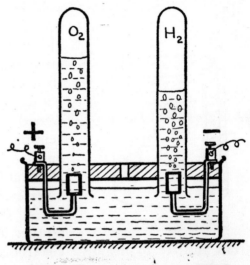

ELECTROLYSIS OF WATER

$$2H_2 + O_2 = 2H_2O,$$

which shows that a molecule of oxygen combines with two molecules of hydrogen to form two molecules of water. It is in keeping with Avogadro's Law that the combining volumes of the gases should also be as 1 to 2.

An electric current will resolve other substances into their separate constituents or at any rate effect chemical transformation. Advantage is taken of this fact in the electro-plating industry. Thus silver nitrate can be resolved by electricity into metallic silver and an acid radicle. The silver will be deposited as a film on the negative electrode of the apparatus, and the acid radicle will appropriate to itself a new atom of silver from the positive electrode if this be made of silver. To silver-plate an article it is only necessary to make it the negative electrode in an electrolytic cell, as shown in the accompanying sketch. The flow of current through the electrolyte (a solution of silver nitrate) resolves the molecules of the silver nitrate ($AgNO_3$) into separate parts which are called "ions." The ions of silver travel to the right, bearing positive electric charges, whereas the ions of NO_3 travel to the left bearing negative charges.

An electrolyte becomes a conductor of electricity by virtue of this splitting up or ionisation of its molecules. The ions are like trains of

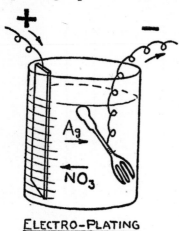

ELECTRO-PLATING

vehicles and they carry electric charges in opposite directions across the gap between the electrodes. The silver ions adhere to the negative electrode when they have parted with their charges, and this is the effect desired, because by degrees the electrode becomes smoothly coated with metallic silver and susceptible to a high polish. The NO_3 ions also part with their charges, but they cannot afterwards exist by themselves and so they enter into combination with the metal comprising the positive electrode to re-form the nitrate. The process in effect transfers silver from positive to negative electrode. The electrolyte lasts indefinitely, but the positive electrode needs renewing from time to time as it is eaten away.

The quantity of silver deposited by electrolytic action is directly proportional to the number of coulombs of electricity expended. For one coulomb (an ampere for a second) we get a deposition of 0·001118 gram. Of any other metal the coulomb will deposit the same number of atoms, or half as many atoms, depending on what is called the "valency" of the metal. A metal which, like silver, has a valency of 1 will be deposited to the same extent, and the weight deposited per coulomb will be

$\frac{m}{s} \times$ 0·001118 gram, where m and s are the atomic weights of the metal

in question and silver respectively. A metal like copper, which has a valency of 2, will be deposited to only half the extent, and the weight

deposited per coulomb will therefore be only $\frac{m}{2s} \times$ 0·001118 gram. The

valency of a metal is the number of atoms of hydrogen it will replace per atom of itself in a chemical transformation. Thus when copper is attacked by sulphuric acid (H_2SO_4), the chemical formed is $CuSO_4$, or copper sulphate, in which an atom of copper clearly replaces two of hydrogen.

If, then, we do copper-plating, using a solution of copper sulphate for our electrolyte, we shall obtain a deposit of $\dfrac{63\cdot5}{2\times108}\times0\cdot001118$ gram per coulomb, because the atomic weight of copper is $63\cdot5$ and its valency is 2. The atomic weight of a substance divided by its valency is called its *chemical equivalent*. Below is given a table of valencies and chemical equivalents for the metals most commonly deposited by electrolysis.

Metal			Atomic Weight	Valency	Chemical Equivalent
Gold	..	..	..	197·0	3	65·7
Silver	..	..	..	108·0	1	108·0
Copper	..	..	..	63·5	2	31·7
Zinc	..	..	..	65·0	2	32·5
Nickel	..	..	..	59·0	2	29·5
Chromium	..	..	..	52·4	3	17·5
Cadmium	..	..	..	111·6	2	55·8

Several of the substances listed above have more than one valency. Copper, for instance, though it usually stands for two atoms of hydrogen, is monovalent in some reactions. Chromium, stated to be trivalent above, is tetravalent (showing a valency of 4) in certain cases. However, in the electro-deposition processes ordinarily used the valencies are as given. To find the weight of any substance deposited by a coulomb of electricity it is only necessary to multiply the chemical equivalent of that substance by the quotient of $0\cdot001118\div108$, that is, by $0\cdot000010352$.

Problem 2.—A certain article is coated with silver weighing x grams in 10 hours by a current of 25 amperes. How long will it take to give another article a coating of nickel weighing $2x$ grams if the current is 40 amperes?

Since the weight deposited per coulomb is proportional to the chemical equivalent, we have:

$$\frac{\text{Deposit of nickel per coulomb}}{\text{Deposit of silver per coulomb}}=\frac{29\cdot5}{108}.$$

$$\therefore \quad \frac{\text{Coulombs needed for nickel deposit}}{\text{Coulombs needed for silver deposit}} = 2 \times \frac{108}{29\cdot5}$$

$$= 7\cdot45.$$

Hours needed for nickel deposit

$$= \frac{7\cdot45 \times 25 \times 10}{40} = 46.$$

Problem 3.—How much copper will be deposited in 24 hours by a current of 5 amperes?

Coulombs of electricity expended $= 5 \times 3600 \times 24$.

Copper deposit per coulomb $= \frac{31\cdot7}{108} \times 0\cdot001118$

$$\therefore \qquad \text{Total deposit} = \frac{5 \times 3600 \times 24 \times 31\cdot7 \times 0\cdot001118}{108}$$

$$= 141 \text{ grams.}$$

It is time now to discuss the production of electric currents by chemical means. This phenomenon is the reverse of the one already discussed in which currents are used to produce chemical effects.

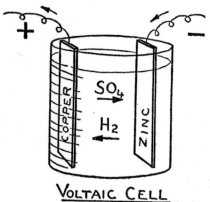

VOLTAIC CELL

In the simple cell described in Volume I on page 155, zinc and copper plates stand in dilute sulphuric acid. When the plates are joined a current flows from the copper (positive) plate to the zinc (negative) plate. This current is maintained as shown in the accompanying sketch by the ionisation of the acid. The ions of hydrogen, carrying positive charges, travel to the copper plate, where bubbles of this gas gradually accumulate. The SO_4 ions travel to the zinc plate where, after giving up negative charges, they combine with the zinc to form zinc sulphate ($ZnSO_4$). Gradually the acid loses its strength and gradually the zinc plate is corroded into a useless sulphate.

This simple cell will provide a limited current, but its internal resistance becomes rapidly greater if hydrogen bubbles are allowed to gather on the copper plate. This leads to a deterioration of performance, the terminal voltage of the cell gradually falling if an attempt be made to keep the current output constant.

All chemical cells are liable to a progressive enfeeblement as a result of hydrogen formation at the positive electrode, and this phenomenon is termed polarisation. Cells required to perform useful work are provided with some depolarising agent which absorbs the hydrogen and so prevents the current-inhibiting action of gaseous bubbles around the positive electrode.

A very successful and widely used chemical cell is the Leclanché, which has a zinc rod for the negative electrode and a carbon rod for the positive electrode. The electrolyte is a solution of ammonium chloride or sal-ammoniac (NH_4Cl). The molecules of ammonium chloride are ionised, so that chlorine ions travel towards the zinc while NH_4 ions travel towards the carbon. After giving up negative charges the chlorine ions become associated with the zinc to form zinc chloride ($ZnCl_2$). The NH_4 ions give up positive charges to the carbon electrode and then become resolved into ammonia (NH_3) and hydrogen (H). The ammonia is dissolved by the electrolyte, and the hydrogen would cause the old trouble of polarisation but for the fact that the carbon electrode is contained in a porous pot filled with crushed carbon and manganese dioxide. The latter chemical (MnO_2) behaves as a depolariser in accordance with the reaction

$$2MnO_2 + H_2 = Mn_2O_3 + H_2O.$$

Very gradually the contents of the porous pot become modified in composition but, meanwhile, the hydrogen is oxidised into water, which effectively disposes of it. The depolarising action is rather sluggish, so that after the cell has been in use for a minute or two it needs a period of rest. In continuous service it evolves hydrogen rather faster than the manganese dioxide can dispose of it. The cell is particularly useful for such intermittent duties as ringing electric bells, operating house telephones, etc., and the open-circuit voltage is $1\cdot4$. The familiar "dry" battery is an assemblage of specially constructed Leclanché cells. The negative electrode of each cell is a cylindrical zinc container partially filled with a pasty electrolyte in which the active ingredient is sal-ammoniac. The carbon rod is contained in a cloth bag packed with the depolarising mixture already described, and the whole is sealed with pitch. Developed primarily for intermittent use in "flash" lamps, dry batteries will nevertheless give a steady continuous output if this is kept well below the limit attainable in intermittent service.

The most common form of electric battery is the accumulator in which the chemical changes occurring during discharge can be reversed by an operation that seems like putting electricity back into the cells to replace what has been drawn out. Cells that are rendered active by "charging" in this way are often termed "secondary" cells to distinguish them from cells which function directly they are put together; the latter are termed primary cells, and the Leclanché is the most useful practical example.

Secondary cells of the lead-acid type give a terminal voltage of 2, and assemblages of such cells are commonly referred to as storage batteries. Although electricity is supplied to them during the "charging" process, they do not really store electricity. The energy supplied in the form of electricity merely modifies chemical substances within the battery. In the process of discharge the chemicals revert to their original condition and electricity is given out while the changes are in progress.

In its most widely used form a secondary cell has electrodes, or plates of lead or lead compounds, and the electrolyte is dilute sulphuric acid. In the charged or active state the cell has a positive plate consisting mainly of lead peroxide (PbO_2) and a negative plate of spongy lead

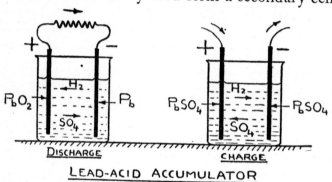

DISCHARGE   CHARGE

LEAD-ACID ACCUMULATOR

(Pb). During discharge the acid is ionised, as shown in the accompanying sketch. At the negative plate the reaction is:

$$Pb + SO_4 = PbSO_4,$$

so that the spongy lead is converted into lead sulphate.

At the positive plate the reaction is:

$$PbO_2 + H_2 + H_2SO_4 = PbSO_4 + 2H_2O,$$

so that the lead peroxide also turns into lead sulphate. Meanwhile, acid is used up and water is formed in its place, so that tests with a hydrometer will show that the specific gravity of the electrolyte gradually decreases during discharge.

When the cell is fully run down (discharged) a current must be driven through it in the reverse direction to restore it to its original condition. The acid is ionised again but, of course, the ions now travel in directions opposite to those previously taken, as shown in the accompanying sketch.

At the negative plate the reaction is:

$$PbSO_4 + H_2 = Pb + H_2SO_4.$$

At the positive plate the reaction is:

$$PbSO_4 + 2H_2O + SO_4 = PbO_2 + 2H_2SO_4.$$

Thus the plates are converted back into their original states and so is the electrolyte, water disappearing in the process and acid reappearing. The battery can be regarded as fully charged when tests with a hydrometer show that the electrolyte in the various cells has regained its original specific gravity.

Recent research has shown that the chemical reactions in a lead-acid accumulator may be rather more complex than those described above, leading to the formation of some Pb_3O_7 on the positive plate, but this is not a matter that can be discussed further in these pages.

Chemistry is, of course, interesting to others besides engineers, but it is not possible in a book of this scope to mention its place in all the arts and industries. The chemistry of vital processes in vegetables and animals is briefly discussed on pages 241 and 242.

CHAPTER IV

THE CONSTITUTION OF MATTER

The notion that all matter consists of minute particles united more or less firmly by a cohesive force is very ancient and the researches of John Dalton greatly strengthened the arguments for this theory. The smallest particle of an element is called an atom, and an atom cannot be subdivided without changing its substance into something else. In all the ordinary chemical and thermal transformations of everyday life atoms preserve their individuality, though they may enter into association with other atoms to form compound substances. Thus an atom of oxygen unites with two atoms of hydrogen to form water. A group of atoms bonded together is termed a molecule, and in general the smallest imaginable amount of any substance is the molecule. Even in elementary substances the atoms may be grouped together to form molecules. We know that in such gases as oxygen, hydrogen, chlorine and nitrogen the atoms are paired. In a compound gas such as steam and carbon dioxide, the molecule consists of three atoms and in many gases the molecules consist of four or more atoms.

A gas is a substance in which the cohesive force between molecules or atoms has been nullified by heat. If the temperature of any gas be reduced sufficiently, it will become a liquid. The molecules in a liquid are under the influence of a cohesive force, but this is not sufficient to prevent relative movement among them. They slide easily over one another. Reduction in the temperature of a liquid causes it to become a solid. The molecules are now bound together by so great a force that in the aggregate they form a more or less rigid body.

Heat is regarded nowadays as molecular motion. The effect of warming a solid body is to communicate to its molecules a restlessness derived from the molecules of another and still warmer body. When this restlessness surpasses a certain limit the molecules break asunder and move freely among themselves, causing the body to assume the liquid state. Elevating the temperature still further is tantamount to accelerating the molecular motions. There will now be such a jostling and bumping between them that at the surface of the liquid many molecules will be buffeted clear of their fellows into space. This explains the phenomenon of vaporisation. A proportion of the escaping molecules will collide with air molecules and be deflected back into the liquid again, but with increasing temperature the number that get clear away will increase.

At boiling-point the inter-molecular cohesive force and the restraining action of the superincumbent atmosphere are both finally overcome and the molecules rush asunder to fill the largest space they possibly can. In any receptacle containing a gas far removed from its temperature of liquefaction, there will be millions of molecules dashing hither and thither at high speeds. You can imagine them to be like tiny balls, and their behaviour suggests that in comparison with the journeys they make their diameter is negligibly small. When molecule collides with molecule the two rebound without there being any loss of energy on the whole, just as though they were perfectly elastic. When a molecule hits the wall of the containing vessel it is deflected with its velocity unimpaired, and the angle of reflection is equal to the angle of incidence.

The pressure that a gas exerts on the inside walls of its container is due entirely to the bombardment of millions upon millions of tiny molecules. These bombardments become more frequent if any given quantity of gas be confined in a diminishing space—a cylinder with a moving piston, for instance—and this explains why a rise in pressure follows a decrease in volume. Heating the gas elevates its temperature, but this is the same thing as saying that it increases molecular motion. Bouncing to and fro at a great speed, the molecules travel even faster when heat is supplied to the gas, heat being in fact merely an increase in molecular motion. If the gas is contained in the same space while being heated, then the pressure on the container walls is bound to rise because molecular bombardments will become more numerous and more energetic.

This molecular theory of the nature of a gas may seem far-fetched, but when it is tested mathematically it gives a very satisfying explanation of the behaviour of a gas. For instance, it shows why a gas must obey the laws of Boyle and Charles (see Volume II, pages 142 and 145).

In unit volume of gas at a given pressure P and temperature T we will assume that there are N molecules each of mass m. The molecules will be moving in all directions with widely differing velocities, but we will consider the velocity of a particular molecule to be v.

Imagine that the gas is contained in a cubical box so that the gas pressure on the walls of this box will be in the three directions perpendicular to them. Let the component velocities of our selected molecule in these directions be v_x, v_y and v_z. The relation between these three velocities and v will be expressed by the relation:

$$v^2 = v_x^2 + v_y^2 + v_z^2$$

this following from two applications of the theorem of Pythagoras (see page 88).

When the molecule strikes a wall of the box it contributes a blow the magnitude of which depends solely on the component velocity perpendicular to that wall. Thus if v_x is the velocity in question, the blow will be proportional to v_x and will be quite unaffected by v_y or v_z. Actually the molecule will have the perpendicular component v_x of its velocity reversed by the impact, so that the change of its momentum in the direction perpendicular to the wall of the box will be $2mv_x$. In the y and z directions there will be no change of momentum. The impulse given to the wall of the box is $2mv_x$ and the pressure on any area s of this wall will be the result of a large number of collisions of this kind.

To evaluate the magnitude of this pressure we must now apply the law of averages. To begin with we must allow that owing to the vast number of molecules, one cubic inch of the gas will be equivalent in a statistical sense to any other cubic inch. If n is the number of molecules having the particular velocity v_x in one cubic inch, then in any other cubic inch the number of molecules having the velocity v_x will also be n. Moreover, in any fractional part q of a cubic inch we can assume that there will be qn molecules having this velocity v_x. The law of averages again obliges us to assume that of n or qn molecules having the velocity v_x, one half will be moving towards the wall of the box and the other half will be moving away from it. Consider now an area s of the wall of the box and imagine what is happening in the space in front of this area to a distance of d away from it. The volume of space under consideration is sd. In this volume there will be $\frac{1}{2}nsd$ molecules moving towards the wall with a particular velocity v_x.

A molecule distant d from the wall and having the velocity v_x perpendicular to it would strike the wall in a time $t = d/v_x$. Consequently the number of blows delivered to the wall in time t by molecules of the velocity group in question must be equal to the number of molecules originally lying within a distance of d from the wall, namely $\frac{1}{2}nsd$.

The combined impulse from all these blows will be (in time t):

$$\tfrac{1}{2}nsd \times 2mv_x.$$

In unit time the impulse is:

$$\tfrac{1}{2}ns\frac{d}{t} \times 2mv_x,$$

and since $v_x = \dfrac{d}{t}$, this simplifies to $nsmv_x^2$ or nmv_x^2 per unit of area.

Now, impulse divided by time is a measure of force (see Volume II, page 22) and therefore nmv_x^2 is the force or pressure exerted on unit area of the wall of our box by molecular bombardment. So far, however, we have considered only one particular group of molecules. The total pressure is the sum of the pressures exerted by all the particular groups, so that we can write it:

$$P = \Sigma nmv_x^2 = m\,\Sigma nv_x^2$$

where Σ is the sign of summation. At this stage we must take into account the fact that v_x differs from molecule to molecule so that, although many will have the same v_x, we could select, if we wanted to, molecules having widely differing values of v_x. Let the average v_x for all the molecules be $_av_x$. Then:

$$\Sigma nv_x^2 = N\,_av_x^2$$

where, as before, N is the *total* number of molecules per unit of volume.

We have then, finally,

$$P = mN\,_av_x^2.$$

The law of averages obliges us to suppose that both $_av_y$ and $_av_z$ will both be equal to $_av_x$. If therefore we put v_a^2 for the average square resultant velocity of the molecules, we obtain the relation

$$v_a^2 = {}_av_x^2 + {}_av_y^2 + {}_av_z^2 = 3\,_av_x^2.$$

Here v_a is not the average molecular velocity but the velocity that a molecule would have to have in order to possess the average amount of kinetic energy. Kinetic energy, it will be remembered, is equal to $\frac{1}{2}$ mass $\times$ (velocity)^2. Thus v_a is the "root mean square" velocity.

Since

$$P = m\,N\,_av_x^2$$

and

$$_av_x^2 = \tfrac{1}{3}v_a^2$$

we can put

$$P = \tfrac{1}{3}m\,N\,v_a^2.$$

Now mN is the mass of unit volume of gas (i.e. the density). If V is the volume of unit mass, we have:

$$mN = \frac{1}{V}.$$

Hence

$$P = \frac{v_a{}^2}{3V}$$

or

$$PV = \tfrac{1}{3}v_a{}^2.$$

This is a statement of Boyle's Law, because if $v_a{}^2$ is dependent solely on the temperature, it follows that for any given fixed temperature PV = constant. If it is a fact that absolute temperature T is simply a measure of the average molecular kinetic energy, then it follows that we can write:

$$PV = RT$$

where R is some constant. This well-known relation was fully discussed in Volume II, on page 148, and it is true of gases which obey Charles's Law as well as Boyle's Law.

Experimental evidence has satisfied physicists that the above description of a gas is approximately correct. With some minor corrections to allow for the finite size of molecules and other details, the kinetic theory of gases explains everything the scientists wish to know. One simple thing it can explain to the engineer is why gas imprisoned by a piston in a cylinder has its pressure increased when the piston is pushed in. A molecule approaching the piston with a velocity of v_x will rebound with a velocity of v_x if the piston is at rest, but if the piston has a velocity of v, then the molecule will rebound with a velocity of $v_x + 2v$, as its velocity relative to the piston after impact must be the same as its velocity relative to the piston before impact (see Volume II, page 25). Obviously the moving piston is increasing the mean velocity of the molecules. This causes both the pressure and the temperature to rise.

An outwardly moving piston reverses these tendencies, minimising the mean velocity of the molecules and so lowering both temperature and pressure.

Modern physical research has dispelled the belief that atoms and molecules could be small elastic spheres, though it is true to say that in some respects they behave as such. The atom is now known to be a complicated and far from solid structure. If it could be magnified to have a diameter equal to the width of this page, it would still be largely invisible because in the main it is just emptiness. There is a massive centre called the nucleus, which carries a charge of positive electricity, and revolving round this at some distance are particles of almost negligible size and mass called electrons, each of which carries the smallest imaginable negative charge of electricity. The particular chemical element represented depends on the constitution of the nucleus, and for different elements the nucleus carries different electric charges. The number of electrons is always just sufficient to be the negative equivalent of the positive nuclear charge. Thus the hydrogen atom has only one electron to balance the lowest imaginable positive nuclear charge. Helium atoms have 2 electrons, carbon atoms 6, oxygen atoms 8, iron atoms 26 and so on, up to Uranium atoms 92. The chemists have now succeeded in making new elements called Neptunium and Plutonium, in which the atoms have 93 and 94 electrons respectively.

The atomic nucleus is not indivisible, but for many years it resisted the chemist's attempts to subdivide it. In radio-active elements it is breaking up spontaneously with effects that are important to mankind. Scientists have long hoped to be able to split up atoms artificially, and this they are now able to do in certain cases. The nucleus of most atoms is made up of positively charged particles called protons and uncharged particles called neutrons. The removal of charged particles from an atomic nucleus always causes a change of element. Thus in course of time atoms of radium become transformed stage by stage into atoms of lead. From what has now been said Nature would seem to be simplicity itself, since matter in all its myriad forms can be regarded as different arrangements of three kinds of elementary particles—protons, neutrons and electrons. (Four kinds if we include positive electrons or "positrons." See page 206.)

The nucleus of an atom is knit together by enormously powerful cohesive forces between its constituent particles. Opposed to this attraction is the mutual repulsion between the positive charges on the protons. In certain circumstances the cohesion force can be overcome and then the electrical force is effective in shooting off particles.

The electrons are obliged by the mutual attraction between positive and negative electricity to circle endlessly round the nucleus in the same way that the planets are obliged by gravitation to circle round the sun. Their orbits define the ultimate size of the atom, so that when atoms are packed closely together (in a piece of iron, say) it does not mean that they can form a truly solid body. The massiveness of the iron is attributable to the atomic nuclei, but its extension is attributable to the large amount of empty space between each nucleus and its neighbours. Solid though the iron appears to be to us, it is really quite open in structure, and certain kinds of radiation will pass through it quite easily.

The loss of nuclear particles by an atom is a phenomenon we still regard as rare and remarkable because it happens naturally to only a very limited extent on our earth, and it cannot easily be made to happen artificially. The loss of electrons is, however, a very common occurrence. An electrically charged block of metal is one in which some of the atoms have an excess or a deficit of electrons. This is a matter which soon remedies itself by a flow of current. Electrical manifestations can be explained as a redistribution of electrons to restore to normality atoms which have in some way or another lost their electrical neutrality through losing or gaining electrons.

A material is never transmuted into another by loss or gain of peripheral electrons alone, but when it loses or gains protons, nuclear electrons or positrons the element is changed. Loss of a nuclear electron corresponds to the conversion of a nuclear neutron into a proton, and loss of a positron corresponds to the conversion of a proton into a neutron. What decides the chemical nature of a substance is simply the positive nuclear charge; this is called the "atomic number" of the substance. The atomic number is equalled by the number of free electrons circling round the nucleus of an electrically neutral atom.

Radio-activity takes a number of forms. Natural radio-active substances send out two kinds of particles, namely alpha particles and beta particles, and also an electro-magnetic wave radiation called gamma radiation. An alpha particle is the same as a helium atom minus its peripheral electrons. It is a nucleus consisting of two protons and two neutrons. In certain circumstances it may be without one of its positive charges so as to consist of three neutrons and a proton. A beta particle is simply a nuclear electron that has been given a particularly high velocity. Gamma rays are caused by the violent vibrations of an atomic nucleus; these are set up when its stability is affected by the loss or gain of a particle. The gamma ray is akin to light- or radio-waves or X-rays, the wavelength giving it a particularly close resemblance to the last mentioned.

An atom stripped of one or more of its external electrons is called an ion; it is a positively charged particle. Alpha and beta particles may ionise the air in the neighbourhood of any naturally or artificially radio-active substance; they do this by colliding with electrically neutral atoms and disrupting them. An ionised gas is electrically conducting, so that a charged gold-leaf electroscope (see Volume II, page 330) in the presence of radio-active substances is soon discharged by leakage through ionised air. Radio-activity is very injurious to human beings, but this simple test with a gold-leaf electroscope will show whether in any particular vicinity there are dangerous radiations. The efficacy of the shields erected round radio-active substances can be tested with the electroscope, and when an atomic bomb has contaminated a whole district with artificially induced radio-activity, the intensity of this can be gauged with the same instrument.

Natural radio-activity goes on for a long time—thousands of years maybe—but, fortunately for us, artificially induced radio-activity is usually short-lived. Seconds, minutes or hours usually suffice to bring it to an end, though occasionally some weeks, months or even years may elapse before the manifestation becomes inappreciable.

The intensity of the radiations from a radio-active material decreases in accordance with a simple law. Thus in 1690 years half the atoms in a piece of pure radium become converted into atoms of lead; thereafter the radium is only half as radio-active as before. In another 1690 years its radio-activity is halved again, and for the same reason. In another 1690 years there is another halving, and so on and so on. This period of 1690 years is called the "half life" of radium. Other radio-active substances have other half lives, and for artificially induced radio-activity the half life is usually very brief—a matter of seconds, minutes, hours or days.

How was radio-activity ever occasioned in the first place? It is believed that the large, heavy, unstable atoms of substances like Uranium and Radium were created under chaotic conditions of enormous heat and pressure at the time of the Creation. They probably represented natural groupings of particles under the conditions then obtaining, but under the conditions with which we are more familiar they cannot hold together permanently and so they are decaying. In course of time the radio-active materials have largely disappeared by transmutation into substances having stable atoms, but a residue remains.

Owing to their rarity the radio-active substances remained undiscovered until comparatively recently. Henri Becquerel, a French scientist, discovered the radio-activity of Uranium in 1896, shortly after the German, Röntgen, had given X-rays to the world (see Volume I, page 206). Radio-activity is made apparent in several ways, but its discovery was due to two effects. Firstly it causes certain substances to exhibit a kind of phosphorescent light when it strikes them—the phenomenon of fluorescence. Secondly it can penetrate the protective wrappings of photographic films and plates, causing the contents to be spoiled as effectively as though light had been permitted to enter.

The work of Becquerel was followed by the researches of the Curies, and credit is usually given to Madame Curie for isolating and thus discovering radium. It is now known that there are many radio-active elements, and that any given element may become transformed by radio-activity into others on its way to stability and quiescence. Scientists have actually succeeded in creating new radio-active elements that are not known in Nature. Neptunium and Plutonium are two of these.

The subject of Atomic Physics is dealt with in the next chapter. To close the present chapter reference should be made to the connection between atomic structure and spectrum analysis.

Heat, as explained in the beginning of this chapter, increases molecular restlessness. When molecules are sufficiently agitated to collide violently among themselves, they may break up into atoms and the atoms may regroup to form new chemical compounds. This is ordinary chemical transformation and heat is often needed to initiate it. A consequence of the violent occurrences occasioned by heat and chemical transformation may be to give sufficiently hard knocks to individual atoms to set them vibrating. A disturbance affecting the outermost electrons occasions vibrations of the kind that generate light-waves, and a disturbance powerful enough to disturb the inner electrons sets up the radiation we call X-rays. Gamma rays result from disturbances within the nucleus and cannot be produced by ordinary thermal or chemical means.

Atoms have their own characteristic modes of vibration, just as pendulums of different lengths have theirs (see the formula on page 39), and chemists can tell one chemical element from another merely by analysing the light emitted by heated (vibrating) atoms. The characteristic light of sodium atoms, for instance, is yellow, and if this yellow light is analysed by a prism, it will be found to consist almost entirely of waves of but one wavelength. For this reason it is called "monochromatic" light. No other element gives just this result, and consequently the presence of sodium can be detected in any light-producing transformation by the simple expedient of spectrum analysis.

For examining spectra a spectroscope is needed. This may be a simple instrument or one of great complexity, depending on the work it is designed to do. In its simplest form it consists of the components sketched on the next page. A light source A is placed opposite a narrow (and usually adjustable) slit B in a tube called the collimator. A convex lens C, having its principal focus coincident with the slit, reduces the light emanating from the latter to a parallel beam. A prism D splits the light into its component colours, giving rise to a spectrum that can be studied through the telescope F. The nature of this spectrum reveals to the experienced observer the composition of the material or materials whose luminosity when heated in a vaporised condition constitutes the light source. As mentioned above, the spectrum for sodium consists of a single band of yellowish hue. The light source will consist of a methylated-spirit lamp having its wick salted with a little common salt (sodium chloride). Other substances provide a characteristic light when they or their salts are volatilised and burnt in the non-luminous flame of a spirit-lamp or Bunsen burner. The light from incandescent solid bodies—e.g. the filaments of electric lamps, the solid carbon particles in the luminous flames of candles and paraffin lamps—is not indicative of the material of the light source, because it is ordinary white or near-white light having

a continuous spectrum ranging through red, orange, yellow, green and blue to violet. The incandescent central core of the sun emits a white light that, by it-self, could not inform us

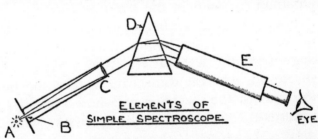

ELEMENTS OF
SIMPLE SPECTROSCOPE.

of anything. However, examination of the solar spectrum shows some gaps. Thus there are dark bands where there should be bars of light corresponding to the hydrogen spectrum. This does not signify the absence of hydrogen from the sun. On the contrary, it proves that there is an abundance of hydrogen in the sun's atmosphere. A relatively cool gas is a powerful absorber of radiation of precisely those wavelengths the same gas emits when very hot, and the conspicuous absence of colour in the hydrogen regions of the solar spectrum is conclusive proof that relatively cool hydrogen is absorbing radiation emitted by the white-hot solar core in the background. Other dark lines in the solar spectrum are characteristic of oxygen; they are caused by absorption in our own atmosphere. Vapours of sodium, calcium and iron in the sun's atmosphere are made clearly evident by still further dark lines; the presence of these cannot be accounted for in any other way. The phenomenon of absorption can be demonstrated quite easily in the laboratory by means of the simple spectroscope. Firstly there must be set up the apparatus for examining the spectrum of, say, sodium. The light source will be the spirit-lamp

with the salted wick, which was mentioned on page 197. When the
characteristic greenish-yellow band is perceived through the telescope,
a second light source is moved into position behind the first. This second
light source must be one which emits an intensely bright white light
having a continuous spectrum; an electric arc lamp will serve admirably.
When this second light is switched on the observer will see only darkness
where formerly he saw the greenish-yellow band characteristic of
sodium. Except for this notable blank, the spectrum of the second light
source will be continuous and complete. Thus the experiment shows the
spectrum of sodium "in reverse" and the solar spectrum is like this; it
shows the spectra of hydrogen, oxygen, sodium, calcium, iron and other
substances in reverse. To the astronomer this seems a conclusive proof
that vapours of these substances lie between us and the solar background,
mainly in the vicinity of the sun itself. The phenomenon of selective
absorption has enabled the astronomer to detect the presence of many
common elements in the remotest stars.

Spectrum analysis has served also to reveal the velocity of approach
or recess of celestial bodies. Due to the Doppler effect (see Volume II,
page 107) the light-waves from a rapidly approaching body will be
shortened, whereas those from a receding body will be lengthened. In
the one case the spectrum will show a bodily shift (small but perceptible)
towards the violet end of the spectrum, whereas in the other case it will
show a shift towards the red end.

Very fine instruments and excellent laboratory technique are needed
to show the Doppler effect and deduce trustworthy figures from indications of its occurrence. Nevertheless, careful observation has shown
that the bright star Sirius must be travelling away from our earth at a
speed of 30 miles a second. Similar observations have revealed a difference between the spectra of the sun at opposite ends of a particular
diameter—a difference that can be accounted for by assuming that on
one side the sun is approaching us and on the other side receding from
us—that, in other words, it is revolving about an axis. The same ingenious technique has revealed the composition of the rings encircling the
planet Saturn. They are now known to consist of myriads of small solid
bodies (meteorites) revolving round the main mass of the planet. Their
speed can be inferred from spectroscopic analysis and it is found to
agree with a prediction of what it must be to accord with the gravitational hypothesis.

Yet another triumph of spectroscopic analysis is its resolution of the
doubt about the composition of nebulæ too far away to be properly

studied by telescope. Many of the closer nebulæ can be distinguished as groups of stars or as masses of gas, but the more remote ones are beyond the ability of a telescope to resolve. However, their spectra show at once whether they are gaseous or in the form of stellar aggregations. Starlight always yields the almost continuous spectrum characteristic of an incandescent solid or liquid, but some nebulæ show the discontinuous spectra characteristic of glowing gases and that is how they can be distinguished.

CHAPTER V

ATOMIC ENERGY

When a molecule of water is formed by the union of an atom of oxygen with two atoms of hydrogen there is a great release of the energy we call heat. The same applies when an atom of carbon combines with two atoms of oxygen. We know now from the molecular theory of matter that the energy which appears is of a mechanical nature, taking the form of increased molecular motion. The molecules dash about faster than they did before, and collisions between them are violent enough to set them vibrating. These vibrations within the molecular structure give rise to the electro-magnetic radiations we call light and radiant heat. Unfortunately for mankind the molecules of most substances found in Nature are like the molecules which result from the above-mentioned chemical changes. Energy was released at the time of their formation long ago, but now it would be necessary to put energy into them to break them up into their elementary substances. A little energy must be provided to make hydrogen combine with oxygen— a lighted match must be applied to initiate combustion—but to recover the oxygen and hydrogen from a quantity of steam or water is quite a different matter. The desired separation needs something more than initiating—it needs to be kept going all the time by the continual supply of energy from some external source. The process is one from which nothing can be gained.

Coal, oil and wood are valuable to us as fuels because they are formed of molecules existing in what is termed the "metastable" state. Only let a little energy be supplied to initiate combustion and a vastly greater amount of energy will be released by a regrouping of the elementary substances in the fuels* to form "stable" as distinct from "metastable"

* Oxygen, whether free or combined, must be included as part of the fuel.

molecules. The energy needed to start this regrouping is called the activation energy, and the resultant energy release, less the activation energy, might be called the "gain." Where there is a clear gain the chemical reaction is an "exothermic" one—i.e. one that gives out heat.

Stable molecules are useless from the power engineer's point of view because they can be broken up into useful combustible substances only by putting into them larger amounts of energy than could ever be wholly recovered. Reactions like this involving, on balance, the absorption of heat energy, are called "endothermic" reactions.

The difference between hydrogen and oxygen in the free state and in the combined state is like the difference between a stone on top of a hill and a similar stone in a valley. With the help of a gentle push the stone on the hill will start to roll down, and in rolling it will give out far more energy than was expended in starting it. The stone in the valley is incapable of providing us with any energy unless we push it all the way up hill to begin with, and even then what it gives us will not be any more than what we put into it; in fact it will be less.

Atoms, like molecules, can be broken up or pieced together, and the transformations are accompanied sometimes by a release of energy and sometimes by an absorption of energy. The evidence accumulated over a number of years before the Great War of 1939–45 suggested that tremendously large amounts of energy were locked up in atoms. Rutherford and others proved beyond all doubt by actual experiment that when an atom was broken in two by the input of a small amount of activation energy from a bombarding particle, the energy gain on fission or rupture of the atom might be impressively large. Hitting atoms with particles proved extremely difficult, however. Millions of shots had to be expended for every bull's-eye, and on balance more energy was expended in the shooting than could be recovered from the atomic fissions actually caused.

The energy in an atom is of two kinds, one derived from the cohesive force binding the nuclear particles together and the other derived from the electric charges on these particles. In a spherical drop of water or mercury we have an illustration of cohesive action, although here it is a comparatively feeble one. When small drops run together to form bigger ones there is on balance a loss of exposed liquid surface, as can be seen when we compare the surface areas of two small spheres made out of the same volume of material as a single larger one.

Let R be the radius of the large sphere and r be the radius of each small sphere. Then, because of the equality between the volumes (see page 148)

$$\tfrac{4}{3}\pi R^3 = \tfrac{4}{3}\pi r^3 + \tfrac{4}{3}\pi r^3$$
$$R^3 = 2r^3$$
$$R = \sqrt[3]{2} \times r.$$

Original area of liquid surface (see page 143)

$$= 4\pi r^2 + 4\pi r^2 = 8\pi r^2 = A.$$

Final area of liquid surface

$$= 4\pi R^2 = 4\pi r^2 \times (\sqrt[3]{2})^2$$
$$= \tfrac{1}{2}A \times 2^{\frac{2}{3}}$$
$$= A \times 2^{\frac{2}{3}-1} = A \times 2^{-\frac{1}{3}}$$
$$= \frac{A}{\sqrt[3]{2}} = 0.795A.$$

Now, the available cohesive energy in a droplet is directly proportional to its surface area, and consequently when two droplets combine there is a reduction in the available energy. In other words, some of the energy is released. In the example given there is a release of energy proportional to $A - 0.795A = 0.205A$. That this is so will be apparent from the way in which the droplets rush together. Their combination is the occasion for a violent agitation or vibration of the fluid mass.

Now, atomic nuclei are rather like liquid droplets, and their fusion occasions a release of energy in the way described. However, because they are electrically charged, energy will have to be expended to bring them together against the force of mutual repulsion. Atoms of the lighter elements such as hydrogen, helium, etc., carry small nuclear charges and consequently, if they can be persuaded to coalesce, there will be on balance more energy released than consumed. The atoms of heavy elements carry big nuclear electric charges, so that the formation of such an atom from two approximately equal parts consumes energy on the whole. More work must be done to overcome electric repulsion than can be got out of the cohesive readjustment. This means that the atoms of the heavier elements are in a metastable condition and would give out energy if they could be split in two. Overcoming cohesion would consume energy, but the flying apart of the fission fragments under the influence of mutual electric repulsion will represent the release of very much more energy. The atoms split by Rutherford included some heavy atoms and consequently they showed this gain effect.

Scientists have now explored the possibility of obtaining energy from combining or splitting atoms and the conclusions they have reached are worth summarising here. Atoms lighter than those of silver will release energy by fusing together, whereas those heavier than silver will release energy upon fission. The gain by fission increases steadily with the weight of the element, and atoms of the very heavy elements such as radium, thorium and uranium are ready to disintegrate in a small way without help from any external agency—in fact, they are doing it all the time. They do not, however, split into equal fragments but merely throw off particles so as to become gradually more stable. The radium atom throws out alpha particles which consist of two neutrons and two protons. It also throws out beta particles (or electrons). The disturbance occasioned within the atom by these readjustments sets up vibrations inside the nucleus. These occasion the electro-magnetic gamma radiation which is akin to X-rays but of even shorter wavelength.

The commoner metals having heavy atoms—lead, gold, platinum, etc.—are not radio-active, although their atoms are metastable and would show a release of energy by fission if they could be suitably bombarded. Effective bombardment is the hardest thing in the world to contrive, and the reasons for this will be apparent presently. So far, the scientists have found only the way to deal with uranium and plutonium.

Would fusion of the lighter atoms be easier to contrive? The answer is that such atoms will fuse together only at enormously high temperatures—temperatures of from tens of thousands to millions of degrees. It is not practicable to work at such high temperatures on the earth, although the conditions for fusing atoms together exist within the interior of the sun and the stars. It is now established beyond question that the enormous output of energy from heavenly bodies—from the sun in particular—is maintained by the alchemical conversion of hydrogen into helium. The process is a roundabout one involving several fusions and readjustments (see page 208) but the net result is a transmutation of hydrogen into helium.

In order to understand how the atoms of a substance can be modified by fusion or fission we must pay more attention to the precise composition of individual atoms. Chemical determinations of atomic weights suggested to a chemist of the nineteenth century named Prout that all atoms might be regarded as concentrations of hydrogen atoms. Thus carbon, with an atomic weight of 12, would be 12 hydrogen atoms; nitrogen and oxygen with atomic weights of 14 and 16 would be 14 and 16 hydrogen atoms respectively. Prout's idea received some attention, and then it seemed to be rebutted by the discovery that chlorine had an atomic weight of $35 \cdot 5$ and therefore could not be a derivative of hydro-gen atoms. Further chemical research showed that many other sub-stances also had atomic weights lying between two integers, and so Prout's idea was abandoned until the year 1919, when a British physi-cist succeeded in demonstrating that chlorine gas contained atoms of two different weights. Careful experiment showed that of every 100 atoms 75 had a weight of 35 and 25 had a weight of 37. The average weight was therefore $(75 \times 35 + 25 \times 37) \div 100 = 35 \cdot 5$. The physi-cist, whose name was Aston, actually managed to sort out the heavy from the light atoms by a machine. This machine is called the Aston mass-spectrograph, and first of all it ionises the atoms by stripping away their outer electrons so that they become positively charged particles. These ions of chlorine are then made to travel at high speed between the oppositely charged plates of an electric condenser. They are deflected by the force arising from the interaction between their own charges and the electric field, and the lighter ions are deflected most on account of their smaller initial momentum. The electric field acts on the ion current almost as a prism acts on a ray of light, causing dispersion. Now to make an optical spectrum on a screen the dispersed ray must be sent through a converging lens; this brings the several light beams to a focus at a screen arranged to receive the different-coloured images. In the mass-spectrograph an ion-converging magnetic field takes the place of a convex lens, and ions of different weights impinge on the screen at different points. It only remains to measure the intensity of the bombard-ment produced by the different ion streams. With chlorine the ions corresponding to an atomic weight of 35 are found to produce 75 per cent. of the total effect, whereas ions corresponding to an atomic weight of 37 are found to produce the remaining 25 per cent.

From this clever experiment it was concluded that chlorine gas was really a mixture of two different kinds of chlorine, one a little heavier than the other but chemically indistinguishable from it. The two kinds are called "isotopes" of chlorine.

Most chemical elements are now known to have two or more isotopes, and it is their mixture in certain proportions in Nature which gives atomic weights to many elements that are not whole multiples of the atomic weight of hydrogen. Isotopes have been separated by the mass-spectrograph and examined separately. Chemically they are found to behave in exactly the same way, so that the properties of an element are now known to be dependent not on the atomic *weight* but on the atomic *number*. The latter is the number of protons in the nucleus or, what is the same thing, the number of electrons circling round it. A chlorine atom of either isotope has a nuclear charge of 17, so that the essential feature of chlorine is the presence of 17 protons in the atomic nucleus. The balance of the nuclear mass is made up of 18 neutrons in the lighter isotope and 20 neutrons in the heavier. The electrons have a weight that is often ignored, since 1840 of them weigh only as much as one proton or neutron.

In a modern table of chemical elements we find more than an average atomic weight; as well we find the atomic weights of the several isotopes and also the atomic number. Beginning with hydrogen, we find the two atomic weights of 1 and 2; the atomic number is always 1. Thus the hydrogen nucleus consists of either one proton by itself or one proton united to a neutron. Heavy hydrogen is present in normal hydrogen to the extent of only about 1 part in 5000, but separation of the isotopes is relatively easy because the heavier atoms are twice the mass of the lighter ones. It is much more difficult to separate isotopes when their masses are close together. For instance, the separation of Uranium 235 from Uranium 238 in a natural mixture is an extremely tedious and costly business, there being a mass difference of only 3 between the masses 235 and 238.

Heavy hydrogen nuclei are called deuterons and light hydrogen nuclei are called protons. The former possess the same electric charge as protons but are of twice the mass, and this massiveness makes them superior to protons as projectiles for bombarding any atoms it is desired to split. Water (H_2O), in which the hydrogen is heavy hydrogen or "deuterium," is called heavy water, and to distinguish it from the common variety it is represented by the formula D_2O where D is the symbol for deuterium. Heavy water can be separated from ordinary water by distillation, but the process is of necessity a slow and elaborate one because the boiling-points of H_2O and D_2O differ by only $1.4°$ C. When water is electrolysed (see page 181) the hydrogen given off is ordinary hydrogen, so that any heavy water present tends to become more concentrated. For this reason the acid solution or electrolyte in lead storage batteries becomes rich in heavy water as time goes on, and it has considerable value to the chemist or physicist for that reason.

Helium, with an atomic number of 2, has two isotopes for which the mass numbers are 3 and 4, the latter being the most abundant. Lithium, with an atomic number of 3, has isotopes of mass numbers 6 and 7. Beryllium, a particularly rare and valuable metal, has an atomic number of 4 and only one isotope of mass number 9. It became of particular interest to the physicist in 1930 when German scientists discovered that it gave off a particularly penetrating kind of radiation when bombarded by the alpha particles from polonium (an element with an atomic number of 84 and seven radio-active isotopes of mass numbers 210, 211, 212, 214, 215, 216 and 218). At first this radiation was believed to be an intense gamma radiation, but in 1932 the English scientist, James Chadwick, proved conclusively that the effects obtained with it could be explained only on the supposition that it was an emission of unelectrified protons, that is, of particles with a mass number of 1 but no positive charge. Chadwick may thus be regarded as the discoverer of the "neutron," as this newly revealed kind of particle was called.

To go through the complete table of elements would make this chapter too lengthy, so that only a summary is possible. Scientists now have a knowledge of elements corresponding to every atomic number from 1 to 94. The isotopes of these 94 elements correspond to mass numbers between 1 and 239, but there are some gaps. Thus no elements appear to have isotopes of mass numbers 5 and 8, or of mass numbers 213, 217 221, 225, 227, 228, 229 and 236, though it is probably too soon to suppose that the last word has been said on this matter. An isotope is often only a temporary condition. For instance, no isotope of oxygen having a mass number of 15 is shown in any table, but this can certainly exist for a time. The nucleus consists of eight protons and seven neutrons. Within 2 minutes of its formation this unstable nucleus emits a positive electron—called a positron—and then there is an atom of nitrogen instead. The mass number is still 15 but the atomic number is 7.

The positron was first discovered in 1932 in the course of research on cosmic radiation. That it takes part in nuclear reactions was discovered by Curie and Joliot, who found that aluminium emitted an unusual radiation when bombarded with alpha particles from polonium. This emission was like ordinary beta emission except that in a magnetic field the particles were deflected in a direction which indicated that they were positively and not negatively charged. Atomic nuclei, then, can either absorb or lose electrons, positrons, protons, neutrons or alpha particles, and in so doing they may become chemically different or they may merely alter in mass number. In radio-active substances the change, whatever it may be, goes on spontaneously. In substances having stable atoms the change will have to be induced by shock tactics, that is to say, by bombarding the atomic nucleus with protons, alpha particles, deuterons or neutrons. The difficulties in the way of doing this are immense and will be described presently. In the meantime here is a table of some of the stable elements giving their atomic numbers and the isotope mass numbers for permanent isotopes. The most abundant isotopes are distinguished by an asterisk.

Element	Chemical Symbol	Atomic Number	Mass Numbers of Isotopes
Hydrogen	H	1	1*, 2
Helium	He	2	3, 4*
Beryllium	Be	4	9*
Carbon	C	6	12*, 13
Nitrogen	N	7	14*, 15
Oxygen	O	8	16*, 17, 18
Aluminium	Al	13	27*
Chlorine	Cl	17	35*, 37
Silver	Ag	47	107*, 109*
Cadmium	Cd	48	106, 108, 110, 111, 112, 113, 114*, 116
Gold	Au	79	197*
Mercury	Hg	80	196, 198, 199, 200, 201, 202*, 204
Lead	Pb	82	204, 206, 207, 208*

The radio-active elements are listed below, beginning with the heaviest. Where they have significance the isotope mass numbers are given, but it must be remembered that the atoms are unstable in every case, so that alpha-particle emission is gradually changing their mass and their chemical nature.

Element	Chemical Symbol	Atomic Number	Mass Numbers of Isotopes
Plutonium	Pu	94	238, 239
Neptunium	Np	93	
Uranium	U	92	234, 235, 238
Protactinium	Pa	91	231
Thorium	Th	90	230, 232
Actinium	Ac	89	
Radium	Ra	88	223, 224, 226
Virginium	Vi	87	
Radon	Rn	86	219, 220, 222
Alabamium	Ab	85	
Polonium	Po	84	210, 211, 212, 214, 215, 216, 218

Oddly enough, the most important atomic-energy releases in Nature are not occasioned by the radio-active elements but by the ordinary elements hydrogen, helium, carbon, oxygen and nitrogen. At the enormously high temperatures obtaining in the heart of the sun and the stars (from 15 to 20 million degrees Centigrade) hydrogen atoms fuse readily with atoms of carbon and nitrogen, so that several nuclear reactions occur which lead to the eventual transformation of hydrogen into helium and also to the release of vast amounts of energy. It is this energy release that enables the sun to go on pouring out heat for millions upon millions of years without showing any immediate sign of cooling or shrinkage.

The theory to account for solar radiation was developed by H. Bethe in America and C. v. Weizsacker in Germany. We can begin our account of the nuclear reactions by imagining a hydrogen atom and a carbon atom to fuse together in accordance with the equation

$$_6C^{12} + {}_1H^1 \longrightarrow {}_7N^{13}$$

or, in words, an atom of carbon, atomic number 6 and mass 12, unites with an atom of hydrogen, atomic number 1 and mass 1, to form a new atom of atomic number $6 + 1 = 7$ and mass $12 + 1 = 13$. The atomic number of 7 is characteristic of nitrogen, but the mass number of 13 does not agree with any of the tabulated isotope masses of nitrogen. However, at the terrific temperature inside the sun, such an isotope can be caused to exist, and indeed *it has been caused to exist in a laboratory* by bombarding a carbon target with fast protons.

The nitrogen atom $_7N^{13}$ is an unstable one, and it soon emits a positron, thereby transforming itself into a carbon atom of mass number 13 in accordance with the equation

$$_7N^{13} \longrightarrow {}_6C^{13} + {}_1e^0.$$

Here, e^0 is the symbol for a positron; the symbol for an electron or beta particle is $-{}_1e^0$. The loss of an electric charge from a nucleus either lowers or increases the atomic number, depending on whether the charge is to be denoted by 1 or $-$ 1. The mass number (not to be confused with the actual mass) remains unaffected, and this explains why the cipher is written against the electron symbol e on the right-hand side.

To continue with what occurs in the sun; another hydrogen atom now disappears by fusing with the newly formed $_6C^{13}$ carbon atom. The reaction, symbolically expressed, is:

$$_6C^{13} + {}_1H^1 \longrightarrow {}_7N^{14}.$$

Thus the result is an atom of the commonest of all nitrogen isotopes. This is not left to rest in peace, for yet another hydrogen atom (equivalent to a proton) seeks to end its existence, and the result is the following:

$$_7N^{14} + {_1}H^1 \longrightarrow {_8}O^{15}.$$

This result is peculiar because no stable isotope of oxygen has a mass number of 15. Within 2 minutes this unstable oxygen atom emits a positron so as to reduce its atomic number from 8 to 7 and so become an atom of a stable isotope of nitrogen. The change is as follows:

$$_8O^{15} \longrightarrow {_7}N^{15} + {_1}e^0.$$

Very soon the atom $_7N^{15}$ captures yet another hydrogen atom, but the result is not what might be expected. Instead of having the reaction

$$_7N^{15} + {_1}H^1 \longrightarrow {_8}O^{16},$$

which would seem to be the obvious conclusion of the whole affair, we have:

$$_7N^{15} + {_1}H^1 \longrightarrow {_6}C^{12} + {_2}He^4.$$

This result has been actually secured in the laboratory, and the explanation appears to be that although an atom of oxygen is formed initially, there is such a huge amount of energy liberated in this fourth proton capture that the resulting vibration breaks up the oxygen atom, making it into a carbon atom and a helium atom.

We must now sum up the results of all these changes. Going into the alchemy described above are four atoms of hydrogen and one of carbon. Coming out of it are two atoms, namely the original atom of carbon back again and an atom of helium. On balance, then, nothing has changed except the hydrogen, four atoms of which have gone to form one atom of helium. The nitrogen and oxygen have appeared only to disappear again. Apart from these material happenings there has been a huge release of energy, and this is what we really appreciate, for it is the basis of solar warmth.

Spectroscopic examination of solar light (see page 197) reveals dark bands where there should be the spectrum of hydrogen. This is conclusive evidence that the sun's atmosphere is rich in relatively cool hydrogen gas. Astronomers affirm that hydrogen is the most abundant element in the universe even now, comprising about one-third of all matter. The sun is believed to have used up only a small fraction of its original store of hydrogen, and an estimate of its useful life to come gives us the comforting figure of "over ten thousand million years."

The problem of securing atomic energy for mankind's use in peace or in war has exercised the minds of scientists for several decades, but nothing practical was achieved until, in the years 1939–45, the fear of what German or Japanese scientists might be doing spurred British and American scientists to make an all-out effort to perfect the atom bomb.

The difficulty of securing worth-while results from splitting atoms by the use of beams of protons or alpha particles has already been mentioned. The nucleus of an atom is only about a ten-thousandth part of the over-all diameter of the atom, and therefore a solid piece of matter is in reality as empty as the inside of a large barn with only two or three small motes of dust floating about inside it. Bombarding particles have to go a long way in space so empty of matter as this before they can hit anything, and therefore millions are lost for every one that achieves an impact.

This is not the worst trouble, however. Atomic nuclei carry positive electric charges and so do the bombarding protons, alpha particles or deuterons. The electric repulsion effects cause the bombarding particles to be thrown off before they can do any damage *unless they are projected with the fearful energy corresponding to a velocity of several thousand kilometres a second.*

Alpha particles from radio-active material have this great velocity, and since their mass number is 4 for a charge of 2 they are better than protons (hydrogen nuclei), which have a mass number per charge of unity. The atomic nuclei of heavy hydrogen (deuterons) are as good as alpha particles because they too have a mass number of 2 per charge. They are not found in Nature with the requisite velocity, however. Deuterons can be made by ionising heavy hydrogen (deuterium) and this obviates the need for rare radio-active sources of particles, but deuterons still have to be accelerated in order that they may have the energy needed to overcome electric repulsion forces and smash right through to the atomic nucleus.

Electric machines for accelerating artificially created protons, alpha particles and deuterons have been set up in many laboratories. The Van der Graaff generator and the Voltage-Doubler of Cockroft and Walton are appliances for applying a helpful electric potential of tens of thousands, hundreds of thousands or even millions of volts to the sluggish particles, causing them to gain enormous speed under electrical attraction and repulsion in a long tubular "speedway" of the kind shown in the left-hand picture opposite. Being positively charged, these particles can easily be influenced by electric and magnetic fields, and the accelerating influence is always an electric field.

The energy gained by particles in the course of their acceleration is

Early cyclotron designed by Lawrence and Livingston. The magnet is not shown and one of the **D**'s has been cut away to reveal the source of the particles. Acceleration of the latter along a spiral path enables enormous velocities to be attained in a relatively compact piece of apparatus.

(By courtesy of the Director of the Science Museum, London, S.W.7.)

Cockcroft and Walton's apparatus for the artificial disintegration of the elements. The tubular electrodes inside the glass are at ascending electric potentials so that descending alpha particles are progressively accelerated to form effective projectiles. (The metal stay-rods and collars have been added for greater safety in the museum, and form no part of the original apparatus.)

(Crown Copyright. From an exhibit in the Science Museum, London, S.W.7.)

measured in electron-volts, the electron-volt being the work done on an electron between points on its path differing in potential by 1 volt. As a rule, the energy needed for atom splitting is very large, so that the practical unit of energy is the Mev (million-electron-volts).

The most modern particle accelerator is the cyclotron of E. Lawrence. This avoids the use of enormously high voltages by the simple trick of applying the same moderate voltage to the accelerating particles again and again. The path of the particles is made to curve by an enormously powerful magnet, and in this way they are caused to pass repeatedly between hollow electrodes each in the form of a letter D. The moderate voltage is applied across the two electrodes, and there is a continual reversal of polarity, this being timed to occur whenever the particles

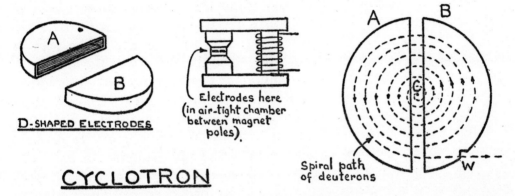

A

B

D-SHAPED ELECTRODES

Electrodes here (in air-tight chamber between magnet poles).

CYCLOTRON

Spiral path of deuterons

reverse their motion relative to the gap between the two D's. The accompanying sketch shows the D electrodes at A and B. They are in a chamber which is completely exhausted of air and any other gas. Ions of heavy hydrogen (deuterons) are admitted at the centre C and these at once start moving from A to B or vice versa. Their path is a curved one because there is an immensely powerful magnetic field passing through the D's in a plane perpendicular to the paper. If a deuteron had a constant speed, its path would be a circle, and the diameter of the circle would be small or large according to whether its velocity was small or large. Actually the deuterons are accelerated with every passage from A to B or B to A, and so they take a spiral course. Faster and faster they go, and ever wider grows their spiralling until, at last, they are in danger of striking the outer periphery of the D electrodes. Before they can do this they are let out by the window W. Here their path is made straight by the action of a deflecting electric field strong enough to neutralise the magnetic field at W. Part of an early cyclotron is shown in the right-hand picture facing page 210.

With rectilinear motion at the rate of thousands of kilometres a second, the deuterons form a beam of immensely destructive projectiles, and targets of various materials put in their path suffer atomic disintegration. But though it is useful for research the cyclotron is incapable of disintegrating matter fast enough to give us an energy release we could use. The power needed to operate a large cyclotron is many times more than the output of energy from the bombarded target. To produce deuterons with an energy of 9 Mev in sufficient numbers to carry a current of 14 microamperes (corresponding to a beam output of 126 watts), involves using an energy input of about 120 kilowatts. The small amount of matter in the beam corresponds to the disintegration of only a gram of heavy hydrogen in several score years.

Two discoveries raised high the originally somewhat forlorn hope of getting useful energy from the atom. Firstly there was the discovery of the uncharged neutron emitted by beryllium under alpha-particle bombardment (see page 206), and secondly there was the discovery in 1939 that bombarded Uranium 235 atoms reacted to neutron bombardment by doing something no atoms were ever known to do before. O. Hahn and F. Strassman, in Germany, discovered that they did not merely throw off protons, neutrons, alpha particles or beta particles under neutron bombardment—they split roughly in half, and the fragments showed energies of about 100 Mev each, which represented a very impressive gain. That there had been real atomic fission was proved by the appearance of barium in the fission products; barium has only a little more than half the weight of uranium.

The difficulties in the way of obtaining useful energy from atomic fission were still enormous, but the Germans were studying the matter with diabolical intent at the outbreak of the war and so perforce the British and Americans had to do so too.

Neutrons are awkward to control because they possess no electric charge. Ideal though they are in being able to get right through to atomic nuclei without meeting a force of electrical repulsion, they nevertheless cannot be accelerated by laboratory or any other methods. As a matter of fact this did not matter, for it was found that to produce fission in Uranium 235 the neutrons had to travel relatively slowly—at about the speed of a rifle bullet—so that they needed slowing down and not accelerating.

Neutrons emitted by bombarded matter are fast neutrons, and these enter Uranium 235 nuclei only to be thrown off again. On being slowed down, however, the neutrons are readily captured by the atoms of U-235, and then they lead to such unstability in the atoms capturing them that fission ensues. Slowed-down neutrons are called "thermal" neutrons because they have speeds of the same order as the molecules of a gas—speeds which as we know occasion a gas to have pressure and temperature (see Chapter IV). The method of slowing down a neutron is to make it collide with the atoms of materials which do not absorb it. It is obliged to share its energy with these atoms, just as a moving billiard-ball shares its energy with any other balls it hits. After a sufficient number of impacts the neutron will have imparted the bulk of its energy to other particles and so it will move with a greatly reduced speed. The impacts are more effective in slowing down neutrons when the element is one having a low atomic weight than when it is heavy. A billiard-ball loses about half its energy when it strikes another ball of its own size, but striking a heavy iron cannon-ball it will rebound with scarcely any diminution of energy. The best materials for slowing down neutrons are called moderators. Very pure graphite (carbon) is one such material and heavy water is another. Neither material absorbs neutrons, but both will convert fast neutrons into thermal neutrons. Incidentally, neutrons pass through steel, lead and other apparently solid screens with their energy almost unimpaired, so that such screens are useless as a defence against neutron radiation. Ordinary water is the best safeguard, and a water wall 3 ft. thick will effectively check them. The metal cadmium is also an effective screen against neutrons—it checks them by absorbing them.

In any lump of U-235 not too large an entering neutron is likely to escape into the open again before it can slow down sufficiently to cause fission. On the average, neutrons will travel 10 centimetres between their collisions with uranium nuclei, and they must make many such collisions before they are sufficiently slowed down; this is because uranium atoms are heavy. When at last one is captured the affected uranium atom will split in two, but the fragments are highly charged, and despite their energy they cannot split up other atoms. However, every atomic fission results in the release of 2 or 3 more fast neutrons, and if these do not escape before being slowed down they may effect further fissions. Plainly there lies here the possibility of neutron multiplication to the point where a chain reaction starts and disintegrates the entire mass of uranium. The crucial factor is the size of the uranium lump. If it is too small, neutrons escape faster than they can be renewed, and so nothing happens. If it exceeds a critical size, however, the fissions generate more neutrons than they absorb, and so fresh fissions are caused.

The whole lump then becomes subject to an atomic-disintegration process of terrifying rapidity and violence. The awful disasters at Hiroshima and Nagasaki were caused by bombs in which one lump of uranium, weighing a few kilograms, was shot by ordinary explosive into another lump of about the same size, so that the combined lump exceeded the critical size. The coming together of the two lumps had to be extremely rapid or in its early stages atomic disintegration might have forced the lumps apart again before the full force of the explosion could be developed. Neutron escape was prevented to some extent by surrounding the uranium with a material that reflected neutrons back towards the interior. Premature expansion of the combined uranium lump was checked by the use of a container possessing great mass or inertia. This was called the "tamper." Mass is of more effect in checking expansion than tensile strength, as the resistance of a material to being accelerated may exceed its resistance to rupture many times over.

Simple in principle though the atomic bomb may be, it was several years before one could be made. Uranium 235 is found admixed with Uranium 238, and the proportion of the former to the latter is about 1 part in 140. Separation of the isotopes is a most difficult and costly process, but in the end it was accomplished. An enormous number of machines like the mass-spectrograph of Aston (see page 240) were set up at the Clinton Engineer Works in the United States, and these were effective in producing Uranium 235 in useful though by no means lavish quantities. The electro-magnetic separator working on the principle of the mass-spectrograph is called the "Calutron."

Another isotope-separation process depends on the relative rates of diffusion through a porous barrier of uranium hexafluoride molecules, those incorporating U-235 passing through a little more rapidly than those incorporating U-238. In time the hexafluoride gas on one side of the barrier shows a slight enrichment in molecules made from U-235. The enriched gas is passed on for a repetition of the process, whereby it is further enriched. After innumerable repetitions, involving barriers aggregating acres of area, the uranium hexafluoride is separated into constituents which are rich in U-235 and U-238 respectively.

Isotopes have to be separated by methods of a mechanical or semi-mechanical nature because they are indistinguishable chemically.

While isotope separation promised in the end enough U-235 for making bombs, the British and American scientists had hopes of making and utilising a new element altogether—the element called Plutonium.

This is as readily fissionable, and it can be made out of the relatively plentiful U-238.

Fast neutrons are readily captured by U-238 in accordance with the relation

$$_{92}U^{238} + {_0}N^1 \longrightarrow {_{92}}U^{239} + \text{Gamma rays.}$$

Atoms of U-239 are unstable and so, in 23 minutes, U-238 becomes converted to Neptunium in accordance with the relation

$$_{92}U^{239} \longrightarrow {_{93}}Np^{239} + {_{-1}}e^0.$$

The transmutation results from the conversion of a nuclear neutron into a proton by the emission of an electron as a beta particle. Neptunium is no more stable than U-239, so that a further beta particle is emitted and gamma rays as well in accordance with the relation

$$_{93}Np^{239} \longrightarrow {_{94}}Pu^{239} + {_{-1}}e^0 + \text{Gamma rays.}$$

This second reaction takes about 2·3 days, and gives a highly valuable fissionable material, namely plutonium, which can be separated from U-238 by relatively easy *chemical* means.

The plant for making plutonium is called a "pile." In effect this is like a huge cake of pure graphite studded with plums of natural uranium. The fast neutrons entering this "cake" are slowed down by the graphite moderator and eventually they produce the fission of a U-235 atom, thereby releasing more fast neutrons. A proportion of these escape capture by the U-238 atoms and are slowed down to the point where they will split more U-235 atoms. In designing a pile care must be taken to see that enough neutrons will split U-235 atoms and keep the reaction going, but not too many. If matters go too fast, the pile becomes more than just warm—it becomes excessively hot and is destroyed. Control of the rate of heat generation is effected by putting sliders of cadmium in the "cake." These absorb most of the neutrons when they are fully operative, but they can be gradually slid out until the chain reaction is going at a safe rate.

Neutrons not captured by U-235 atoms may escape into space (or into the protective water wall usually built round a pile) but many of them will be captured by U-238 atoms before they have a chance to be slowed down. U-238 atoms have a strong partiality for fast neutrons going at a particular speed. This capture of neutrons by U-238 is called "resonance" capture, and in a large lump of natural uranium so many neutrons suffer this fate that no chain reaction is possible.

The spacing of uranium plums in a moderator gives most of the neutrons resulting from the fission of U-235 a chance to slow down well below the critical speed for resonance capture before they can collide with U-238 atoms. At thermal speeds they are safe from capture by U-238 atoms and are available for fission capture by U-235 atoms.

Resonance capture by U-238 is desirable up to a point because it causes U-238 to become Plutonium 239. The designer's chief care must be to see that, in his anxiety to get plutonium, he does not let U-238 seize more neutrons than the pile can afford to lose. For every neutron set free by the fission of U-235 at least one must be spared for causing further fission. Actually it proved difficult to conserve the neutrons, and a pile was not made until calculations showed that about 1007 neutrons could be made available for fission for every 1000 causing fission. The balance were lost or absorbed in some way or another, some doing the useful work of turning U-238 into Pu-239.

The energy release from a pile is so great that in order to make a kilogram of plutonium a day the pile must give out the heat equivalent of from 500,000 to 1,500,000 kilowatts. The first pile ever to be made operated at 200 watts, and would have taken at least 70,000 years to produce enough plutonium for a bomb ! To accelerate the production of plutonium the Americans erected some huge piles on a site that became known as the Hanford Engineer Works. The heat from these piles was wasted in heating river water.

Piles built to withstand high temperatures might be put to peaceful uses; they could generate steam for use in turbo-electric generating stations. However, piles of the present type cannot be very small in size, and when protective screens are added to obviate the risk of injury by neutrons to bystanders, the weight and bulk are very great. Atomic piles are not likely therefore to become yet awhile the source of motive power for motor cars, ships or aeroplanes.

Whence comes atomic energy? In 1905 Einstein said that mass and energy were convertible one into the other. He gave a formula connecting the two, namely:

$$\text{Energy} = \text{mass} \times C^2,$$

where C is the velocity of light. This formula shows that a gram mass is interchangeable with $8 \cdot 9 \times 10^{20}$ ergs of energy. In other words, one pound mass converted to energy is equivalent to 15,000 million horse-power hours. Ordinary chemical releases of energy are so small in comparison with the total amount of matter involved that no change in the mass of this matter is perceptible, but atomic-energy releases are on a different scale altogether and physicists have detected the disappearance of mass. Nuclear particles are conventionally described as being of unit mass, but mass-spectrograph investigations show that protons and neutrons differ slightly in mass when apart (one weighs 1·0076 whereas the other weighs 1·0090). Together they weigh less than their arithmetical sum (2·0142 instead of 2·0166). These differences have to do with differences in potential energy. When a proton and a neutron combine to form a deuteron (nucleus of heavy hydrogen atom) there is a release of energy equivalent to the apparent loss of mass (2·0166 − 2·0142). This energy amounts to 2·2 Mev. To break them asunder again, precisely 2·2 Mev of energy needs to be supplied by the bombarding particle, whether it is a proton, an alpha particle or a neutron.

The arithmetical sum of the masses of the particles (two neutrons and two protons) making an alpha particle (nucleus of helium atom, isotope 4) is 4·0332 (twice that of the component parts of deuteron), but the actual mass of the alpha particle is 4·0027 which is not, as you might have expected, twice that of a deuteron; that would be $2 \times 2 \cdot 0142 = 4 \cdot 0284$. The mass loss here (4·0332 − 4·0027) is the equivalent of no less than 28 Mev of energy. Alpha particles would evidently need a lot of energy to destroy them, and this explains why they are so effective as projectiles in atom-splitting experiments; they do damage without being broken up themselves.

In the solar transformation of hydrogen to helium, four protons, having a combined weight of $4 \times 1 \cdot 0076 = 4 \cdot 0304$, come together to make an alpha particle having a weight of 4·0027. The loss of mass is $4 \cdot 0304 - 4 \cdot 0027 = 0 \cdot 0277$, and this is equivalent to 25·5 Mev. Very gradually, then, the sun is decreasing in mass, but the return in energy given out is enormous and there is enough matter in the sun to keep the process going for thousands of millions of years to come.

CHAPTER I

THE ORIGIN OF THE EARTH

In this book pride of place has been given to what are termed the experimental sciences in which the observer plays an active part, testing his theories and conclusions by practical work in the laboratory or workshop, or by the mathematical examination of his findings with microscope or telescope.

We come now to some sciences that are rather different in character, being studies of natural phenomena in which the observer is obliged to play a more passive part by merely collecting data and reserving judgment as to explanations or theories until the data suggest a likely hypothesis. Geology is a science of this kind and so is biology. The natural events being studied occur at a rate that may be very slow by human standards, and the scale on which they take place may be too vast for imitation in the laboratory. The changes that are going on may not be perceptible when they are observed by ordinary scientific methods, but their occurrence can often be inferred from a study of the relics of bygone ages. Thus the process of sedimentary rock formation is too slow to be noticeable or reproducible by man, but its occurrence is borne out by the examination of geological strata.

A microscope shows that chalk consists of the calcareous remains of minute sea-water organisms. Their precipitation and consolidation on the sea bed in the course of millions of years led to the formation of the sedimentary layer of rock we know as chalk. Without seeing it happen, or being able to imitate such a happening in the laboratory, we know that chalk must have originated in this way, and we can infer that the rolling hills made of chalk in Sussex and Berkshire must once have formed part of the bed of the sea. From other evidence we infer that the exposure of the chalk was due to an upthrust of the sea bed and not to a fall in the general level of ocean waters.

Conclusions of this kind belong to the realm of science because they are reached by methods that scientists regard as valid. Neither guesswork nor legend plays any part in the scientific reconstruction of the remote past, though, admittedly, there are gaps and uncertainties which may have to be filled temporarily by suppositions. These suppositions are brought to the test whenever fresh data come to light. Thus the supposition of Charles Darwin that man might be descended from the same ancestral stock as the apes has been examined afresh with every new fossil discovery bearing on the question. For a long time the chain of evidence remained incomplete. The gradual evolution of the man-like form could be traced through a line of sub-human creatures up to a certain point; then there occurred a gap in the evidence, and when it could be followed again the fossils showed unmistakably human characteristics. Nobody could be certain that fossils of an intermediate age would ever be found or, if found, that they would establish a connection between ape-like beings and man-like beings. Darwin's theory lacked confirmation because of this "missing link." Within recent years the missing link has been found and Darwin's theory is now regarded as finally established. Even now, however, scientists are not able to prove this theory up to the hilt by breeding men from monkeys in a laboratory; in some respects, therefore, the inductive science of biology, like the inductive science of geology, falls short of being as convincing and satisfactory as the science of electricity, say, or the science of mechanics.

Theories in the inductive sciences cannot be proved by demonstration but only by amassing vast amounts of evidence in their favour and by ensuring that the collected data include no facts that are irreconcilable with them. The old saying that "the exception proves the rule" finds no place in true science. Anything that seems to be in violation of natural law stands to the discredit of that law unless it can be explained away as a mistake in observation. Newton's law of universal gravitation was for a time discredited by the irregular behaviour of the planet Uranus, but it was gloriously vindicated by the subsequent discovery of the planets Neptune and Pluto, whose gravitational influence had not previously been suspected or allowed for. At a later stage Newton's theory was again put on trial because of peculiarities in the motions of Mercury. The verdict has not been so favourable to Newton this time. Einstein and others are still working out true expressions for cosmic laws—expressions for which Newton's Law has turned out to be only an approximation.

Sometimes a student thinks he has found evidence that disproves an accepted tenet of scientists, but the conflict is more apparent than real, for it is found to originate usually in some error or omission in his experiments. Only when the often-repeated experiments of experienced scientists show disparities and discrepancies are established theories put in doubt.

In the inductive sciences again the evidence of the inexperienced may not be of much value. A fossil of a trilobite found in the earth under a nineteenth-century house would not prove that trilobites roamed the world during the reign of Queen Victoria, though some excited amateur geologist might imagine that it did. An examination of the facts by a cautious expert would certainly show that the fossil had come to occupy its unnatural place through some human or other accidental agency. The same kind of discovery has to be made many times and in circumstances that preclude the possibility of human inter-ference, before the trained scientist will regard it as conclusive evidence of natural happenings. The conclusions of geology and biology are, in the main, based on similarities between the findings of research workers in many different localities. Freak findings are recorded, but judgment as to their value in proof or disproof of accepted theories is reserved until more can be ascertained about them. You might find a nugget of gold on a Welsh mountain and affirm that it was of meteoric origin, but the Astronomer Royal would not attach much importance to your deduction. You might send it to the Geological Museum in London claiming to have discovered a vein of gold-bearing rock in Wales, but again your statement would probably be discredited. An advertisement in a provincial paper a week later might then inform you of the truth that the nugget fell from the pocket of a traveller who subsequently missed it and decided to offer a small reward for its return by a possible finder. Many and great are the disappointments of the amateur scientist unless he is properly grounded in his subject and able to curb his fancy.

No great space can be given to the inductive sciences in this book because they constitute vast accumulations of data which cannot be described even in summary. All that can be done here is to point to some of the conclusions reached by the students of this data—by the accredited astrophysicists, geologists and biologists. Human curiosity has pro-pounded many seemingly unanswerable questions, but science is gradu-ally finding the likely answers, and it is to these answers that the remaining chapters of this book must be confined. Very little can be given of the evidence in support of these answers, as this would entail reproducing the records of many learned societies and making the present work into a vast catalogue of facts.

Oldest perhaps of all questions is that concerning the creation of our planet. How was it formed and when? Astronomy suggests that the stellar bodies, of which our sun is one, originated as condensations of gaseous matter in vast nebulæ. Our telescopes show us stellar galaxies in various states of evolution. Some nebulæ are still in a tenuous and almost invisible state. Their existence is imperceptible to the eye but is proved by the impression made on a photographic plate long exposed to their faint luminosity. Other nebulæ are brighter and more compact. They assume the form of vast gaseous discs relatively thick at the centre and thin at the edge, where they may be tails and streamers of gas giving them the appearance of the firework known as the Catherine Wheel. A slow contraction and a slow rotation seem to characterise the nebular existence. In time the nebula breaks up by condensation and centrifugal action into huge globules of gas which become intensely luminous by reason of their rising temperature. These gaseous globules draw to themselves all the matter originally contained in the nebula and then there remains only a collection of stars. The number of these may run into billions and the space they occupy will be vast almost beyond comprehension. It is thought that all the stars we see around us, including those of the Milky Way, were derived from a single nebula. Their grouping retains the disc form and our own position is near the edge of that disc. Looking towards the edge on a clear night, we see more stars than when we look along the axis; in fact we see so many that we are conscious of an extra luminous band all round the heavens; the band that we call the Milky Way, which powerful telescopes resolve into millions upon millions of separate stars.

In the ordinary way the stars are at vast distances from one another, but under certain conditions two stars may form a linked pair, gravity causing them to keep close together and rotate about their common centre of mass. Such a system is termed a binary system and the sun is thought to have been the smaller partner of such a system hundreds of millions of years ago. The partnership terminated when all the hydrogen in the larger partner had been turned into helium giving rise to internal temperatures and pressures too terrific to endure. An explosion occurred and the sun's partner became reduced in large measure to mere fragments which formed a huge dust-cloud in the neighbourhood of the sun. Such a cloud would be gravitationally unstable as the particles would tend to draw together by mutual attraction. The earth and the other planets took shape in this way. For a more complete account of this new theory of the formation of the earth the reader is referred to the printed lectures of Mr. Fred Hoyle on "The Nature of the Universe" in *The Listener* for February 9th, 1950, and succeeding issues.

The theory shows that a great deal of time must have elapsed before the dust-cloud could have formed aggregates as large as our earth but that once such aggregates had been formed their growth would be increasingly rapid. On account of the energy imparted to the growing mass by every additional particle of matter attracted to it these aggregations acquired rotation and also a high temperature. Certain of them became too large for stability and broke up into fragments or "blobs." It is thought that the earth and its attendant satellite, the moon, were the outcome of such a rupture. The same applies to the other relatively small planets.

The older theory that the earth and the planets may originally have formed part of the sun has been discredited by the students of atomic physics. The sun consists almost wholly of hydrogen which, indeed, seems to be the predominant material in the universe. No known process could account for the present composition of the earth, assuming that it started as hydrogen. The iron and other heavy elements present in it must have come from a star in a more advanced state of evolution than the sun, though this star could very well have been a partner of the sun.

Such heat as the earth has manifested in its interior from time immemorial may be in part the residue of such heat as was developed at the time of its formation under the influence of gravity. The accepted view to-day, however, is that much unstable or radio-active material entered into its composition and that heat has been continuously developed in the earth's interior by the breakdown of this material. It is clear from the evidence of geology that the earth was once much hotter than it is to-day.

CHAPTER II

THE ELEMENTS OF GEOLOGY

Terrific heat tends to break down all substances into their elements, but when the temperature abates the elements may come together to form compounds. We can imagine that in the first state of the earth oxygen and hydrogen existed independently of one another, just as they will in any fiery furnace. Below a certain temperature, however, oxygen and hydrogen combine to form a new gas which we call steam. Other substances besides hydrogen have a strong affinity for oxygen, so that as the earth began to cool the amount of free oxygen or, indeed, of free elements of any kind became progressively less. It is supposed that the earth eventually developed a liquid core and that heavier elements such as iron gravitated to the centre, while lighter substances floated to the surface where cooler conditions prevailed and where much chemical interaction was able to take place.

Eventually there was a solidification of the scums and drosses forming the outside layer of the fluid globe. Free gases, including oxygen, nitrogen and steam, formed an atmosphere round this gradually solidifying planet. A time must have come when the steam in the outer layers of this atmosphere began to condense as clouds of water droplets and even to fall as rain. This falling rain might never reach the earth's surface but be re-evaporated by the terrific heat still radiated by the hot surface crust. The falling of water as rain and its subsequent re-ascent as steam served to carry away the heat of the earth by a very efficient convection process, and eventually conditions were ripe for a descent of nearly all the water vapour in the prolonged downpour that gave us our oceans. All that was then left of the earth's atmosphere was a residue of still uncombined oxygen and nitrogen, together with some other gases including, very probably, a considerable percentage of carbon dioxide.

By now the earth had a relatively thick and stable solid crust. Neverthe-less, it would not always have seemed stable to a human onlooker, could there have been one present so many millions of years ago. The fluid interior of the earth shrank and shrank as it lost its heat, so that the solid outer crust was continually wrinkling and crumbling like so much un-supported pie crust. Large areas of it would be pushed up slowly or else with violent rapidity into huge ridges that assumed the form of mountains tens of thousands of feet high. Earthquakes must have been of daily and perhaps hourly occurrence. Every now and then gaseous products from the earth's interior would force an opening through the crust and belch forth with eruptive violence just as steam belches up from hot porridge. Molten matter from the interior would be carried up at the same time and would spread over the outside of the earth's crust in what we would now call a sea of lava.

Such volcanic activity was liable to become manifest anywhere. On the moon it left permanent scars and pock marks which you can see as "craters" if you look through a telescope. On the earth many traces of volcanic activity were obliterated by the torrential rains already men-tioned. The same might have occurred on the moon but, being much smaller, the moon was unable to retain its atmosphere. For want of a large enough gravity force to hold it in subjugation, the moon's atmo-sphere wandered away molecule by molecule into outer space. The high mountains and volcanic cones, elevated on the earth's surface in the early stages of its history, were erased by the subsequent effects of weather. Storms of unbelievable violence and duration carried away all loose volcanic matter. Torrential rivers charged with rocks and grit carved great courses of their own to the sea, where they let fall this sediment to cover vast tracts of the sea bed.

For a time there seemed to be direct competition between fire and water, for each continually obliterated the efforts of the other in an endeavour to put a finishing touch to the earth's exterior. No sooner did lava overflows spread a covering of igneous rock over the land than deluges and flood water came down to disintegrate this covering and spread it in the form of sand or mud over the sea bed. Often the land would sink beneath the level of the sea, and just as often the sea bed would be lifted up high enough to become dry land. A good idea of the rough treatment suffered by the earth's crust in a former Age is given by the pictures opposite page 226. These show the folding or crumpling effect of endwise pressure.

When the earth lost so much heat as to be dependent on the sun to keep the water on its surface from freezing, a new force, namely ice, came into the picture as a formative agent. Water which percolates into rocky crevices and then freezes has the same disruptive action as a wedge driven in by a hammer. Many a proud mountain of enormous size has been gradually levelled down into an untidy scatter of small fragments by the expansive force of freezing water within its surface interstices. Moreover, soft snow on the heights has a habit of sliding into ravines and valleys, there to become consolidated into hard ice. This ice works its way down the valley as a slow-moving glacier which is capable of exerting a huge pressure on rocky knobs and prominences in its path. That a glacier breaks away many fragments of rock both large and small from the sides of the valleys down which it courses will be evident to anyone who has stood at the lower extremity of such a glacier. Here, where the ice melts to form a turbulent stream, you can see an accumulation of abandoned boulders and rocky fragments forming what is called the terminal moraine. The stream of icy water coming from the glacier is itself charged with rocky fragments and, as it courses its muddy way on to level land, there to flow more slowly and spread more widely, it deposits these fragments, gradually building up the level of its bed at the expense of the mountain it has left behind.

At the present time volcanic action is on a negligible scale. Up-heavals and subsidences may likewise be unimportant. Fire has practically finished its work of giving surface-contours to the earth. Not so ice and water, however. The grand wrinkles of rock we call mountains are being broken down and worn down by weathering, and their substance is being scattered broadcast over land, but more especially over the sea bed, without there being any adequate compensatory mountain or land-building process. It seems as though the impact of the weather on our earth is destined to wash all dry land into the sea at last. Here and there man manages to hold up the process, or even reclaim submerged land, but the best delaying agency is vegetation. The roots of trees, grass and other plants hold the surface soil together even on steep hillsides, so that the rain is unable to carry it away down the slope and via streams or rivers to the sea.

If we take a section through the earth's crust, cutting into a hillside for instance, in search of chalk or gravel, coal or iron, we shall find that it is built up in layers or "strata." This is just what we should expect from the story we have told above. Fire lays down a bed of rock which water subsequently covers with sediment. Fire may try again, over-laying sedimentary rock with lava, and then, perhaps, subsidence has given the sea a chance to lay down vast thicknesses of chalk. Further accidents of Nature may cause gravel or sand to be piled on the chalk. The story of what has occurred in a given locality over huge periods of time is recorded wholly or incompletely by the rocks we can find there. I say "or incompletely" to include cases where the record may have been partially obliterated by weathering or erosion. An alluvial deposit may be laid down at one epoch only to be washed away in the next.

We can only know for certain what has occurred in any one place if we compare its geological record with the records of neighbouring places, carrying out our survey over a very wide area. The foregoing account of the formation of the earth's crust is the end product of much patient investigation by innumerable geologists. The rocks which form the earth possess characteristics which differ according to their composition and the manner of their formation; consequently a study of the rocks provides many a clue to past events. Some rocks disclose their igneous origin, being obviously the solidification of minerals that were once molten. If cooling was very slow the rock will be crystalline, if sudden it will be without structure (amorphous) and it may be like glass (vitreous). Igneous rocks formed by slow cooling under great pressure at great depths are called "plutonic" rocks, and granite is a good example. Other igneous rocks are termed "volcanic" because they represent ancient overflows of lava from craters or fissures in the earth's surface. Volcanic rocks are mainly amorphous on account of their rapid cooling; some are riddled with blowholes caused by the expansion of imprisoned gases. In pumice the effect of these gases on the molten material was to blow it up into a kind of froth which subsequently petrified.

Chemical analysis shows that many so-called sedimentary rocks are nothing more than a consolidation of minute particles of igneous rock. Thus, sandstone consists of minute particles of quartz, and it can be inferred that these particles resulted from the gradual disruption of granite exposed to the destructive agencies of sunshine, wind and water. Laid down under water, layer by layer, these particles of sand formed a thick sediment which, in the course of centuries, became consolidated into a hard rock. In red sandstone the particles are cemented together by iron oxide (rust) which was left behind by oxide-impregnated water percolating through them.

Clay is formed from the debris of granite which consisted of felspar rather than of quartz; the felspar was chemically changed and disrupted by water containing carbon-dioxide gas in solution. That sandstones

A severe case of folded strata.

Folded strata are here seen in process of denudation by the sea.

When subjected to horizontal compressive forces the stratified crust of the earth wrinkles or folds. The folding seen here is on a small scale. *Crown Copyright Reserved.*

Much of the earth's crust is formed of deposits laid down layer by layer under water to form strata, as shown here.

(Both by courtesy of the Geological Survey and Museum.

and clays were formed under water is proved conclusively by the discovery in them of the fossil remains of fish and other marine organisms. From the presence of sedimentary rocks in any given area the geologist will conclude that the particular area of their occurrence must once have been under the sea. Quite often these sedimentary rocks containing marine fossils are found at considerable elevations above sea-level and, since it is unthinkable that the sea should have subsided, the geologist concludes that what was formerly a sub-merged part of the earth's crust must have been lifted up by subter-ranean forces. This can be seen from both the pictures opposite this page which show examples of stratified rock uplifted in this way. The picture on the right shows that on a small scale a certain amount of folding has occurred also.

Many rocks fail to fit into the categories of "igneous" or "sedimen-tary," and it would seem that they are the result of a transformation. Thus, a layer of sedimentary rock loses its original character if it is baked to a high temperature by an intrusion of lava, or if affected chemically by water laden with some active impurity. Rocks affected by such influences to the point of taking on new characteristics are called "metamorphic." Marble deserves to be called metamorphic because it was made by subjecting chalk or limestone to great heat at a depth where the pressure of the superincumbent strata was sufficient to prevent the escape of the resulting carbon-dioxide gas. Such heating at atmospheric pressure results in the production of quicklime (see the section on Chemistry, page 169), but at higher pressures melting occurs without chemical change, and slow cooling then leads to crystallisation. It is in this way, then, that formless chalky limestone is converted into the crystalline rock we call marble. The process can be imitated in the laboratory.

Other crystalline limestones have resulted from a different process; the original sedimentary rock was dissolved by water impregnated with carbon dioxide and then precipitated in crystalline form by the subsequent evaporation of the water.

Pressure alone may change the nature of a rock by causing its crystals to assume a new alignment with their long axes parallel to the direction of the applied force. A rock so formed is termed a "schist" and its structure appears to be stratified. However, not being laid down layer by layer, as is the case with a truly stratified rock, a schist is best described as "foliated." A schist can generally be split quite easily into thin laminæ if it is divided along the planes defined by the crystal layers; such planes are termed "cleavage" planes. Schists may be formed from sedimentary rocks by their being heated and then slowly cooled under great pressure. Crystals are formed and these assume the alignment needed to define cleavage planes. The latter do not always run parallel to the original bedding planes or planes of stratification. Schists are of many different kinds, e.g. clay schist, quartz schist, mica schist, etc., depending on the material which was originally processed. Slate is a clay schist and gneiss is a granite-like schist resulting either from volcanic rock subjected to pressure or sedimentary rock subjected to heat.

Of the elements comprising the earth's crust oxygen is the most abundant. This statement is true even when water is left out of the account; oxygen has been estimated to comprise nearly 50 per cent. by weight of the solid materials forming the crust. It is, moreover, nearly eight-ninths by weight of all ocean waters, and there is a sufficiency of these to cover the whole globe to an average depth of 2 miles. After oxygen the most abundant element is silicon, this being nearly 30 per cent. by weight of the earth's crust. The estimated percentage figures for some of the other abundant elements are 8 per cent. for aluminium, $4\frac{1}{2}$ per cent. for iron and $3\frac{1}{2}$ per cent. for calcium. In order of their occurrence, magnesium, sodium, potassium, hydrogen and carbon come next. Carbon represents less than one-eighth of 1 per cent. of the earth's crust and yet it is the main ingredient of valuable coal and petroleum deposits.

Many substances have so great an affinity for oxygen that they cannot exist as elements in the natural state. Silicon is scarcely known to anybody in its pure form, yet, as silica, which is an oxide of silicon (SiO_2), it is one of the most familiar of materials. Quartz is its igneous crystalline form occurring in granite, and sand consists mainly of quartz particles torn from granite by the disintegrating influences of climate or by the battering of boulder-laden ocean waves. Silicon is also present in the minerals termed "silicates," which are compounds of silica and metallic oxides. Silicates are said to comprise nine-tenths of the earth's crust, being the basis of all rocks except sandstones, quartzites and carbonates.

Aluminium is represented chiefly in a silicate known as felspar and in clay, which is derived from felspar by the deteriorating effect of chemically impregnated water. It is, of course, present also in slate and other rocks formed out of clay by such agencies as extreme heat and extreme pressure.

Rocks coming under the head of carbonates are limestone and chalk.

These consist mainly of calcium carbonate ($CaCO_3$). This substance is present in sea water and it is used by minute sea organisms to build up shell and skeleton. Chalk consists of the imperishable remains of billions of these organisms. Thus it is sedimentary in character, though the primary cause of its formation was organic.

Another rock of the same chemical composition is built up originally as coral. The creature responsible for this was thought by Charles Darwin to be incapable of living at a depth of more than 150 feet below the surface of the sea, yet coral reefs are known to be based on ocean beds thousands of feet deep. The supposition is that the coral animal depends on a gradual subsidence of the sea bottom for the continuity of its activity. When the sea bed rises instead of subsiding, the coral reefs are thrust above water to become the rocky substance of dry land.

Limestones originated in several different ways, among others by the metamorphosis of chalk and coral. Calcium carbonate is soluble in water containing carbon dioxide, so that limestone could also be the accumulation of a precipitate in water that evaporated or otherwise lost its solvent capacity. The well-known caves in the limestone hills of Derbyshire and elsewhere are gradually eaten out by water with solvent properties. This water, impregnated with calcium carbonate, is capable of reconstructing in another situation the limestone it has eaten away. Part of this work of reconstruction may be accomplished in the original cave. Droplets of water hanging to the roof may evaporate before they become large enough to fall. They deposit their load of calcium carbonate at the point of their disappearance and in course of time the accumulated deposit grows into a long pendent finger of limestone called a "stalactite." Sometimes the drops evaporate after falling, so that the finger grows *upwards* from the floor of the cave instead of *downwards* from the ceiling; in this case it is called a "stalagmite." The top picture facing page 230 shows stalactite formation in a cave.

In the course of time rocks exposed to the weather become reduced to fragments which may be called boulders, stones or gravel according to their size. In general boulders become reduced by the mischances of time to fine gravel and ultimately to sand, but not infrequently they become embedded in soft sand or clay, there to remain while this matrix becomes hardened. Rock consisting of boulders in sandstone or clay is called conglomerate; the second kind is also called boulder clay.

If the boulders are newly broken from a rocky cliff or mountain, they are likely to be angular with some sharp points and edges, but boulders that have been much rolled and buffeted by swiftly moving water assume rounded forms. The pebbles on a shingle beach are rounded fragments of rock or of flint.

The origin of flint is thought to be organic. Certain sea creatures (including sponges) utilise the silica in sea water for their skeletons instead of calcium carbonate. Their remains after death serve as nuclei for the deposition of more silica directly from the sea water. Thus a flint is a growing thing, yet it never becomes very large. Nodules of flint abound in chalk and other marine sediments. Our prehistoric ancestors discovered that flints could be easily chipped into the form of tools or weapons (see Volume I, page 2), and their dependence on flint implements characterised the dawn of civilisation during what we call the "stone age."

That rocks of different kinds lie on top of one another in the form of strata is common knowledge, and everyone has a rough idea of how stratified formations come into being. When the earth first acquired a solid crust all rock must have been of the unweathered igneous variety. Lava eruptions might cover an old igneous rock with a newer one, and possibly there would be an intervening layer of dusty volcanic deposit or of volcanic mud. The level of the earth's surface would be constantly raised in the neighbourhood of volcanic vents, but far more important as an agency of uplift would be the constant crumpling of the earth's crust to accommodate a shrinking central core. The earth wrinkled on a grand scale, just as an ageing apple wrinkles on a small scale, and the result was proportionately more impressive. Huge ranges of mountains were thrown aloft; and the process being haphazard must have produced other irregularities in the form of seams, clefts and chasms.

When sunshine and rain began to attack the volcanic landscape the tendency was for the rocky heights to be gradually disintegrated and carried piecemeal into the valleys, there to be deposited as boulders, stones, gravel, sand or mud. Water loses its ability to convey solid matter in suspension when its velocity of travel abates; consequently a river drops the sediment in its waters when it becomes broad and slow moving. It tends to become silted up near its mouth with the debris of the mountains at its source. The level of the plain is gradually raised by the same river that, farther up, will be carving for itself an ever wider and deeper channel out of mountain rock. Geologists believe that vast irregularities in the earth's surface have been created and eroded several times over as a consequence of the war between the earth's internal fires and the levelling atmospheric influences.

Our present mountains are the relics of the last of the great fiery

Limestone is soluble in water containing carbon dioxide, so it is often dissolved out by underground springs to cause caves. Limestone-charged drops of water on the roof may evaporate and cause the limestone to be left behind. Over a period of centuries these minute deposits of limestone form stalactites.

Frost produces an expansive action on water, so that ice forming in the interstices of rock will cause the latter to split and crumble. Here can be seen a mountain which is gradually being reduced to rubble by this force of Nature.

(*Both by courtesy of the Geological Survey and Museum. Crown Copyright Reserved.*)

upheavals. The bulk of the material formerly entering into their composition is now scattered broadcast. Some lies at their feet in the form of screes or glacial moraines; some forms deposits of clay or mud over nearby plains, but most of it is spread over the bottom of the sea as sand or mud near river mouths. The bottom picture facing page 230 shows a mountain in course of reduction to rubble by the action of sun, frost, wind and rain.

Most of the scenery of the existing world is provided by the levelled-out debris of mountains and hills, and even the hills that are visible may themselves be only the upthrust debris of former hills. Of sandstone hills this must be true; likewise of hills made from derivatives of clay. The areas where we can see primitive igneous rocks such as granite still rearing aloft and withstanding the processes of decay are much more restricted than could have been the case millions of years ago. The Alps in Europe and the Himalayas in Asia are magnificent relics of our plutonic past, but they are destined to be worn away at last by sun, wind, rain and ice. The mountain scenery of Scotland is provided very largely by metamorphic rock.

CHAPTER III

THE DAWN OF LIFE

The practical requirements of mankind necessitate such activities as quarrying, mining and well boring, all of which result in the exposure of ancient beds of rock. Cutting away the side of a hill to obtain gravel or sand or chalk leaves a cliff the face of which will tell a competent geologist a great deal about the past history of that particular locality. Such a cliff, if vertical, represents the sort of section of the earth's crust that geologists would like to have made everywhere to help them form

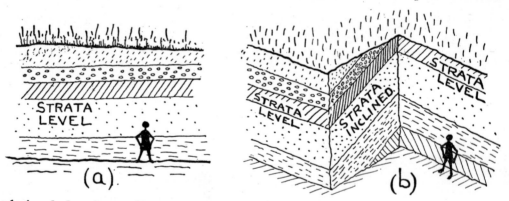

their deductions. Fortunately for these investigators, every locality possesses its quarries, mines and wells or, alternatively, such naturally provided sections as sea-formed cliffs, river-worn ravines, etc., etc. Enough data have been accumulated from such sources to enable us to determine in some detail how our own island kingdom was laid down layer by layer or stratum by stratum.

The evidence of a cliff may point to a quiet or tumultuous past, but the testimony of a single section needs to be studied in conjunction with that of one at right angles before definite conclusions can be drawn.

Sketch (*a*) on page 232 shows a cliff in which the strata are horizontal and suggestive of long ages of quiet sedimentary deposit unaffected by volcanic or other earth movements. Sketch (*b*) shows how false this impression could be; here the plane of section is turned through 90 degrees and we see at once that the strata, so far from being horizontal, are steeply inclined. To learn all we can from rocky sections we must choose our section plane with discrimination or, alternatively, make two sections at right angles to one another. The section of least interest is the one which shows horizontal stratification for strata that are known to be inclined; such a section plane always exists, but the plane at right angles to this—the plane of steepest inclination—is the one that tells the whole story.

In general the geological sections representative of the rocks at a

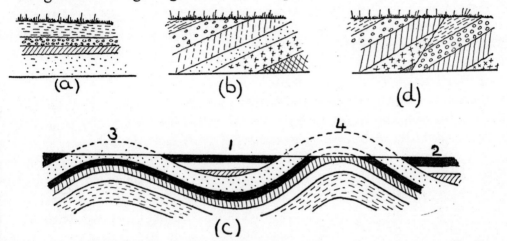

(a)   (b)   (d)

(c)

particular place will be taken in the direction of greatest slope for the various strata; we are free to suppose that in the perpendicular direction the strata lie horizontally for a greater or smaller distance. Typical sections are shown on this page. A truly horizontal disposition of the strata as shown at (*a*) is characteristic of undisturbed sedimentary rock, but, of course, it could also apply to a terrain that had undergone uplift or settlement after the rock was formed, this movement being of the straight up or down variety without tilting. Sometimes a horizontal stratification results from the accidental cancellation of one tilt by a subsequent tilt in the opposite direction. To what the rocks reveal there may be several plausible interpretations, and the geologists' business is to sift all the evidence, comparing the indications at one place with those in neighbouring places, in order to eliminate all but the right interpretation.

Examples of inclined strata are sketched at (b) and shown in the left-hand picture opposite. The inclination, whether it be great or small, is the result of the wrinkling or folding of the earth's crust that occurred after the stratified sedimentary rocks were laid down. When the course of the strata can be followed by studying borings or excavations at wide intervals, we find great humps and hollows in what must once have been level horizontal deposits. Sketch (c) shows an example of this crumpling or folding of stratified rock. Naturally a good deal may have occurred since the folding took place. Further sedimentation may have filled up the hollows (as at 1 and 2), whereas the erosive effects of wind, water, ice and temperature fluctuation may have removed the humps (as at 3 and 4). In the right-hand picture opposite truncated strata have been overlaid by fresh deposits. A fault, as at (d) occurs where the strata are thrown out of alignment by cracking of the earth's crust followed by relative movement of the rocks on the two sides of the fissure. A fault may develop gradually, or with alarming suddenness; a good example is shown in the top picture opposite page 235.

Geologists know enough about the earth's crust now to be able to recognise its different shells or layers as having certain ages. Despite their distortion and mutilation by events following their formation, the rocky layers cannot but occur in the order of their formation and, except in regions where folding has been so extreme as to cause "inversion," the oldest rocks lie deepest and the newest rocks lie at or near the surface.

The classification of rocks according to their age is perhaps the most interesting of all geological classifications and it links up with the evolutionary account of how the multitudinous life forms came into existence. Embedded in the rocks are the remains of animals, birds, fishes, reptiles, plants, insects, etc. etc., of long ago. Sometimes the remains consist of actual bones or shells or teeth; sometimes again they take the form merely of the impressions of such things, these having remained after the things themselves have decomposed and vanished. In certain muddy deposits we find the footprints of huge reptiles, now extinct, and even the impressions made by raindrops falling millions of years ago. Made in soft mud that rapidly baked hard in the sun, these imprints have been preserved under further deposits which, fortunately for us, did not melt or merge with what was laid down before.

The oldest of all rocks are the igneous rocks of plutonic origin. These are known as Archæan rocks and they commonly exist in the form of granite, gneiss and schists. They are sometimes referred to as "Azoic" because they are lifeless, that is to say, without any fossils or

Here the remains of folded, or inclined, strata have been subsequently overlaid by new deposits.

Folding on an ample scale produces inclined strata, an example of which is shown here. Notice the embedded fossil tree trunk.

(Both by courtesy of the Geological Survey and Museum. Crown Copyright Reserved.)

Ancient deposits may in time lose their underlying support, or they may receive a local upthrust. In either case a shearing force causes them to rupture and they lose their horizontal continuity. A rupture of this kind is termed a "fault."

A mixture of fine sandy material or clay with boulders or gravel constitutes the debris left behind by glacial action on rock.

(*Both by courtesy of the Geological Survey and Museum. Crown Copyright Reserved.*)

impressions that point to the existence of life on the earth at the time of their formation. Of course, the mere absence of such remains does not afford conclusive proof of the absence of life; some of the first life forms may have been too lacking in substantial parts to leave any trace. Thus nobody could expect to find much evidence of the existence of a prehistoric jellyfish!

The next geological division embraces the so-called Primary rocks, known also as Palæozoic because they contain traces of the earliest-known life forms. Then come the Secondary rocks (Mesozoic) corresponding to the middle period in the development of life. Here we find the remains of the enormous reptiles and reptile-like birds that feature so prominently in the naturalists' story-book of bygone ages. The Tertiary rocks bring us to the remains of early mammals, such as the mammoth and the sabre-toothed tiger. This epoch is characterised by the term Cainozoic, signifying a more recent development in life forms. The Quaternary rocks date from the last great ice age and they are still in process of formation.

Evidence of man's existence cannot be traced back very far. It abounds in Quaternary rocks, but the first man-like remains make their appearance in the later Tertiary rocks. The origin of man would seem to date from about half a million years ago, but bones and skulls like those of modern men go back to only about 50,000 years ago. The record of the rocks, beginning with the igneous granites and their derivatives, is thought to go back about 1000 million years, and calculations based on astrophysical data, nuclear physics and so on put the age of the earth at from 2000 to 3000 million years. There were, of course, no rocks until the earth developed a solid crust.

The years taken to form a layer of sedimentary rock can be gauged from its thickness if the rate of deposition is known. The latter factor cannot be known with certainty since it is dependent on influences which vary from age to age. We can measure the rate at which sediments are formed and laid down to-day, and use this figure as a basis for our estimates, but it is almost certain that Nature worked in a more energetic fashion hundreds of millions of years ago when the internal fires were still causing world-wide earthquakes and volcanic eruptions. Storms of wind and rain must have been far more violent and destructive. The risk, then, is that we shall over-estimate rather than under-estimate the age of the rocks. Thus the geologists who reckon that rock formation commenced about 1000 million years ago are not without rivals, who would put the figure at 100 million years, which is only a tenth as much.

The Primary or Palæozoic age is variously stated to have commenced at from 60 to 600 million years ago; the Secondary or Mesozoic age at from 14 to 140 million years ago and the Tertiary or Cainozoic age at from 4 to 40 million years ago.

The oldest (Archæan) rocks include the various granites which are made up of quartz, felspar and mica; also the metamorphic gneisses and schists. The Primary rocks include old red sandstone, a variety of limestone, and the slates of Wales; also the coal measures. The term Cambrian applies to the Primary rocks found in Wales, Silurian to those found in Shropshire (where an old British tribe called the Silures used to dwell), Devonian to Primary rocks found in Devonshire and Carboniferous to Primary rocks associated with coal seams.

It should be understood that names like Cambrian, Silurian and Devonian are of more than local significance, as they apply to all rocks of certain types and ages irrespective of where they are found. It is perhaps unfortunate that geologists should have conferred on these rocks names suggestive of particular districts, but at the time it seemed a natural procedure, the rocks having been found and studied in the places concerned before they were encountered elsewhere.

Secondary rocks are divided into three groups, Triassic being the oldest and Cretaceous the youngest, with Jurassic in between. The term Jurassic applies to the kind of rock of which the Jura mountains are composed, so that this is another rather misleading distinction. The so-called "new" red sandstone is in the Triassic group, and chalk is the most important rock in the Cretaceous group. It is in chalk that flints are found.

Clay and loose sands are chief among the Tertiary rocks, which are grouped according to age under the heads of Eocene, Oligocene, Miocene and Pliocene, the oldest being the Eocene group. The Quaternary rocks fall under the heads of Glacial or Pleistocene, and Post-Glacial or recent. Clay containing boulders (boulder clay) is the chief formation for which the ice ages are noted. This type of material is shown in the bottom picture opposite page 235. When the softer material is washed away, and only the boulders are left behind, a strange panorama may be created, as shown in the top picture opposite this page. Rocks rounded and gullied, as in the bottom picture opposite this page, bear the marks of weathering, but smooth contours accompanied by scratches usually denote abrasion by glacial ice.

The rocks are arranged in layers like the pages of a postcard album and they abound in pictorial records of the past. Known as fossils these relics include bony remains, moulds or impressions and mineral

Water or other eroding influences acting on glacial deposits may remove all but the heaviest boulders.
These are sometimes left precariously perched on small bases, as shown here.

Hard rock, subjected to the eroding effects of weather, sometimes becomes grooved, gullied and smooth-
contoured as shown here.

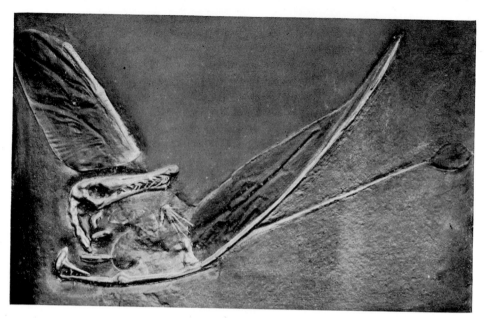

Buried in ancient deposits are the remains of prehistoric creatures.   The cast shown here is of the remains
of a reptile-like bird called the Pterodactyl, prototype of the dragon of folk-lore and legend.

(Crown Copyright.   By courtesy of the British Museum of Natural History, London, S.W.7.)

The bony remains shown here are of a prehistoric creature called the Hypsilaphadon.

(Crown Copyright.   By courtesy of the British Museum of Natural History, London, S.W.7.)

transformations. The last mentioned are a product of substitution; some shell or other object is removed by chemical action and its place is taken, particle by particle, by some different substance until a durable image or cast is formed of the whole. Soft-bodied creatures like sea urchins and lumps of animal excrement have had their likenesses preserved in this way. The oldest remains prove that life began in a small way with unimpressive creatures dwelling wholly in water. These were elaborated by degrees into backboned fish, but some species developed the ability to breathe air and move about on land without losing all their aquatic habits; these were the first amphibians. At a later stage some of the amphibians specialised in the land-way of life, becoming reptiles, with no further interest in lake or sea. This was the epoch of the monsters whose remains are shown in the pictures facing pages 238 and 239. The branching of life into new forms did not stop here. Fossil finds show that certain reptiles, for example the pterodactyl shown fossilised in the top picture opposite, developed the ability to fly. These strange forms reigned supreme for some millions of years and then became extinct, being superseded by cleverer and less clumsy adaptations from the original stock.

With the disappearance of the more impressive reptilian remains we come upon bones like those in the pictures opposite of creatures that quite clearly were the ancestors of present-day birds and animals. We can follow the record through for the horse, which was once a creature no bigger than a dog and walked on feet having five toes. A similar pedigree has been drawn up for the elephant and even for man. It seems clear that man shares his ancestry with the higher apes, notably the chimpanzee and the orang-utan.

No mention has been made of the relics of plant-life and insects, but we have evidence of the existence millions of years ago of dragon-flies with a wing span of over two feet, and of trees and ferns unlike anything occurring to-day.

Only a few hundred years ago men believed that the world was created a matter of five to six thousand years before, with all the familiar plants, birds and beasts perfected once for all. Geological research revealed the untruth of this supposition, for it showed that existing creatures were derived from earlier and different creatures which in turn were derived from earlier creatures still, and so on back to an age when the most advanced representative of bony individuals was the humble trilobite. Indeed, there was reason to think that the trilobite itself could be traced back further hundreds of millions of years to origins more unpretentious still. Perhaps the earliest living things were only microscopic blobs of jelly or slime occurring in the warm waters of the primeval sea. No traces of life's ultimate origins can be found and, indeed, it is not to be expected that the rocks should bear the impress or remains of creatures so unsubstantial.

A problem of more concern to biologist than geologist is to discover the mode of progression of one life form to the next. It could be supposed that several separate acts of creation provided the world with its earliest species of living creatures, and that subsequent miraculous happenings caused new creatures to take the place of old ones. However, as the evidence accumulated, it became clear that Nature did not work in jerks like this but by smooth and almost imperceptible degrees. The fossil record showed that creatures changed gradually as generation succeeded generation, possibly becoming larger and more clearly remarkable for one feature or another until the amount of change, taken over tens of thousands of years, was considerable enough to entitle the end product to be regarded as a new creature quite distinct from the ancestral root.

A number of naturalists supposed that living creatures could alter themselves by struggling to meet difficulties in their circumstances and that such alterations were passed on to the offspring. This theory, called "the inheritance of acquired characteristics," explained the evolution of new and better types from types less fitted to the conditions of existence, but nobody accepts such a theory to-day because there is no evidence that acquired characteristics can be transmitted to the next generation. A man who makes himself exceptionally strong in the arms by exercise does not have children with similarly developed arms; a lamb having its tail cut off does not grow up to produce naturally tailless lambs.

Charles Darwin put forward a different and more credible theory to account for evolutionary change. He noticed that certain *natural* differences existed between creatures of the same kind and that these might indeed be transmitted in the process of generation. Thus naturally tall parents have, on the average, taller children than naturally short parents. Darwin did not attempt to explain *how* individuals came to differ; he just accepted it as a fact that no two were ever exactly alike. Circumstance favoured individuals which were stronger or swifter or taller or cleverer than their fellows, so that in the struggle for existence they might survive where others perished. Thus the competition for the scanty food available in a time of famine might leave only those creatures which were particularly well endowed in the matter of tooth

Skeleton of the Diplodocus, most enormous of the monsters that roamed over the earth millions of years ago.

(Crown Copyright. By courtesy of the British Museum of Natural History, London, S.W.7.)

In size and proportions the Arsinoitherium is more like the animals of our own Age than some of the other prehistoric creatures.

(Crown Copyright. By courtesy of the Museum of Natural History, London, S.W.7.)

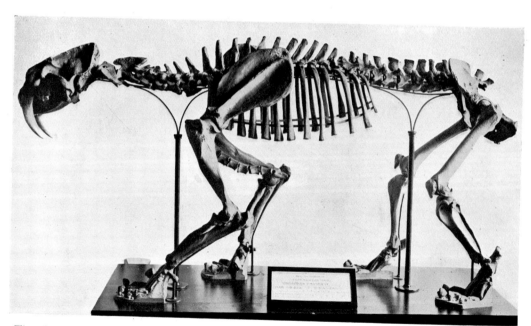

The sabre-toothed tiger was a creature destined to leave a line of descendants reaching down to our own time.

(Crown copyright. By courtesy of the British Museum of Natural History, London, S.W.7.)

and claw. This sifting of the fittest creatures from those not so fit Darwin called "natural selection," and the result of this sifting he termed the "survival of the fittest." The offspring of the fit comprised the whole of the next generation and so the average length of tooth and claw in such generation might be considerably above what it had been in the previous generation, i.e. before it had been decimated by famine. Darwin put forward this argument to explain how, for instance, teeth might turn into tusks, flippers into arms, fins into legs, and so on.

It is evident from a comparison between the animals of sea, land and air that the basic idea of backbone and four limbs is common to all, and that the existing species could very well be special adaptations of what was once a fishy four-finned creature. The whale is fitted for an aquatic existence by having well-developed fore-fins, but corresponding to rear fins there are only vestiges of bony structures. In animals the limbs are no longer fins but mobile supports called legs. In birds two of the limbs are modified to form wings and in man (as well as in the apes) these same limbs have become arms. A certain reptilian form may have been the common ancestor of all these widely differing creatures, one branch of the family finding success in becoming adapted to a marine existence, another succeeding in some terrestrial mode of existence and a third branch taking to the air.

Darwin's theory has undergone some modification since the laws of natural inheritance have become better understood, but it is substantially as described here and biologists accept it as true despite the apparently well-founded objections of such naturalists as Fabre (the great French student of insect life) and one or two others. The fault Fabre found with Darwin's evolutionary theory lay in its apparent inability to account for the development of characteristics that needed to be perfected in a single step. Wings, for instance, are not wings and can confer no advantages on their possessor until they are effective as instruments of flight. They could not have evolved by easy stages from useful flippers, fins or legs because a process of degeneration would then have preceded the acquisition of an advantage, and how could it have profited any creature to degenerate?

Certain insect habits are successful because they represent an instinctive skill in doing something rather complex. At no half-way stage could this skill have availed the insect in the least, as its actions must always have been perfectly right or else the result would have been disaster. How did the insect acquire by stages an ability that was worse than valueless ere it became infallible?

The answers to these objections can be looked for in the mutability of circumstance. Thus the skill needed by an insect to-day would only have been needed by the insect of a million years ago, provided that its prey were in all respects the same a million years ago as it is to-day. Fabre was inclined to overlook the fact that an insect's tactics in dealing with other insects could have been cruder in the days when these other insects also were cruder. Also, success might very well have come to an insect species on the hit-and-miss principle. Thus, since insects breed at the rate of tens of thousands of progeny per couple per season, it might well be that success was at first only a matter of luck. The early insects may have been fumblers, but if as many as a tenth of one per cent. achieved success by accidentally doing the right thing, the species would be preserved and the survivors would hand on to some of their progeny a similar "accident-proneness." Instinctive skills may have become universal in the insect world merely as a result of this hit-and-miss process.

As for the evolution of wings, we could envisage the process for this too. The penguin has flippers which help him to swim. On land he stands erect and uses his flippers to balance himself when running. Were penguins to be benefited by great swiftness in running, it is possible that this balancing function of the flippers would become of paramount importance as giving extra speed in running or hopping. With time the flippers might become effective as fans or paddles, actually giving forward impetus during hops by beating back the air. A heavy duck is not able to fly, but she will flap her wings when running fast and this will give her extra speed. Wings may therefore have had some value in their unperfected form as aids to running or hopping. It is easy to see that under the continued pressure of circumstances the power of sustained flight might be evolved from a gradually increasing ability to hop with the help of flippers. It is conceivable that monkeys or men could be bred so as ultimately to fly because they already use their arms as aids to walking and running. It is not conceivable, however, that pigs could be bred with wings, because pigs use their fore-limbs for supporting part of their weight, and while limbs are used for this purpose they cannot possibly undergo an adaptation for any other purpose. The penguin could never be bred for flight while it still needed its flippers for swimming.

The story of biological evolution is extremely interesting from many points of view and it raises the question of whether man is still profiting as a result of natural change or only degenerating. This question cannot be discussed in this chapter.

CHAPTER IV

THE ELEMENTS OF PHYSIOLOGY

In whatever form life first became manifest on the earth there must have been embodied the peculiar principle possessed to this day by all the manifold organisms of the vegetable kingdom, and that is the ability to obtain nourishment from *non-living* or inorganic matter. At a later stage it was possible for one kind of creature or organism to subsist by preying on other kinds, but to begin with the only available foodstuff for building tissue and providing energy was some simple chemical substance, or a group of such substances.

The peculiarity of modern vegetable organisms is their ability to subsist almost entirely on water from the soil, carbon dioxide from the atmosphere and sunlight. The earliest life forms must have been as simple as this in their requirements. Water from suitably formed soil will contain traces of various chemical compounds in solution and these assist in the tissue-building process. Such compounds are returned to the soil when plants die and decompose, for their remains are then assimilated by the earth. The main body of every plant is built up by the action of sunlight on its leaves, this being responsible for a process known as photosynthesis. Moisture taken in at the roots is constantly rising to the leaves where most of it is passed away as a vapour by "transpiration." At the same time the leaves "breathe in" atmospheric carbon dioxide, converting this, with the help of sunlight and a green substance called "chlorophyll," into the complex carbon compounds needed for growth. The leaves owe their green colour to chlorophyll.

From the date of its first appearance animal life has been dependent upon vegetable life, because the peculiarity of an animal is that it must have food of a self-sufficient kind. Regardless of whether the sun is shining or not the animal must have heat energy and body-building substances, and consequently its food must be a ready-prepared store of all that is essential to its being. The substance of vegetable organisms and of other animals answers to this requirement, which explains why animals live by preying on plants and other animals. The term "animal" is here used in a very general sense and it includes birds, fishes and even insects. What such creatures need from the atmosphere is not carbon dioxide but pure oxygen, as the food they assimilate is oxidised or "burnt" in order to make it produce heat. A product of this oxidation is carbon dioxide, so that, whereas plants absorb this gas from the atmosphere, animals give it back again.

We can see from this brief account that the entire panorama of life is made possible in the first place by the action of sunlight on green leaves. The energy of the sun breaks up a useless incombustible carbon compound and enables the carbon to enter into new compounds that are the basis of vegetable life. These same compounds, assimilated as food by animals, undergo combustion through being combined with atmospheric oxygen, and then they give back as animal heat the energy that was derived in the first place from the sun. Once more there results an incombustible carbon compound, and for a continuation of the cycle this compound must again be assimilated by green leaves with the help of sunlight and be remade into vegetable tissue.

Animals that subsist wholly on a vegetable diet are called "herbivorous" animals; horses, cattle and sheep are examples. Life is rather more complicated for animals needing a diet of animal food; examples of flesh-eating or "carnivorous" animals are wolves, lions and tigers. The human being should be termed "omnivorous" because his diet includes practically every kind of consumable vegetable and animal food.

The relationship between all living things hinted at by the evolutionary hypothesis of Darwin is borne out by anatomical examination of familiar creatures, and by the identity of their life stories. In his birth, way of life and death, man is essentially the same as dog, cat or any other animal. To all the organs comprising his body there are comparable organs in the bodies of animals. Man's only claim to superiority over other creatures seems to lie in the exceptional development of the organ called the brain. Mental processes are possible in man that are far beyond anything of which animals are capable. Nevertheless, a careful study of animals shows that they possess a rudimentary power of thought, and when the same trouble normally expended in educating human children is expended in training monkeys, dogs or other higher animals, the results are by no means negligible.

A person's education is not thought complete nowadays unless he knows something about his own body, and to conclude this book a few notes will be given on the complicated mechanism that is ourselves. We are distinguished from worms and other "invertebrate" creatures by having a bony framework that gives rigidity to our several members. The framework is articulated or jointed to enable the body and its attachments to take up different attitudes or configurations. Almost everything we do—eating, running, writing, etc., etc.—involves the movement of limbs or other parts relative to the trunk or body. And in breathing we constantly move our ribs up and down. The motive power for all these movements is provided by the connections between bone and bone that we call "muscles." To every joint there is necessarily a pair of muscles. Each forms an elastic attachment not unlike a spring or band of rubber, and whereas one muscle tends to move the joint one way, the other tends to move it the other way. We achieve the movement we want by giving one muscle an ascendancy over its opposite.

Mechanical Model of Joint & Muscles
J = Joint
m and M = muscles
(Varying the tension in m and M alters the angle between A and B)

The muscle is a fleshy band attached to bone at both ends and having its body or central part contractable. Under the requisite nervous impulse the muscle tends to become thicker and shorter, and it exerts a considerable force in so doing—the force that enables us to lift weights, spring into the air or nod our heads. When it is in action a muscle performs work and the energy it needs is drawn from the glucose in the blood. It takes both glucose and oxygen from the blood, returning water and carbon dioxide as waste products.

Nearly all the flesh of our bodies consists of muscular tissue, and blood streams through it constantly under the pumping action of the heart. The entry is by way of an artery and it passes back to the heart by a vein. The entering artery subdivides again and again until it forms a network of extremely fine capillaries that can be seen only under a microscope. The subdivision of the blood-stream nevertheless leads to the provision of a greater area of flow, so that whereas the velocity of the blood in a large artery may be of the order of 1 ft. per second, in a capillary it will be nearer to 1 inch per minute. The capillary walls are exceedingly thin so that this, in conjunction with the slowness of the blood flow, enables an interchange to take place between the blood and the cellular tissue of the muscle. The blood loses glucose and oxygen while gaining water and carbon dioxide. If the muscle is being over-worked, or if the blood flow is too sluggish, carbon dioxide and water will accumulate to excess so that we shall feel fatigue. Normally the heart responds to vigorous muscular exercise by pumping the blood round faster. If the heart is diseased and unable to respond to our normal needs, we may suffer from the accumulation of water in our blood that is known as dropsy.

After the blood has served its purpose in the muscle its multitudinous streams recombine to form wider and ever-wider veins. In the veins it recovers its former speed of about 1 ft. per second, though the energy for this acceleration comes only in small part from the heart. Arteries are elastic, and you can feel the pulsations of the heart by pressing on an artery, but almost none of this energy from the heart gets through the capillaries to the veins, so that you cannot feel any pulsation by pressing on a vein. Movement of blood in a vein is promoted mainly by external pressure on the vein itself. If we exercise ourselves vigorously we shall help the blood to travel along the veins by compressing them or squashing them at intervals, their position in the muscles obliging us to do this.

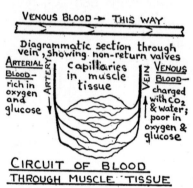

CIRCUIT OF BLOOD THROUGH MUSCLE TISSUE

Because external pressure tends to drive the blood *both* ways along the vein, non-return valves are provided at intervals along its length; these allow blood to flow towards the heart but not backwards towards the capillaries. We can see now that when the circulation of the blood needs to be most rapid, muscular exercise contributes to the desired end by its mechanical action on the veins just where the influence of the heart is at its feeblest. Blood brings warmth to our muscles, this being one of the results of the oxidation of glucose, so that on a very cold day we can dispel the feeling of numbness by stamping our feet and swinging our arms across our chests.

The importance of blood as a vehicle for the fuel needed by our muscles is now self-evident. We have mentioned its circulatory function and said that the heart is a pump that maintains its flow. Where does the blood acquire its oxygen and its glucose? For answer we must refer to the respiratory system and the digestive system. Blood leaving the muscles is impoverished in both respects, so the heart must contrive to pump it to regions in the body where its proper condition is restored. The blood from every muscle in the body goes first of all into a great trunk main leading to what is termed the right heart (because it is the right-hand portion of that organ) whence it is pumped at once to the lungs to have its oxygen deficiency corrected. The lungs are in the chest cavity that we alternately expand and contract in the act of breathing. Our ribs rise and fall and in rising they spread outwards just as the drooping handle of a bucket spreads out when we first begin to lift it from its lowest position; this enlarges the chest cavity. Separating the chest cavity from the abdomen is a muscular wall called the diaphragm, which we also use in breathing; we depress this when we expand our chests and, by squashing up our abdominal organs, we produce an extra bulge in our bellies.

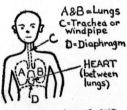

A&B=Lungs
C=Trachea or windpipe
D=Diaphragm
HEART (between lungs)

POSITION OF LUNGS AND HEART IN CHEST CAVITY

The lungs are a pair of similar organs in the variable chest cavity. Entering each lung is a wide air tube (the bronchus) which subdivides again and again into smaller and ever-smaller branches. Each of the ultimate branches terminates in a tiny elastic air sac the surface of which is covered with blood capillaries. When we expand our chests we create a partial vacuum in the chest cavity. Air in our lung sacs is thus able to expand by blowing out the sac walls like tiny balloons. When the air pressure in a lung sac falls, more air rushes in to make good the deficiency, and therefore we are conscious of inhaling or "taking a breath."

The blood in the capillaries lining the lung air sacs has come straight from the heart via a great artery called the pulmonary artery, that divides and subdivides until it reaches the tiny capillaries. The blood here is deficient in oxygen and in the nutrimental principle called glucose, but once it reaches the thin walls of an air sac filled with fresh atmospheric air it can give up its load of carbon dioxide and acquire a fresh charge of oxygen. Having done this, it passes from the lung capillaries into common veins which run together to form at last the great pulmonary vein taking oxygen-enriched blood back to the heart (the left heart this time).

The blood entering the lung is a dark colour tending to purple, and even blue, but when its oxygen content is restored to normal it becomes bright scarlet again, so that the pulmonary vein carries scarlet blood to the left heart. The vehicles for the oxygen are the tiny red corpuscles of the blood. These are shaped like the sweets known as fruit gums and, although of microscopic size, their numbers are great enough to give the blood its characteristic colour. Apart from the red corpuscles the blood consists of a colourless fluid carrier medium and the so-called "white" corpuscles which serve a variety of purposes to be mentioned in due course.

The left heart receives all the blood from the lungs and delivers this to arteries all over the body. The great artery by which it starts on its way is called the aorta, but this soon splits up into branches going to muscles everywhere. In parallel with the circuits from artery to vein through muscles are two other circuits which are very important. The so-called

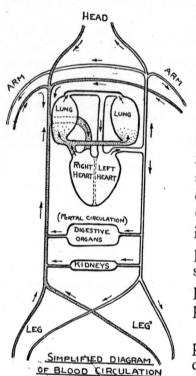

HEAD

ARM   ARM

LUNG   LUNG

RIGHT | LEFT
HEART | HEART

(PORTAL CIRCULATION)
DIGESTIVE
ORGANS

KIDNEYS

LEG   LEG

SIMPLIFIED DIAGRAM
OF BLOOD CIRCULATION

portal circulation leads blood to the digestive organs, where it is able to make good its deficiency of glucose. Only a proportion of the aortic blood-stream is dealt with in this way. The other parallel circuit is through the kidneys, where the blood yields up its surplus water. Here again only a proportion of the aortic blood is involved. Thus the blood is refurnished with the nutrimental principle and made free from surplus water on what engineers would call the "bypass" system. Oil from the lubrication circuit of an engine is generally filtered and purified on the same plan. The entire circulation of the blood, so essential to the maintenance of the life process, is shown diagrammatically on this page.

Each half of the heart is a two-stage pump. The intake portion, called the auricle, is thin walled, and when it contracts it delivers the blood through a non-return flap valve to the ventricle. Valves in the veins prevent any back-flow of blood at this point. The ventricle is provided with very thick muscular walls, and for this reason it can deliver blood at a relatively high pressure—2 to 3 lb. per square inch. The outlet from each ventricle is provided with a non-return valve. The pulsations of the heart occur at a rate of about seventy a minute, and the capacity of the heart is sufficient to bring the blood round to itself again every half minute or so. However, the rate of circulation is governed by the use of the muscles. When very hard work is being done both heart and lungs must deal with the blood at a rate in excess of normal. If we run in a race, we shall be conscious that our heart is pounding and that our breathing is accelerated to the point of distress.

We feel the need for more oxygen directly we exert ourselves, but the store of glucose in our blood is sufficient to last a considerable time. Carbon dioxide we get rid of through our lungs, and the rate of riddance is regulated by our breathing at the same time that this governs our oxygen intake. Normal atmospheric air contains about 0·04 per cent. of carbon dioxide (by volume) and air exhaled from our lungs contains about 4½ per cent. of this gas. The oxygen content drops from about 21 per cent. to about 16 per cent.; so that the net result of our breathing is to replace about a fifth of the atmospheric oxygen with carbon dioxide.

Exercise results in the production of much water in our blood and the kidneys will not rid us of all of this. Some water is passed away in our exhaled breath—we can see it as a cloud on cold days—and some will pass away through our skins as perspiration.

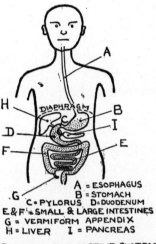

A = ESOPHAGUS
B = STOMACH
C = PYLORUS   D = DUODENUM
E & F = SMALL & LARGE INTESTINES
G = VERMIFORM APPENDIX
H = LIVER   I = PANCREAS

DIAGRAM OF DIGESTIVE SYSTEM

To complete the picture of vital processes in the human body we must describe the digestive system and the portal circulation it serves; we must also say a little more about the excretory system or kidneys.

Food is the source of energy and tissue-building material, and digestion permits the assimilation into the blood-stream of what the body needs from the food. The digestive process begins in the mouth and is completed in stages throughout what is called the alimentary tract. This tract is a tube of variable width and great length which runs through the body without having direct communication with it at any point.

Whatever passes from the alimentary tract into the body must do so through the walls of capillary vessels into the blood-stream. Soluble materials such as salt and sugar are ready for assimilation directly they are dissolved in water, and the saliva in the mouth is a digestive secretion that can begin at once to turn starch into sugar. However, the bulk of the food proceeds by way of a tube called the œsophagus to the stomach, which is a bag-like swelling in the alimentary canal just below the diaphragm. The walls of the stomach secrete another fluid that is able to break down meat and allied foodstuffs into simpler substances soluble in water. Hydrochloric acid is a constituent of the stomach juices.

The exit from the stomach is controlled by a valve called the pylorus, which opens periodically to permit the digested food to enter the duodenum, whence it passes to the small intestine. Food may stay in the stomach for several hours, and in this time it is subjected to a churning motion by muscular agitation of the stomach as well as to the chemical action of the gastric juice. In the duodenum it is joined by secretions from the liver, gall bladder and pancreas, but in the long, narrow intestine it gives back to the body such substances as are needed for the maintenance of the life processes.

The walls of the intestine are interlaced with blood-vessels forming part of the portal circulation; and the dissolved nutriment from the food passes through the walls of these blood-vessels to become assimilated by the blood-stream. Glucose is the chief material absorbed in this way.

From the small intestine the food residue passes into the large intestine, where it becomes more or less solid as a result of the assimilation of water by the intestinal blood-vessels. From the terminal portion of the large intestine the food residue is periodically expelled. It was once believed that undue retention of this waste matter in the bowel resulted in progressive self-poisoning, so that drastic purges were habitually used to ensure a daily evacuation. The truth is that once matter has entered the large intestine it loses nothing to the blood-stream other than water, so that it can do little harm. The disorder resulting in headache, furred tongue and constipation has nothing to do with the lower bowel but rather with the digestive and assimilation processes higher up. The food consumed may be of a kind to overload the system with an excess of fat or sugar or some other substance. Or it may be that insufficient water has been imbibed. What we feel when we are indisposed may be the strain put on organs that have been given an excessive amount of work to do under difficult conditions. Quite naturally the orderly passage of digested matter through the intestines will be suspended if the food is of a kind that requires exceptional activity of stomach glands or liver or pancreas. There may have to be a long wait before the necessary chemical transformations can be wholly accomplished.

If poisonous or indigestible matter is taken, the stomach may return it instead of letting it pass on by way of the pylorus. We vomit when the stomach is unable to reduce its contents to an assimilable condition. The same thing occurs when some inflammatory condition of the intestinal tract (e.g. a diseased appendix or a duodenal ulcer) makes it dangerous for the pylorus to open and impose fresh work on weakened tissue. If a laxative or purging medicine be administered in such a case, the result to the patient may be a fatal rupture or perforation of the intestinal tract at the point of inflammation. Once intestinal matter escapes into the cavities of the body it will occasion the dangerous condition called peritonitis.

The passage of the food along the intestinal tract is promoted by rhythmical contractions of the latter known as "peristalsis." The tube closes down on its contents at particular points and then the points of contraction advance along the tube so that there is a pushing action on all contained matter. Before the peristaltic movement is over the tube recovers its normal diameter, but then the cycle begins all over again. The "waves" of contraction travel in only one direction under normal conditions; reversed peristalsis is a reaction to disease and can only lead to vomiting.

Blood which has assimilated glucose and other substances from the intestines passes straight to the liver, a function of which seems to be to store this glucose in one form or another and deliver it to the main blood-stream in response to the body's needs. The portal circulation includes the liver.

When a muscle is used, glucose is used up and water is formed. The liver at once restores the missing glucose and the kidneys remove the excess water. The pancreas plays a part in this process by secreting a substance known as insulin into the blood-stream. If the pancreas is diseased or missing, the muscles do not utilise the glucose properly and the net result is a tendency for the glucose or sugar content of the blood to become excessive. The victim of this complaint is said to have diabetes, and the unequivocal symptom is the appearance of sugar in his urine, since the kidneys of the diabetic individual must rid the blood of excess sugar as well as excess water. Diabetes is successfully treated nowadays by introducing insulin into the blood artificially by means of injections.

The kidneys are bean-shaped organs high up in the abdominal cavity behind the other organs. On its way through them the blood gives up excess water and any other substances it does not need for the proper performance of its functions. Blood assists in the process of tissue repair and renewal that is constantly going on, but it must also carry away the products of decay. Dead tissue is taken up by the blood with other soluble waste matter, and consequently the urine is never pure water even when the individual is perfectly healthy; it contains nitrogenous matter which gives it a characteristic colour and odour. The secreted urine passes drop by drop from the kidneys to a receptacle called the bladder, where it gradually accumulates. The tubes conveying it from the kidneys to the bladder are called ureters, and there is one for each kidney. When the bladder is unable to hold any more urine, discomfort is felt and its expulsion becomes imperative. The passage from the bladder to the exterior is called the urethra. Common experience shows that much more water passes from the body by way of the kidneys at some times than at others. It is relatively greater, for instance, in cold weather, because then the loss by perspiration is decreased. Its amount is reduced in hot weather for the opposite reason, unless the individual partakes of more water or beer or tea to compensate for excessive perspiration.

Being the vehicle for ridding the body of much waste matter, urine becomes unduly thick and coloured if it is too scanty. For the preservation of good health it is desirable to drink plenty of water, particularly

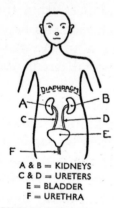

A & B = KIDNEYS
C & D = URETERS
E = BLADDER
F = URETHRA

DIAGRAM OF EXCRETORY
SYSTEM

between meals. When the kidneys are diseased or deprived of the chance to function properly, various waste products may not be completely eliminated from the body. A particularly painful complaint, called gout, is attributable to the presence of uric acid in the system. The cure is to avoid certain acid-forming articles of diet on the one hand and to assist the kidneys in their work of eliminating uric acid on the other hand.

The healthy body is liable to become prey to micro-organisms, and such well-known diseases as measles, whooping-cough, tuberculosis, rheumatism and smallpox are the effect of microbic invasion. The body reacts to attack in certain well-defined ways. First the blood temperature increases. This excess of temperature deters many microbes because it renders them incapable of multiplying. When a fever is beneficial the doctor lets it run its course, knowing that only mischief could result from giving the patient cold baths or drugs to abate the blood temperature. Microbe attack has been observed to lead to a great increase in the white corpuscles of the blood, particularly in any disease-affected region. One purpose of these white cells would appear to be to resist microbic invasion. The cells actually attack and engulf the injurious germs. The white cells appear also to have an important part in restoring wounded tissue and no doubt they make good in some way the normal wear-and-tear that goes on in the several organs of the body. This question, however, belongs to the more detailed department of physiology which needs the microscope for its study. Using this instrument, we perceive that every part and organ of our bodies is made up of minute individual organisms called cells.

Every individual human being or animal begins life as the result of two microscopic cells fusing together to form a single cell. Thereafter growth results from cell multiplication. A cell multiplies by growing and then dividing in two. Thus one cell becomes two, two cells become four, four cells become eight and so on. The growth of the individual proceeds apace and eventually there are millions of cells to give him substance and form. The remarkable thing about growth is the way in which the cells become differentiated from one another, ultimately becoming of many different kinds. These specialist cells group together to form different kinds of tissue, such as muscle, bone, cartilage and so on. They combine to form organs such as stomach, liver, brain and so on. From the outset they appear to be motivated, knowing exactly how to become arranged to make a human being.

The original cell from which the individual starts is provided jointly by mother and father, and, simple as it appears to be when seen under a microscope, it is known to embody the form and character of the person destined to grow from it. All that we comprehend under the name of heredity is contained in this one cell that is first parent to all cells.

Most living creatures, whether vegetable or animal, are equipped with special organs for generating the cells that are needed to make new individuals of their own kind. Some creatures are able to make both the cells whose fusion inaugurates a new life, but in man and other complex creatures the individuals are of two kinds distinguished as male and female. Each makes but one of the necessary cells, so that joint action between two individuals is needed to inaugurate a new life. The distinction of sex runs through almost the whole of Nature, so that even flowers and trees may be said to have maleness or femaleness.

The expedients for bringing male and female cells together are extremely diverse, and in the vegetable kingdom insects may be called upon to carry the male cells (pollen) from flower to flower. Pollinated flowers produce fertile seeds that grow and form new plants under favourable conditions. No seeds can form in a flower that is deprived of pollen, because the unfertilised cells in its ovary come to nothing.

In the kingdom of animals, birds, fishes and insects we find the same principle obtaining. A cell from a female source must be merged with another from a male source in order to create a life-giving composite cell. In the higher animals and in human beings the encounter is arranged to occur in the person of the female, who subsequently brings forth the new individual in a very immature form. Insects, fish, reptiles and birds generally produce eggs which require hatching, but the higher animals retain the new organism until it has a life of its own. The human baby cries directly it is born, and it must be given nourishment within a day or two of its first appearance.

Nobody can explain with finality why the responsibility for multiplication in the vegetable and animal kingdom should have become a divided one calling for the joint action of the sexes, but the probability is that the arrangement was one of Nature's tentatives that proved successful in the evolutionary scheme of things. If we could know anything about the first living things ever to divide this labour of reproducing themselves, we should probably discover that they had stolen a march on their competitors in the struggle for existence and became immensely successful at their rivals' expense. We can only imagine how this might be, as we cannot pretend to give the actual facts.

Among animals the sexes find pleasure in associating with one another, and in human beings the association is usually an association for life. The mother is helped by the father to protect and nourish the offspring. The chance of survival in the struggle for existence is enormously increased where creatures develop moral qualities such as courage, loyalty and love of offspring, so that these qualities are as certainly the outcome of natural selection as is the great length of the giraffe's neck. The vast reptiles of prehistoric times became extinct for a reason we cannot know with any assurance, but one guess as good as any other is that they failed to develop the requisite interest in their eggs or progeny. In an increasingly crowded world neglected eggs and defenceless infants would frequently become prey to a ravenous enemy; creatures had the alternative of adapting themselves to the new order of things or of becoming extinct. One successful adaptation was to lay more and more eggs; insects and fishes did that and so they survive to this day. A better adaptation, much less wasteful of life, was to submit to necessity and begin guarding the eggs. Birds followed this course of action. The great reptiles failed to adapt themselves either way and so they perished from the earth.

TABLES OF LOGARITHMS

LOGARITHMS

The difference columns are grouped as "1 2 3 4 | 5 | 6 7 8 9" (Mean Differences). For the upper rows (10–19) two difference lines are given; both are shown separated by a line break.

	0	1	2	3	4	5	6	7	8	9	1	2	3	4	5	6	7	8	9
10	0000	0043	0086	0128	0170	0212	0253	0294	0334	0374	4 4	9 8	13 12	17 16	21 20	26 24	30 28	34 32	38 37
11	0414	0453	0492	0531	0569	0607	0645	0682	0719	0755	4 4	8 7	12 11	15 15	19 19	23 22	27 26	31 30	35 33
12	0792	0828	0864	0899	0934	0969	1004	1038	1072	1106	3 3	7 7	11 10	14 14	18 17	21 20	25 24	28 27	32 31
13	1139	1173	1206	1239	1271	1303	1335	1367	1399	1430	3 3	7 7	10 10	13 12	16 16	20 19	23 22	26 25	30 29
14	1461	1492	1523	1553	1584	1614	1644	1673	1703	1732	3 3	6 6	9 9	12 12	15 15	18 17	21 20	24 23	28 26
15	1761	1790	1818	1847	1875	1903	1931	1959	1987	2014	3 3	6 5	9 8	11 11	14 14	17 16	20 19	23 22	26 25
16	2041	2068	2095	2122	2148	2175	2201	2227	2253	2279	3 3	5 5	8 8	11 10	14 13	16 15	19 18	22 21	24 23
17	2304	2330	2355	2380	2405	2430	2455	2480	2504	2529	3 2	5 5	8 7	10 10	13 12	15 15	18 17	20 19	23 22
18	2553	2577	2601	2625	2648	2672	2695	2718	2742	2765	2 2	5 5	7 7	9 9	12 11	14 14	16 16	19 18	21 21
19	2788	2810	2833	2856	2878	2900	2923	2945	2967	2989	2 2	4 4	7 6	9 8	11 11	13 13	16 15	18 17	20 19
20	3010	3032	3054	3075	3096	3118	3139	3160	3181	3201	2	4	6	8	11	13	15	17	19
21	3222	3243	3263	3284	3304	3324	3345	3365	3385	3404	2	4	6	8	10	12	14	16	18
22	3424	3444	3464	3483	3502	3522	3541	3560	3579	3598	2	4	6	8	10	12	14	15	17
23	3617	3636	3655	3674	3692	3711	3729	3747	3766	3784	2	4	6	7	9	11	13	15	17
24	3802	3820	3838	3856	3874	3892	3909	3927	3945	3962	2	4	5	7	9	11	12	14	16
25	3979	3997	4014	4031	4048	4065	4082	4099	4116	4133	2	3	5	7	9	10	12	14	15
26	4150	4166	4183	4200	4216	4232	4249	4265	4281	4298	2	3	5	7	8	10	11	13	15
27	4314	4330	4346	4362	4378	4393	4409	4425	4440	4456	2	3	5	6	8	9	11	13	14
28	4472	4487	4502	4518	4533	4548	4564	4579	4594	4609	2	3	5	6	8	9	11	12	14
29	4624	4639	4654	4669	4683	4698	4713	4728	4742	4757	1	3	4	6	7	9	10	12	13
30	4771	4786	4800	4814	4829	4843	4857	4871	4886	4900	1	3	4	6	7	9	10	11	13
31	4914	4928	4942	4955	4969	4983	4997	5011	5024	5038	1	3	4	6	7	8	10	11	12
32	5051	5065	5079	5092	5105	5119	5132	5145	5159	5172	1	3	4	5	7	8	9	11	12
33	5185	5198	5211	5224	5237	5250	5263	5276	5289	5302	1	3	4	5	6	8	9	10	12
34	5315	5328	5340	5353	5366	5378	5391	5403	5416	5428	1	3	4	5	6	8	9	10	11
35	5441	5453	5465	5478	5490	5502	5514	5527	5539	5551	1	2	4	5	6	7	9	10	11
36	5563	5575	5587	5599	5611	5623	5635	5647	5658	5670	1	2	4	5	6	7	8	10	11
37	5682	5694	5705	5717	5729	5740	5752	5763	5775	5786	1	2	3	5	6	7	8	9	10
38	5798	5809	5821	5832	5843	5855	5866	5877	5888	5899	1	2	3	5	6	7	8	9	10
39	5911	5922	5933	5944	5955	5966	5977	5988	5999	6010	1	2	3	4	5	7	8	9	10
40	6021	6031	6042	6053	6064	6075	6085	6096	6107	6117	1	2	3	4	5	6	8	9	10
41	6128	6138	6149	6160	6170	6180	6191	6201	6212	6222	1	2	3	4	5	6	7	8	9
42	6232	6243	6253	6263	6274	6284	6294	6304	6314	6325	1	2	3	4	5	6	7	8	9
43	6335	6345	6355	6365	6375	6385	6395	6405	6415	6425	1	2	3	4	5	6	7	8	9
44	6435	6444	6454	6464	6474	6484	6493	6503	6513	6522	1	2	3	4	5	6	7	8	9
45	6532	6542	6551	6561	6571	6580	6590	6599	6609	6618	1	2	3	4	5	6	7	8	9
46	6628	6637	6646	6656	6665	6675	6684	6693	6702	6712									
47	6721	6730	6739	6749	6758	6767	6776	6785	6794	6803	1	2	3	4	5	6	7	7	8
48	6812	6821	6830	6839	6848	6857	6866	6875	6884	6893	1	2	3	4	5	5	6	7	8
49	6902	6911	6920	6928	6937	6946	6955	6964	6972	6981	1	2	3	4	4	5	6	7	8
50	6990	6998	7007	7016	7024	7033	7042	7050	7059	7067	1	2	3	3	4	5	6	7	8

	0	1	2	3	4	5	6	7	8	9	1	2	3	4	5	6	7	8	9
51	7076	7084	7093	7101	7110	7118	7126	7135	7143	7152	1	2	3	3	4	5	6	7	8
52	7160	7168	7177	7185	7193	7202	7210	7218	7226	7235	1	2	2	3	4	5	6	7	7
53	7243	7251	7259	7267	7275	7284	7292	7300	7308	7316	1	2	2	3	4	5	6	6	7
54	7324	7332	7340	7348	7356	7364	7372	7380	7388	7396	1	2	2	3	4	5	6	6	7
55	7404	7412	7419	7427	7435	7443	7451	7459	7466	7474	1	2	2	3	4	5	5	6	7
56	7482	7490	7497	7505	7513	7520	7528	7536	7543	7551	1	2	2	3	4	5	5	6	7
57	7559	7566	7574	7582	7589	7597	7604	7612	7619	7627	1	2	2	3	4	5	5	6	7
58	7634	7642	7649	7657	7664	7672	7679	7686	7694	7701	1	1	2	3	4	4	5	6	7
59	7709	7716	7723	7731	7738	7745	7752	7760	7767	7774	1	1	2	3	4	4	5	6	7
60	7782	7789	7796	7803	7810	7818	7825	7832	7839	7846	1	1	2	3	4	4	5	6	6
61	7853	7860	7868	7875	7882	7889	7896	7903	7910	7917	1	1	2	3	4	4	5	6	6
62	7924	7931	7938	7945	7952	7959	7966	7973	7980	7987	1	1	2	3	3	4	5	6	6
63	7993	8000	8007	8014	8021	8028	8035	8041	8048	8055	1	1	2	3	3	4	5	5	6
64	8062	8069	8075	8082	8089	8096	8102	8109	8116	8122	1	1	2	3	3	4	5	5	6
65	8129	8136	8142	8149	8156	8162	8169	8176	8182	8189	1	1	2	3	3	4	5	5	6
66	8195	8202	8209	8215	8222	8228	8235	8241	8248	8254	1	1	2	3	3	4	5	5	6
67	8261	8267	8274	8280	8287	8293	8299	8306	8312	8319	1	1	2	3	3	4	5	5	6
68	8325	8331	8338	8344	8351	8357	8363	8370	8376	8382	1	1	2	3	3	4	4	5	6
69	8388	8395	8401	8407	8414	8420	8426	8432	8439	8445	1	1	2	2	3	4	4	5	6
70	8451	8457	8463	8470	8476	8482	8488	8494	8500	8506	1	1	2	2	3	4	4	5	6
71	8513	8519	8525	8531	8537	8543	8549	8555	8561	8567	1	1	2	2	3	4	4	5	5
72	8573	8579	8585	8591	8597	8603	8609	8615	8621	8627	1	1	2	2	3	4	4	5	5
73	8633	8639	8645	8651	8657	8663	8669	8675	8681	8686	1	1	2	2	3	4	4	5	5
74	8692	8698	8704	8710	8716	8722	8727	8733	8739	8745	1	1	2	2	3	4	4	5	5
75	8751	8756	8762	8768	8774	8779	8785	8791	8797	8802	1	1	2	2	3	3	4	5	5
76	8808	8814	8820	8825	8831	8837	8842	8848	8854	8859	1	1	2	2	3	3	4	5	5
77	8865	8871	8876	8882	8887	8893	8899	8904	8910	8915	1	1	2	2	3	3	4	4	5
78	8921	8927	8932	8938	8943	8949	8954	8960	8965	8971	1	1	2	2	3	3	4	4	5
79	8976	8982	8987	8993	8998	9004	9009	9015	9020	9025	1	1	2	2	3	3	4	4	5
80	9031	9036	9042	9047	9053	9058	9063	9069	9074	9079	1	1	2	2	3	3	4	4	5
81	9085	9090	9096	9101	9106	9112	9117	9122	9128	9133	1	1	2	2	3	3	4	4	5
82	9138	9143	9149	9154	9159	9165	9170	9175	9180	9186	1	1	2	2	3	3	4	4	5
83	9191	9196	9201	9206	9212	9217	9222	9227	9232	9238	1	1	2	2	3	3	4	4	5
84	9243	9248	9253	9258	9263	9269	9274	9279	9284	9289	1	1	2	2	3	3	4	4	5
85	9294	9299	9304	9309	9315	9320	9325	9330	9335	9340	1	1	2	2	3	3	4	4	5
86	9345	9350	9355	9360	9365	9370	9375	9380	9385	9390	1	1	2	2	3	3	4	4	5
87	9395	9400	9405	9410	9415	9420	9425	9430	9435	9440	0	1	1	2	2	3	3	4	4
88	9445	9450	9455	9460	9465	9469	9474	9479	9484	9489	0	1	1	2	2	3	3	4	4
89	9494	9499	9504	9509	9513	9518	9523	9528	9533	9538	0	1	1	2	2	3	3	4	4
90	9542	9547	9552	9557	9562	9566	9571	9576	9581	9586	0	1	1	2	2	3	3	4	4
91	9590	9595	9600	9605	9609	9614	9619	9624	9628	9633	0	1	1	2	2	3	3	4	4
92	9638	9643	9647	9652	9657	9661	9666	9671	9675	9680	0	1	1	2	2	3	3	4	4
93	9685	9689	9694	9699	9703	9708	9713	9717	9722	9727	0	1	1	2	2	3	3	4	4
94	9731	9736	9741	9745	9750	9754	9759	9763	9768	9773	0	1	1	2	2	3	3	4	4
95	9777	9782	9786	9791	9795	9800	9805	9809	9814	9818	0	1	1	2	2	3	3	4	4
96	9823	9827	9832	9836	9841	9845	9850	9854	9859	9863	0	1	1	2	2	3	3	4	4
97	9868	9872	9877	9881	9886	9890	9894	9899	9903	9908	0	1	1	2	2	3	3	4	4
98	9912	9917	9921	9926	9930	9934	9939	9943	9948	9952	0	1	1	2	2	3	3	4	4
99	9956	9961	9965	9969	9974	9978	9983	9987	9991	9996	0	1	1	2	2	3	3	3	4

Note.—These tables are so constructed that the fourth figure of a logarithm obtained by their use is never more than one unit above or below the best 4-figure approximation. E.g. if the logarithm found is 0·5014, the best 4-figure approximation may be 0·5013, 0·5014, or 0·5015. Greater accuracy than this cannot be obtained by the use of a uniform table of differences of this kind.

INDEX

INDEX

261

Electricity—*continued*

Inverse Square Law in electrostatics, ii. 333
Inverse Square Law in magnetism, ii. 255
ionisation in gases, i. 209; iii. 194
ionisation in liquids, iii. 182
Joule, definition of, ii. 284
kettle, electric, ii. 284
Kirchoff's rules, ii. 299
Leclanché cell, i. 162; iii. 185
Leyden jar (*see* Condensers, electric)
lighting, electric, i. 158, 164, 166, 169, 172, 174, 181; ii. 179, 182, 183, opp. 184
lightning arrester, i. 177
lightning conductor, i. 155; ii. 342
lightning, energy of, ii. 337
lodestone, ii. 253
Lodge, Sir Oliver, i. 189, 190
magnetic circuit, ii. 322
magnetic effect of electric current, ii. 274
magnetic moment, definition of, ii. 262
magnetic permeability, ii. 323
magnetic pole, unit, definition of, ii. 257, 261
magnetic reluctance, ii. 323
magnetic theory of Blackett, ii. 273
magnetism, i. 152, 156; ii. 253, 322
magnetism, molecular theory of, ii. 270
magnetism, terrestrial, ii. 266, 270
magneto, i. 110
magnetometer, ii. 265
magnetomotive force, ii. 322
magnetron, i. 204, opp. 205
magnets, steel for, ii. 254
Marconi, i. 189, 190
Maxwell, Clerk, i. 188, 189
microfarad, definition of, ii. 312, 336
microphone, i. 170, 171
motor, direct-current, theory of, ii. 314
motors, electric, i. 158, 163, 168, opp. 168, 174, opp. 176, 178, 183, 184; ii. opp. 63, opp. 68, 289, 347
Oersted, i. 156
ohm, definition of, ii. 282
Ohm's Law, definition of, ii. 282
oscillatory circuits, theory of, i. 181; ii. 347
permeability, magnetic, ii. 323
photo-cell, i. 198
Pixii's machine, i. 172, opp. 172
Planté, i. 164
polyphase current, ii. 347
post-office box, ii. 293
potentiometer, ii. 294
power factor, i. 183
power-factor correction, i. 184
power in A.C. circuit, i. 181
radar, i. 187, 201, opp. 204, opp. 205
radio, i. 186; ii. 350
rating, current, of electric machines, ii. 289
reluctance, magnetic, ii. 323
resistance, measurement of, ii. 290
resistance of batteries, ii. 302
resistance, specific, of metals, ii. 305

Electricity—*continued*

resistances in series and parallel, ii. 295; iii. 47, 56, 67
resonance in A.C. circuits, i. 185, 190; ii. 347
Röntgen ray, production of, i. 206, opp. 206
Siemens dynamo, i. 110, 158, 164, 172; ii. 315
solenoid, i. 163; ii. 277
spark telegraphy, i. 188
squirrel-cage motor, i. 179
static electricity, i. 152; ii. 327
Sturgeon, William, i. 160
synchronous motor, i. 178, 184
tangent galvanometer, ii. 275, 279
telegraphy by wire, i. 153, 160
telegraphy, wireless, i. 186
telephone, i. 169
telephony, wireless, i. 195
television, i. 198, opp. 200
thermionic valve, i. 192
three-phase current, ii. 347
thunderstorms, i. 152, 155
toy motors, i. 163
trains, electric, i. 168, 180
trams, i. 168
transformer, i. 157, 171, 173; ii. 345
transmission systems, i. 171, 174, 177; ii. opp. 344, 345, opp. 346
trolley buses, i. 168
velocity of propagation of electricity, i. 154, 186
Volta, i. 156, 161
volt, definition of, ii. 282
voltmeter, ii. 287
Ward-Leonard control, i. opp. 168, 169; ii. 67, opp. 68
Watson, Sir William, i. 154
watt, definition of, ii. 284
Wheatstone, i. 158
Wheatstone bridge, ii. 291, 299
Wimshurst machine, i. 206; ii. 341, opp. 342
wireless waves, i. 186
X-rays, production of, i. 206, opp. 206
Electro-chemistry, iii. 181
Electro-plating, iii. 182
Electrostatics (*see* Electricity)
Elements (*see* Chemical elements)
Ellipse, properties of, iii. 103
Energy, atomic (*see* Atomic energy)
Energy, conservation of (*see* Mechanics)
Energy conversions, i. 22, 49, 82, 86, 102, 104, 185, 207; ii. 47, 111, opp. 112, opp. 113, opp. 114, 150, 283, 289
Energy from matter, iii. 216
Energy, kinetic and potential, ii. 46
Energy of a vibrating body, ii. 76
Engineering, electrical, i. 152
Engineering, mechanical, i. 1
Engines (*see* Steam engines *and* Internal-combustion engines, Hot-air engines)
Equation clocks, i. 241
Equation of time, i. 240, 154
Equations (*see* Mathematics)